INTRODUCTION TO THE THEORY OF STATISTICS

HARPER'S MATHEMATICS SERIES

Charles A. Hutchinson, *Editor*

INTRODUCTION TO THE
THEORY OF
STATISTICS

VICTOR GOEDICKE

Associate Professor of Mathematics
Ohio University

HARPER & BROTHERS · PUBLISHERS · NEW YORK

INTRODUCTION TO THE THEORY OF STATISTICS

Library of Congress catalog card number: 53-5077

To Misha

CONTENTS

13 Statistics and Common Sense   248

1. Introduction. 2. Inadequate Information About Data.
3. Non-Representative Sample. 4. Correlation and Causation.
5. Inappropriateness of Data. 6. Fallacy of Large Numbers.
7. Excessive Refinement of Weak Data. 8. Some Useful Precautions.

Appendixes

PREFACE

In a field already covered by many textbooks, the presentation of a new book requires special justification.

The study of statistics has two aspects. First, there is a set of operational procedures to be mastered, leading to standard conclusions drawn according to standard rules. The student can learn to apply these procedures without understanding the principles underlying their validity. This, of course, is the part of the subject which the student must master if he is to make any practical use of statistics. Secondly, there is a body of mathematical and logical analysis which demonstrates the validity of the procedures. It is not necessary to master this mathematical analysis in order to use statistics; nevertheless there are cogent reasons for studying it. In the first place, an understanding of the theoretical basis for a procedure often brings with it an understanding of the limitations of the procedure, and the statistician with theoretical training is not likely to apply his procedures to situations where they are not suitable. In the second place, knowledge of the theory makes statistics a far more versatile tool in the hands of the worker. With the theory, he is capable of modifying his procedure to fit unusual situations, whereas a worker who knows only a set of specific operational procedures is helpless if the problem contains an unusual or unexpected ingredient. And in the third place, there is far more intellectual satisfaction for the student in carrying out procedures which he understands than there is in carrying out procedures which he accepts on someone else's authority.

All textbooks must make a compromise of some sort between these two aspects of statistics. In general, books for beginners are wholly or mainly operational, whereas intermediate and advanced books mix theory with application in varying proportions. To understand most of the principles used in elementary statistics it is generally necessary for the student to master books used in advanced courses, which usually require calculus and sometimes differential equations. Most students, however, take only one course in statistics and have neither the time nor the mathematical background to continue to the advanced courses. Their mastery of statistics consequently is almost entirely operational.

It is the thesis of this book that it is possible and desirable to give beginning non-technical students a deeper understanding of theory than is customarily attempted. Many of the principles which ordinarily must be "taken on faith" by the elementary student are here derived in terms of simple mathematics not involving calculus. These derivations have been used with success in classes composed of students in psychology, sociology, biology, education, and other non-mathematical fields. This book is written for such students and also for the many workers in industry, medicine, conservation, and other fields who use statistics in their work and are curious about the theoretical basis for their tools.

The possibilities of making theoretical mastery available to beginning students are necessarily limited. Much of the elementary theory of statistics is intrinsically technical and hopelessly beyond the reach of the beginner, and much of the remainder can be brought to the beginner only with some sacrifice of mathematical exactness. In a few cases the derivations are accomplished by means of simplifications which perhaps conceal some of the logical difficulties, and in a very few cases derivations are omitted altogether. But with these minor exceptions the student participates fully in the development of the subject and verifies for himself the derivations of all theoretical results. Furthermore, he has an opportunity to follow the development of the basic ideas and to understand the needs which led to the formulation of our various statistical concepts.

The data used in the illustrative problems and exercises are fictitious unless otherwise noted. The use of fictitious data has made it possible to illustrate the principles of statistics with a minimum of time devoted to extended computations.

The book is intended for use in a single semester introductory course of three or four semester hours. For use in a three-hour course, the following omissions are suggested: Chapter 2, Article 2; Chapter 3, Articles 6 and 11; Chapter 5, Articles 4, 5, and 11; Chapter 6, the technical details of Article 4; Chapter 7, Articles 5, 6, 7, and 8; Chapter 8, Article 9; Chapter 9, Second Method of Article 11 and all of Article 13; Chapter 11, Article 3.

I wish to record my gratitude to Professors George Starcher and Carl Denbow for their criticism of the manuscript, and to Misha Goedicke, Mae Simon, and Norma Albaugh for their assistance in criticizing, typing, and proofreading. I am also indebted to many of my students in Ohio University who have worked with the material and particularly to Eugene Dunn, Shirley Stevens, and Lawrence Talley, who have checked all the exercises for numerical errors.

I am indebted to Professor Ronald A. Fisher, Cambridge, to Dr. Frank Yates, Rothamsted, and to Messrs. Oliver and Boyd Ltd., Edinburgh, for permission to reprint Table IV from their book *Statistical Tables for Biological, Agricultural, and Medical Research*.

VICTOR GOEDICKE

January, 1953

INTRODUCTION TO THE
THEORY OF STATISTICS

CHAPTER
• 1 •
OBJECTIVES OF STATISTICS

1. INTRODUCTION

"Statistics" is a term somewhat loosely used to include various methods of presentation, analysis, and interpretation of mass numerical data. Some writers prefer to use the term "statistical methods" for these various procedures and to reserve the term "statistics" for the data itself, but this convention will not be followed in this book.

The purpose of this introductory chapter is to explain to you the scope and purpose of the branch of mathematics which you are about to study. For this purpose a verbal definition of the word "statistics" is probably of little use. A more effective procedure is to examine a set of representative situations which require statistical methods of attack and to see for yourself what statistics means in practice and what it is used for. The presentation of such a set of statistical problems is the primary task of this chapter.

A preliminary orientation of this sort is desirable in any field of mathematics, but the need is probably greatest in statistics. The transition from the objectives of other mathematics courses to those of statistics is not an easy one, and many students soon find themselves floundering hopelessly, with a feeling that they have missed the central idea. Their specific comments are likely to describe one or the other of the following impressions:

(1) Statistics is a grab-bag of unrelated techniques, without an underlying core of common principles and without a continuous thread of mathematical development.

(2) The "results" of statistical study are vague and hard to grasp; the methods rarely give you a flat "yes" or "no" answer to any problem, but only a diffuse statement about likelihoods or probabilities.

It is the author's hope that a careful reading of this chapter will give you a little insight into the purposes of statistical analysis and help you to avoid this typical feeling of disorientation.

2. NATURE OF STATISTICAL DATA

In most fields of mathematics we deal with a few specific numbers, each of which is considered to be exactly known and to have a specific relation to the other numbers involved in the problem. In statistics we usually deal instead with a collection of numbers, all measuring in some way the same thing and each containing some element of uncertainty. We then draw conclusions from the *trend* of the data as a whole, rather than from any individual items in it. Furthermore, if two variables are involved, we do not assume that a specific relationship exists between them; instead we frequently find that the second variable is only partly controlled by the first and is partly independent of it. Indeed, it is frequently the duty of the statistician to *measure* the amount of relatedness of the two variables, that is, to separate the part of one variable which is controlled by the other from the part which is independent of it.

Suppose, for example, that a scientist applies a varying voltage across a circuit, with the purpose of finding how the voltage affects the amperage, and obtains the following results:

Trial No.	Voltage	Amperage
1	120	24
2	110	22
3	100	20
4	90	18
5	100	20
6	110	22

He would conclude that, for this circuit, amperage is proportional to voltage. Since this law works *exactly* for all his measurements, he can further conclude that in this situation the amperage is controlled *solely* by the voltage. There is no element of uncertainty in the figures, and statistical analysis would add nothing to his knowledge.

Now let us suppose instead that the apparatus is subject to an irregular change of temperature and that the resistance of the circuit, unknown to the scientist, changes with temperature, so that the measures are as follows:

TABLE 1-2-1.   Voltage and Amperage

Trial No.	Voltage	Amperage
1	120	23.8
2	110	22.1
3	100	19.7
4	90	18.0
5	100	20.2
6	110	22.2

The principle that amperage is proportional to voltage now fails; furthermore, no law whatever can work exactly, because the same voltage does not always produce the same amperage. It is evident that some other cause or causes, not measured by the scientist, are at work, and the situation is now one in which statistical analysis can add to the scientist's knowledge.

But, you may ask, "Why doesn't the scientist study, in turn, all the possible causes of the uncertainty?" For example, why doesn't he keep every other factor constant and vary first the temperature alone, then the barometric pressure alone, and so forth, to see whether the amperage changes or not with each of these other factors? In short, why does he not isolate and eliminate the statistician's "element of uncertainty" and get the experiment back onto the solid and familiar ground of exact measurement?

This is, of course, exactly what the scientist does *when he can*. It is better to isolate and to measure the effect of each variable separately, by controlling the experiment, than it is to begin by measuring a quantity which is controlled by a hodgepodge of causes all acting simultaneously and then to try to separate them later by mathematical analysis. Unfortunately the scientist is not always able to control his experiment completely

The degree of control which an experimenter exerts over his experiment varies over a wide range. At one end of the range we have the chemist or physicist exercising complete or almost complete control over an experiment in a laboratory; at the other end we have the social scientist studying the causes of such things as mass shifts of population in a large city. Somewhere along this continuous range we cease to refer to the study as an "experiment" and call it an "observation," in acknowledgment of the increasingly passive role of the investigator, but the dividing line is not sharp. In all cases the uncontrolled part of the experiment is likely to be somewhat larger than it appears at first glance.

Consider, for example, the scientist who is studying the relation between voltage and amperage in a complex circuit. He can eliminate the effects of temperature, barometric pressure, humidity, and every other physical variable which occurs to him, but there may still remain one source of uncertainty. If he wishes to formulate a law which will be accurate to four decimals and if his instruments are capable of measuring amperage only to three decimals, *then his own inability to measure with sufficient accuracy* constitutes an element of uncertainty, and to make further progress he must use statistical tools. It is for this reason that statistics is becoming increasingly important in the exact sciences. The early investigators in any field always discover the easy "knock-down-and-dragout" laws, which are obvious as soon as some rough measures are assembled. The later investigators must in many cases study the subtler relationships which were at first overlooked. In order to make progress they must utilize the full precision of their instruments, and then, having reached the limit set by the instruments, they must use statistical methods to extract the greatest possible amount of information from the uncertain part of their measurements.

In medical research the uncontrollable elements are more obvious. It is common practice to test the effectiveness of a medicine by dividing the patients into two groups which are identical, so far as possible, in average age, severity of illness, general health, and so forth, and to give the medicine to one group and not to the other. But who is to decide when all other possible variables are identical for the two groups? Mrs. Schmidt and Mrs. Bartolacci are both 62 years old, weigh 147 pounds, and have three children each. But Mrs. Schmidt worries acutely about her son, who is in Eastern Germany, so that her appetite is poor and her interest in her treatment is low; Mrs. Bartolacci's son has a fine job in Brooklyn and writes to his mother every day. Mr. Ericson and Mr. Thomas receive identical dinners of poached eggs, toast, and tea. Mr. Ericson thrives on this food, but Mr. Thomas develops an allergic reaction to eggs and breaks out in a severe case of hives, with a mounting temperature!

Even if two identical sets of human beings could be found, the doctor's freedom of action in varying their conditions is limited. He might suspect that malnutrition has in the past been a contributing factor in the failure of a particular treatment, but he can hardly withhold food from some of the patients in order to test his theory. And even if he had complete freedom of investigation, he could never cope with the sheer number of possible contributing factors, which stretch on to infinity. Furthermore, many of these factors are intrinsically unmeasurable. Who can measure, for example, the patient's motivation to recover?

In practice, the doctor who suspects that malnutrition has had an effect on the success of a treatment need not admit defeat simply because humane considerations prevent him from starving his patients. Instead he can test his hypothesis by collecting data from hospitals all over the world and taking advantage of the fact that malnutrition unavoidably existed in some areas.* But the doctor who uses such data must reckon with a number of new and irrelevant effects, since the hospitals in malnutrition areas can be expected to differ from each other and from American hospitals in many ways other than the degree of malnutrition of their patients. In this situation, all hope of using a "controlled experiment" type of analysis must be given up, and the doctor must now attempt to separate the causes as well as he can by means of statistical analysis.

---

*At the end of World War II, for example, some important information about the effect of malnutrition on tooth decay was obtained by a statistical study of the diets and the condition of teeth in Italy, where malnutrition had been serious for several years.

3. PROBABILITY IN STATISTICAL RESULTS

You will find that statistics differs in a second way from the branches of mathematics with which you are familiar. Statistical analysis frequently leads you not to a flat statement that a given answer is correct, but to a statement that, out of the various possible answers, a given one is the most likely to be correct. Furthermore, the likelihood or *probability* that it is correct is itself determined exactly by statistical analysis. Statistics is in part the analysis of the degree of uncertainty of results. Because of this emphasis upon probability, students sometimes begin to feel that they are treading a quicksand of uncertainty and to wish for the cold precision of the familiar "let x equal the unknown number" sort of mathematics.

A little reflection, however, will show the reader that in dealing with human affairs the concept of probability is vital. We must frequently base important decisions upon incomplete evidence, simply because some aspects of the evidence are not available to us. Even if all the evidence is potentially available, we often do not have time, in our finite lives, to scrutinize all possible factors in minute detail; we must observe what we can and make the most reasonable possible hypothesis about the remainder. Having done so, we must be aware of the *degree of uncertainty* contributed to our final decision by the various uncertainties in the separate factors, and this can be done accurately only with the aid of a mathematical analysis of probabilities. The study of statistics will perhaps make you more specifically aware of the role played by chance in your affairs, and will help you to develop some skill at computing probabilities or "estimating the odds." It is to be hoped that after you have studied statistics you will be less likely to be caught in an unwise action which depends for its success upon the occurrence of demonstrably unlikely events.

Statistics is in large part the science of gambling and is valuable to us precisely because human affairs consist of a long series of unavoidable gambles. We engage in a gambling operation when we choose a career, when we buy a house or a car, when we choose an insurance policy, or even when we plant a tree. Whether or not to gamble is a choice not left to us; we can choose only whether we should gamble blindly or whether we should analyze our bets and place them to the greatest possible advantage. And if we make the second choice, then a mastery of the basic laws of probability becomes a necessary tool.

4. SURVEY OF STATISTICAL PROBLEMS

A more specific acquaintance with the scope and purposes of statistical study is best obtained by an examination of specific problems to which the methods are applicable, and the remainder of this section consists of a sample set of such problems. These will of course not be phrased in the more exact language used later in the book, but their insertion here will introduce you to the basic ideas and give you a background for the more exact formulation to come later.

It is suggested that you answer all these questions to the best of your ability, using any common sense methods of reasoning which may seem appropriate to you, and that you record your answers for future comparison with the results you will obtain when you solve these same problems by statistical methods. If you believe that some of the problems do not contain enough data to justify an answer, record this statement as your answer.

I. Table 1-4-1 contains the results of recording the maximum temperatures reached during the illnesses of forty patients with a given kind of

TABLE 1-4-1.   Maximum Temperatures of Forty Malarial Patients

104.3	104.8	104.0	104.0	105.4
105.0	103.9	105.8	104.4	104.5
103.3	104.5	104.4	103.7	104.9
104.5	105.3	103.7	105.0	104.2
104.0	104.2	104.5	103.9	104.0
103.4	104.4	105.0	105.7	105.5
104.4	104.8	103.7	105.0	103.7
104.9	104.3	105.3	104.4	104.5

malaria. How can this data be summarized or presented in a more concise form so that a reader can grasp the essential points at a glance instead of having to form an impression by studying the forty separate numbers?

II. Table 1-4-2 contains the maximum temperatures of twenty additional patients who were given an experimental treatment designed to reduce temperature during the illness. What are the essential differences and the

TABLE 1-4-2.   Maximum Temperatures of Twenty Experimental Patients

104.5	104.9	104.5	104.1	103.6
104.6	104.8	104.1	105.1	104.6
104.4	103.8	104.7	104.0	104.8
103.8	103.9	104.7	104.5	104.2

essential similarities between the treated group and the non-treated group? What form of description of the two sets of data is best suited for making a quick and exact comparison between the two?

III. The average temperature for the untreated patients is 104.48, while that for the treated patients is 104.38. At first glance this suggests that the treatment had some small success in reducing the temperatures of the patients. However, the difference is only 0.10, which is very small, particularly if we compare it with the range of 2.50 degrees which exists between the smallest and the largest in the untreated group. Since the temperatures differ so much from one patient to another, it is possible that the difference between the two groups exists only because the treated group happened accidently to include an unusual percentage of patients with tendencies to have slightly lower than average temperatures. In other words, the difference may be due to chance. Is it reasonable to believe that the difference of 0.10 arose from such an accidental selection of patients, or is the difference too large to be explained in this way? In short, is it more reasonable to believe that the treatment had an effect on temperatures or to believe that it did not have an effect?

IV. Although their averages are practically identical, there are nevertheless important differences between the two sets of numbers. For example, there are far fewer extremely high temperatures in the treated group than in the untreated group, which might be a more important basis for action than a difference between the averages. How can we best measure these other differences and express them in a convenient and concise way?

V. In a wire factory, the wire made by one machine is tested by taking fifty wires from its day's production and measuring the tension required to break them. The results are shown in Table 1-4-3.

TABLE 1-4-3.   Breaking Strengths of Fifty Wires

205	204	204	203	205
203	203	203	204	204
206	207	202	202	204
206	203	205	204	204
205	205	203	204	206
201	204	202	207	205
203	203	204	204	205
203	205	201	202	202
204	204	205	206	205
203	204	204	203	204

A purchaser wishes to buy a carload of the wire, under a contract which guarantees all wire to withstand a pull of 200 pounds, and which permits the purchaser to void the contract at any time (at considerable expense to the manufacturer) if any wires subsequently tested break under a pull of 200 pounds. Would you advise the manufacturer to sign such a contract or not? Would you advise signing if the guaranteed strength were reduced to 195 pounds?

VI. In the above situation, what would your answer be if the contract specified instead that the *average* breaking strength of any wire subsequently delivered must not be below 202 pounds? Would the contract under this stipulation contain any perceptible risk to the manufacturer?

VII. Suppose instead that the purchaser offered a contract specifying that not more than 1 per cent of any sample subsequently selected from the delivered wire should break at 200 pounds. Would this be a better or a worse contract than the ones described above, from the manufacturer's viewpoint?

VIII. In question VI, do you think that the manufacturer should safeguard himself by specifying in the contract the number of wires to be included in the sample to be tested? If so, how large a sample yould you recommend?

IX. A man who suspects that he has a serious disease consults a physician. The physician finds that there is free acid in the man's stomach, and this is one of the characteristic symptoms which is always present in the disease. However, it is not an absolute symptom upon which a diagnosis can be made, because many people who do not have the disease nevertheless exhibit the symptom. Specifically, for men in the same age group as the patient about 18 per cent of the men who do not have the disease nevertheless exhibit the symptom. The patient is found to exhibit three other symptoms of the disease, for which the corresponding percentages are 12 per cent, 5 per cent, and 9 per cent. If the symptoms are independent of each other for people not having the disease, how likely is it that this man has the disease? Do you feel that you need more information to answer the question? If so, what?

X. A university gives all applicants for admission an entrance examination. To judge the usefulness of the examination, records are kept of the grades subsequently made by the examinees in their college courses. The first column of Table 1-4-4 gives the score made by the examinees on their entrance examination, and the second column gives the average grade which each man has made in the mathematics courses which he has taken during the following four years. An examination of these two columns reveals that a high test score is almost always followed by a high mathematics grade, and a low test score by a low mathematics grade. It is evident that the test measures some of the abilities which enable students to earn high mathematics grades, but it is equally evident that there must be other factors present which help to determine the mathematics grade, but which the entrance test does not succeed in measuring. It follows that the entrance scores of new students can be used fairly successfully to predict their mathematics grades, but that the prediction will be subject to a certain amount of error. A number of practical questions arise:

(a) How can predictions of mathematics averages best be made? In particular, if Tom Jackson, who is now applying for admission, makes a score of 18 on his entrance test, what mathematics average might he reasonably be expected to make in college if he is admitted?

TABLE 1-4-4.   Records for Twenty-Five Students

Entrance Test Score	Subsequent Mathematics Grade	Subsequent Language Grade	Experimental Test Score
(E)	(M)	(L)	(X)
15	51	58	209
17	60	47	148
18	54	51	181
18	54	77	239
20	64	52	184
21	49	63	214
21	60	61	217
22	66	54	162
22	65	70	224
22	68	77	214
23	67	90	231
23	64	59	171
24	76	76	218
24	68	82	208
24	74	83	217
24	69	66	182
25	80	74	200
25	96	49	147
27	84	98	188
30	95	79	183
30	81	84	184
30	89	68	158
31	94	88	163
31	78	74	174
32	88	93	218

(b) How can the accuracy of this prediction be measured? The two men who also scored 18 both made subsequent averages of 54, which is below passing. Since Jackson also scored 18 on his entrance test, it is reasonable to predict that he also will fail. But the prediction is not absolute; for example, the second man on the list scored only 17, which is lower than Jackson's score, but he nevertheless made a subsequent mathematics average of 60, which is a passing grade. If Jackson has three chances in ten of passing and wishes very much to try, perhaps he should be admitted. But if his chances are only one in a thousand, it would be foolish to admit him. Exactly what are his chances of obtaining a mathematics average of 60 or higher if he is admitted?

(c) The third column gives the subsequent grades which the admittees made in language courses. A comparison of these grades with the entrance

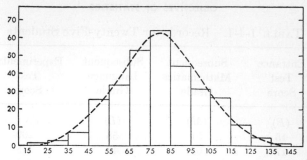

Figure 1-4-1. Distances of Baseball Throws by 303 High School Girls. (Based upon data by Leonora Steward and Helen West, the Froebel School, Gary, Indiana. Reprinted by permission of Prentice-Hall, Inc., from "Applied General Statistics" by Croxton and Cowden. Copyright 1939 by Prentice-Hall, Inc.)

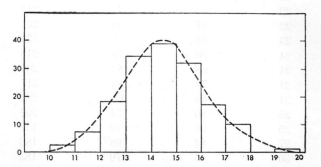

Figure 1-4-2. Percentage of Dry Matter in 160 Mangel Roots. (Based upon data from "The Combination of Observations" by David Brunt, by permission of the Cambridge University Press.)

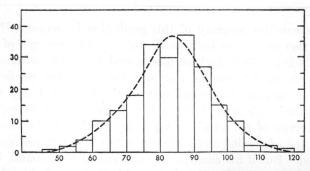

Figure 1-4-3. Scores of 206 Freshmen on the Thorndyke Intelligence Test. (Based upon data from "Statistics in Psychology and Education" by Henry E. Garrett, by permission of Longmans, Green, and Co. Copyright 1947 by Longmans, Green, and Co., Inc.)

scores shows that a high entrance test score *frequently but not always* goes with a high language grade, and vice versa. The entrance test, in other words, is not a very successful measure of the abilities which enable students to make high grades in language, although it is not altogether unsuccessful either. Can you devise a numerical measure for stating exactly *how much* better the entrance test is for predicting mathematics grades than it is for predicting language grades?

(d) The entrance officials have for some time been dissatisfied with the entrance test being used in the university and have considered replacing it with a test of a somewhat different type, in the hope of securing more accurate predictions of subsequent performance. This second test was given to the same twenty-five men who took the regular test, with the objective of comparing the two tests critically and choosing the better one for future use as soon as enough subsequent data about the twenty-five men became available. The scores on the experimental test are shown in column four of Table 1-4-4. Which is the better of the two tests for predicting mathematics grades? Is it also better for predicting language grades?

XI. A dealer who purchases a consignment of dice suspects that they are defective. To make a quick test he throws one of the dice twenty-four times and finds that a 6 came up seven times, a 5 twice, a 4 three times, a 3 four times, a 2 once, and a 1 seven times. If the die were perfect, one would of course expect that all faces would turn up approximately four times apiece in twenty-four trials. It would not be reasonable, however, to expect each face to turn up *exactly* four times, because of the presence of the element of chance. But how large a deviation from this expected frequency of four is to be regarded as normal? In other words, how large must the deviations from the expected frequency of four become in order to convince us that the die is defective? In particular, from the evidence presented above would you conclude that the die is certainly defective, or probably defective, or probably not defective?

XII. A surveyer has found by experience that his measurements of angles are frequently in error by more than one minute of arc but that if he measures an angle five times and averages the results, the average will almost always be within one minute of the true value. He undertakes a new assignment in which the angles must be measured with sufficient precision so that errors rarely exceed one-half of a minute of arc. Can be achieve this precision by increasing the number of times he measures the angle? If so, how many measures should he make to insure the required accuracy?

XIII. All the preceding problems have been of practical nature; that is, they have illustrated the use of statistical analysis as a tool for gaining insight into practical problems. The following question is of an entirely different nature; it is concerned instead with the *theory* of statistics.

Figure 1-4-1 is a diagram which shows the distances which 303 freshman high school girls in Gary, Indiana, were able to throw a baseball. The height of each column indicates the number of girls whose throws were between the limits given across the bottom of the diagram. Thus, reading from the left, the diagram tells us that only one girl threw less than 25 feet, two girls threw farther than 25 feet but less than 35, seven threw farther than 35 but less than 45, and so forth. (Such a diagram is called a histogram and is a useful and widely used tool in statistics. The construction and use of histograms will be discussed in Chapter 2.)

In Figure 1-4-2 the same sort of representation is used to show the percentage of dry matter in a sample of 160 mangel roots. Two of the mangel roots contained between 10 and 11 per cent dry matter, seven contained between 11 and 12 per cent, and so forth. Figure 1-4-3 shows the scores of 206 freshmen examinees on an intelligence test.

As one examines these three figures, one is struck by the fact that there is an unmistakable similarity in the fundamental nature of the three curves. The width of the vertical bars is different in each case, but this is determined by the range which the tabulator chooses to include in each group, and has nothing to do with the physical nature of the distribution. To help eliminate this extraneous factor, the author has sketched a smooth curve in each figure, which follows the general trend of the tops of the bars. We see that in all three cases the curve is convex upward in the center and that it changes to convex downward on each side of the central peak, then levels off to a horizontal direction as it reaches the zero line. Other examples will show that the same sort of curve is obtained when we plot such diverse things as the sizes of the eggs of a certain marine snail in Greenland, the neck sizes of male college students, the batting averages of baseball players, and many other types of data. These curves are so similar that a single equation can be used to describe all of them.

This similarity raises some interesting questions: Is there a hidden essential similarity between the "forces" governing the distribution of intelligence among American college students and those governing the egg sizes of marine snails in Greenland? If so, what are the "forces" and how do they operate? For any new collection of data, can we tell in advance whether we should expect this same type of distribution or not?

5.   SCOPE OF STATISTICS

The list of human activities and interests in which statistical thinking plays a part is a very long one. The following outline will suggest to the reader the variety of the fields in which statistical procedures are being or can be used.

I.   The Exact Sciences

We have already indicated that the physicist, chemist, or astronomer uses statistical analysis to estimate the amount of uncertainty present in measurements and to trace the effects of this uncertainty through his subsequent computations and conclusions. But many further uses can be cited. For example, the physicist frequently deals with problems involving the behavior of things too numerous to study individually, such as the separate molecules in a gas. In such cases he uses statistical formulations based upon the probability that a given molecule will have a given velocity, and with the aid of this treatment he is able to predict the behavior of the entire population of molecules, that is, of the gas as a whole. There are individual molecules with erratic or exceptional velocities, just as there are individual human beings whose behavior is unusual, but so long as we are able to measure the *probability* that a given individual atom or human being will have a given type of behavior, we can allow for the net effect of these mavericks.

In the last few decades there has grown up a fascinating new branch of modern physics called quantum mechanics, which has dramatically overcome the long-standing problem of the fundamental nature of light and matter which has bedeviled physicists for centuries. In this new interpretation, light and atoms merge into one entity, which can only be described as "probability density," or probability (per unit volume) that the atom or photon will be found to be occupying a given position in space. A light wave is a wave of this "probability density," and so is a moving atom! The need for advanced statistical theory here has been so urgent that the physicists have surpassed the statisticians in developing some specialized branches of the subject.

II. The Biological Sciences

The usefulness of statistics in these fields is so obvious that a single example will suffice. If an agricultural research worker measures the yield of an experimental variety of corn, he is observing the results of a common factor (the genetic properties of the variety) overlaid by a number of random factors which differ for each plant (soil conditions, availability of water and sunlight, and so on), and he must use statistical methods to isolate and measure the common factor, in which he is primarily interested. This combination of a constant ingredient with a random ingredient is so nearly universal in these fields that some knowledge of statistics is a basic necessity for all workers in biology, zoology, botany, livestock breeding, agricultural experimentation, and so forth.

III. The Social Sciences

The situation here is much the same as for the biological sciences; almost every quantity which the investigator can measure is affected by a number of factors, some of which are always random with respect to the other variables in the study. If a sociologist wishes to study the connection between poverty and crime, he can readily collect data for a number of communities showing the distribution of incomes and the incidence of crime; but in interpreting his data he is faced with the fact that the sociological pressures behind each individual crime were very complex and included many factors besides that of poverty. If a teacher tries to evaluate the effectiveness of a given textbook, he can test the students who used the book and compare their proficiency with that of students who used other books instead. But he must reckon with the fact that a certain amount of random variation from class to class is to be expected as a result of chance, and he must be sure that any observed difference is too large to be explained by chance before he can conclude that the textbook has made a difference.

An example of a statistical approach is to be found in the December, 1949, *Atlantic Monthly*, in an article which analyzes the attitudes of the members of the Supreme Court in cases involving alleged violations of civil rights. The author points out that there are some apparent contradictions in attitude among the Justices, and goes on to say:

" . . . Does this not make it plain, some member of the bar may ask, that nothing of value is to be concluded from grouping cases and aligning Justices for statistical review?

"The question should answer itself. Obviously not much is to be told by only three cases. But a great deal may be learned from a study of twenty times three. Who would say that since three roll calls give little insight into the voting attitudes of a member of Congress, sixty roll calls would be no more informative?

"Justices generally do not like to be put in tables. They may prefer to think that the work they do cannot be counted up in columns of figures. No impertinence is intended in the suggestion that they had better begin to get used to some numerical analysis. Legal scholars are using it and doubtless they are going to use it more and more."*

The data referred to in this passage is used as illustrative material for problems in Articles 7 and 8 of Chapter 11.

IV. Industry

There are a number of more or less unrelated uses for statistics in industry. A few of them are as follows:

A. PRODUCTION CONTROL AND ANALYSIS. An industrial machine usually turns out a product which is almost uniform, but which nevertheless contains a small random variation of size, or weight, or strength, or color. If the product is destined for use in precision machinery, this small variation must be studied and controlled.

B. ECONOMIC FORECASTING. When a business is to be established or

---

*Reprinted from "Truman Reshapes the Supreme Court," by Irving Dilliard, December, 1949, by permission of the Atlantic Monthly and Mr. Dilliard. Copyright by the Atlantic Monthly, 1949.

a factory built, the owners must frequently commit themselves to an expenditure which can be recovered only by twenty or thirty years of successful operation. They must therefore not only know the present demand for the product, availability of raw materials, and transportation facilities, but they must also make the most reasonable possible prediction of the future course of these factors. When a life insurance company fixes its rates, it is making a forecast concerning the average longevity of the men in each group who pass the physical examinations. This forecast cannot be based merely upon the assumption that longevity of any group in the future is going to be the same as the longevity of a similar group has been in the past; it must be based also upon the presence of various changing factors in medicine, nutrition, and general health.

C. PERSONNEL. Statistical studies concerning employees are undertaken for a wide variety of reasons. Abilities are sometimes measured by standard tests, and the results are used to assign the employees to other tasks where their abilities will be used more effectively. A recent study was made by a trucking company which indicated that many of the drivers had far more accidents than they were entitled to "on the law of averages"; in other words these drivers had at any time a higher probability of having an accident than other drivers. The company saved many lives (and, of course, saves themselves much money in damages) by simply reassigning these employees to non-driving duties. We do not know *which* of these drivers would have had fatal accidents, and undoubtedly many drivers were transferred who would have been lucky enough to avoid further accidents. But *as a group* these drivers were accident-prone, and the accident rate went down after their transfer.

D. PUBLIC RELATIONS. Many businesses, particularly those involved in selling directly to the public, can improve their effectiveness by studying public opinion and modifying their product or their approach to meet the wishes of their customers. In many industries the public opinion poll is a matter of course. For example, some manufacturers in the automobile industry recently polled the public about their wishes concerning various details of automobile design, such as body size, amount of chromium trim, and quality of upholstery. Another example is that of the motion picture industry. In this industry it is obvious that the customer has no first-hand information about the quality of the product until after he has purchased it, that is, until he has seen the picture. At the time of his decision to see it, he frequently knows only such things as the name of the picture and the leading actors or actresses in it. Statistical studies have shown that the name of the picture has a strong effect on the attendance, and these studies have led to the formulation of general principles which must be followed in choosing profitable names for new films. (The author is tempted to add the slightly acid remark that the studies have evidently persuaded some manufacturers that it is better to produce a good name for a picture than it is to produce a good picture.)

V.   Literature and Arts

It is a little surprising to find statistical methods used in studies of literature, where one might expect the material to be totally unsuitable for numerical measurement of any kind.   However, studies have shown that such things as the pattern of frequency of use of various words or frequency of various lengths of sentences are remarkably stable and remain more or less the same for any given author.   Several questions of disputed authorship have been settled by a study of the frequency distribution of lengths of sentences.   Recently the frequencies of use of various words have been tabulated for a large number of literary (and non-literary) works, and a very remarkable general law has been found to describe all these distributions.*

VI.   Statistics for the Layman

For a man who is not engaged in any of these fields, is there any purpose in studying statistics?   There are several.   Every man is a taxpayer, or a voter, or an insurance purchaser, or an investor in real estate, or a purchaser of consumer goods.   Many laymen are interested in consumer cooperative groups of various sorts.   All people have a financial interest in the economic trends in their communities.   Everyone is subjected to advertising which uses (and sometimes misuses) statistical data or reasoning.   And we all live in an age of political propaganda, in which news from all parts of the world has been "slanted" in such a way as to affect our opinions.   We must learn to discount the interpretation which is put upon the data by people whose interests are at stake and try to discern for ourselves the justifiable conclusions.   At the time of this writing the American people are being subjected to a set of arguments concerning the desirability or undesirability of what is generally called "socialized medicine."   As interpreted by one side, the data prove that the American people are now receiving adequate medical care, while the other side uses the same data to prove that medical care for some income groups is grossly inadequate.   In self defense the ordinary citizen must equip himself to draw his own conclusions!

And, for one last point, the ordinary citizen needs a little statistical knowledge to protect himself against amateur statisticians!   We have commented upon the misuse of statistics by the unscrupulous, but it is also misued by the inept.   It is a field in which a little knowledge is a dangerous thing, and many an unwarranted conclusion is urged upon the unsuspecting public in the name of statistics.   This topic will be discussed at some length in Chapter 13, which deals with some of the particular pitfalls of statistical logic.

---

*See, for example, G. K. Zipf, *Human Behavior and the Principle of Least Effort.* Addison-Wesley Press, Cambridge, Mass., 1949.

6.   HOW TO STUDY STATISTICS

As in any branch of mathematics, the process of learning statistics consists chiefly in operating with it. A procedure which is only *described* to you will be vague and shadowy, but if you simultaneously *apply* it while you read, you will master it more quickly and at a deeper level. Study with plenty of paper and pencils at hand, and carry out for yourself the mathematics of all derivations, supplying all the missing steps. Then carry out for yourself the computations in the illustrative examples, using the figures in the textbook only as a check upon your own work.

The theoretical derivations in the book form an interlocking series in which a great deal of space is saved by cross references to previous results. Each equation to which reference is made is numbered in such a way as to indicate the chapter and the number of the article in which it occurs, and the task of locating the equation is further facilitated by the fact that the chapter and article numbers are given at the head of each double page throughout the book. You can therefore refer to any equation with little loss of time.

For quick reference to frequently used equations a table is provided in Appendix VII. Perhaps you will find it advantageous to mark this and other tables in the back of the book with tabs to make them readily accessible.

At the end of each chapter is a summary of the operational procedures described in the chapter. These summaries will be useful for review of the procedures and their interpretations. Also, for the inexperienced mathematician who finds himself occasionally carried beyond his depth, these summaries will provide a means of following the thread of the operational aspects of the subject.

CHAPTER

・ 2 ・

FREQUENCY TABULATION

1. INTRODUCTION

The raw data with which a statistician begins his work usually consists of a large number of more or less related indiviudal measurements or other numerical information. The investigator's first task is to organize or summarize this body of data; that is, to reduce it to a form in which its essential character can be perceived and in which it can be compared quickly and accurately with other similar sets of data. This organizing operation is a necessary preliminary to any further statistical analysis of the data which might be undertaken.

The basic procedure for accomplishing this objective consists of grouping together the quantities which are alike or nearly alike, counting the number in each group, and tabulating the results of the count in a standard form. Such a count is called a frequency tabulation.

When such a tabulation has been made, it is often useful to express the results in graphical form. Two graphical devices for this purpose, with slightly different uses, are the *histogram* and the *ogive*. The construction and the uses of frequency tabulations, histograms, and ogives will form the chief content of this chapter.

2. PROCEDURE FOR MAKING TABULATION

The procedure of forming a frequency tabulation can be demonstrated most quickly by means of an example. Table 2-2-1 consists of a list of forty numbers which represent the breaking strengths of a sample set of

TABLE 2-2-1.   Breaking Strengths of Forty Wires

204	201	207	206	208	207	208	203
206	207	202	204	205	207	202	206
203	207	205	204	203	208	203	206
205	205	207	205	206	207	204	206
206	205	207	203	207	205	206	206

wires taken from a day's production of the machine. An inspection of the table shows us that there are only eight different numbers represented, from 201 to 208 inclusive. We begin by listing these eight numbers vertically, beginning with 201 and continuing to 208. The first number in the table is 204, and we enter this number in our tabulation by placing a checkmark opposite 204. We continue in this way until all the numbers are entered in the tabulation, as shown in Table 2-2-2. The last step of

TABLE 2-2-2. Frequency Tabulation

Breaking Strength	Tally	Frequency
(x)		(f)
201	$\mid$	1
202	$\mid\mid$	2
203	⤒⤒	5
204	$\mid\mid\mid\mid$	4
205	⤒⤒ $\mid\mid$	7
206	⤒⤒ $\mid\mid\mid\mid$	9
207	⤒⤒ $\mid\mid\mid\mid$	9
208	$\mid\mid\mid$	3

the operation consists of finding the total of the tally for each line and entering it at the right in the column headed "frequency."

In future discussions it will be convenient to have a standard terminology to describe the elements of this procedure. The original numbers are called *variates*. The symbol x_1 stands for the first variate in the list (204 in our case), x_2 stands for the second variate (206), and so forth, while the letter x, without a subscript, stands for any variate. Each group of variates in the frequency tally is called a *class*, and the number of variates in any class is called its *frequency*, for which f is a standard abbreviation. The sum of all the frequencies (i.e., the total number of variates) is customarily denoted by the letter N.

PROBLEMS

1. Form a frequency tabulation of the data in Table 1-4-3.
2. In Problem 1, what is the numerical value (a) of x_3? (b) of N?

3. BOUNDARIES AND LIMITS

In general, if we group only identical numbers together into classes, there will be too many classes and too few variates in each class. This is true, for example, for the data in Table 2-3-1. In this table the temperatures range from 98.1 to 99.9, so that we would require nineteen classes if we let each separate temperature constitute a class by itself. Some of

TABLE 2-3-1. Temperatures of Forty Patients

98.4	99.0	98.1	98.6	98.9	98.8	99.5	98.5
98.6	99.0	99.5	99.3	98.8	98.9	98.9	98.1
98.8	98.8	99.3	98.7	99.4	99.5	98.5	98.9
99.0	98.6	99.3	99.9	99.1	98.8	99.3	98.6
99.3	99.7	98.3	99.0	98.1	99.3	99.2	98.5

these classes would be empty, while others would contain only one or two entries, and the tabulation would fail to fulfil its objective of presenting the data in a quickly graspable form.

In such a case the tabulation will be more informative if we group together a small range of variates which are nearly alike, instead of grouping together only those which are exactly alike. For these forty temperatures, for example, we can obtain a useful tabulation by grouping together all temperatures within a range of 0.3 degrees, as shown in Table 2-3-2.

TABLE 2-3-2. Temperatures of Forty Patients

x	f
98.0 to 98.2	3
98.3 to 98.5	5
98.6 to 98.8	10
98.9 to 99.1	9
99.2 to 99.4	8
99.5 to 99.7	4
99.8 to 100.0	1

From an inspection of this table, it is obvious that the nature of the distribution has been made more clearly apparent than it would have been if we had assigned only identical temperatures to each class.

Again, a standard terminology is useful in discussing the procedure: The smallest and the largest values which are to be included in any class are called the *class limits*. In Table 2-3-2, for instance, 98.9 is the *lower limit* of the fourth class, and 99.7 is the *upper limit* of the sixth class.

If we are interested in precise results, it is necessary to consider carefully the exact extent of each of the classes. It is reasonable to assume, unless we have evidence to the contrary, that each of the temperatures recorded in Table 2-3-1 has been rounded off to the nearest tenth of a degree, that is, that the observer has recorded, in each case, the tenth of a degree which is nearest to the actual reading of the thermometer. If, for example, the mercury level is between 98.5 and 98.6, but closer to the latter, then the recorded temperature will be 98.6 and the variate will fall in the third class. If, on the other hand, the mercury is closer to 98.5

than it is to 98.6, then the recorded temperature will be 98.5 and the variate will fall in the second class. The dividing line between the second and third classes is therefore halfway between 98.5 and 98.6; it is in other words exactly at 98.55. Such dividing lines are called *class boundaries*. The value 98.55 is the *lower boundary* of the third class; it is also the *upper boundary* of the second class. It is important to notice the distinction between limits and boundaries. The boundary between two classes is always midway between the upper limit of one class and the lower limit of the following class.

The midpoint of any class is called the *class mark*. It is the value midway between the lower limit and the upper limit of the class. For example, the class mark of the second class is 98.4, while that of the third class is 98.7. The width of each class, from boundary to boundary, is called the *class interval*, and is customarily denoted in equations by the symbol C. In the above example, the class interval is 0.3. A list of these terms, with their standard abbreviations and instructions for computing them, will be found in the summary at the end of the chapter.

PROBLEMS

1. Form a frequency tabulation of the forty temperatures in Table 1-4-1, using a class interval of 0.5, and starting with 103.0 for the lower limit of the first class. Form a similar frequency tabulation* of the twenty temperatures in Table 1-4-2. Describe in words the chief similarities and the chief differences between these two distributions, as revealed by the tabulations.

2. What is the upper limit of the fifth class in Table 2-3-2? What is the upper boundary of this class? What is its class mark? What is the lower boundary of the sixth class? What is the lower limit of the sixth class?

3. What is the upper boundary of the first class in Table 2-2-2? What is the class mark of this class?

4.   GRAPHING OF FREQUENCY TABULATIONS

The inspection of a distribution, or the comparison of one distribution with another, can be facilitated greatly if we present the distributions in graphical form. The simplest and most widely used graphical form is the *histogram*, which consists of a plot in which the horizontal scale represents the values of x of the various classes, and the vertical scale represents the frequencies of these classes.

The construction of a histogram will be illustrated with the data in Table 2-3-2. We begin by laying off a horizontal scale running from about 97.5 to 100.5, or enough to include all the classes. We then locate on this scale the points corresponding to the boundaries of the classes, at 97.95, 98.25, 98.55, and so forth. These points divide the scale into segments,

---

*It is suggested that you retain these tabulations for use in future problems.

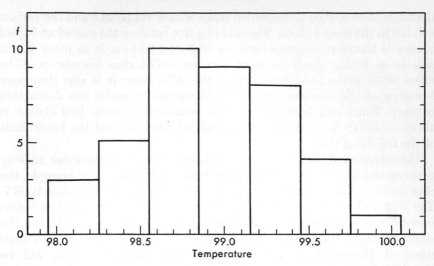

Figure 2-4-1.   A Histogram.

each of which corresponds to one class. Upon each such segment we erect a column whose height gives us the frequency of the class. The completed histogram is shown in Figure 2-4-1. It is important to notice that the base of each column consists of that portion of the x-scale corresponding to the interval between the upper and lower *boundaries* of the class, rather than its upper and lower *limits*.

A distribution is sometimes represented graphically by means of a *frequency polygon*, which is similar to a histogram except that a single point

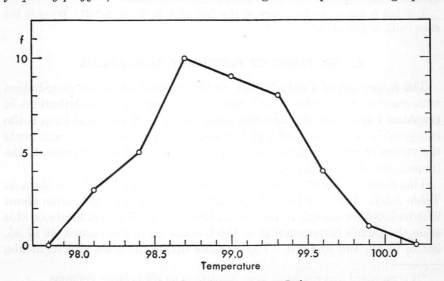

Figure 2-4-2.   A Frequency Polygon.

is plotted for each class, at the class mark, and these points are then connected by straight lines. An example is shown in Figure 2-4-2, based upon the same data as the preceding figure. Of the two, the histogram is more widely used, perhaps because it emphasizes the fact that the location of the individual variates inside the class is no longer specified when the data is in the form of a frequency tabulation.

PROBLEMS

1. Draw histograms of the distributions shown in Tables 1-4-1 and 1-4-2, using the tabulations which you made in the first problem of the preceding section. Do these graphs add to your knowledge of the differences between the two distributions?

2. Draw frequency polygons of these two distributions.

3. Make a histogram of the data in Table 2-2-2. (Note that the boundaries between classes should be placed at 200.5, 201.5, and so forth.)

4. Collect a set of data from your own observations, form a frequency tabulation from it, and construct a histogram. Retain this data for future practice exercises. If you cannot think of a source for suitable data, read the following suggestions. Ask each of twenty students how much money he has in his possession at the moment, or how many cigarettes he smokes per day, or what his grade average is, or what his weight and height are. Measure with a millimeter ruler the lengths of twenty or thirty leaves chosen at random from a single tree. Record the number of yards gained by your team on each play during a quarter of a football game. Attend a target shooting contest and record the number of shots in each zone of the target. Record the number of spades, or the number of cards higher than a ten, in each hand you hold during a game of bridge. (If you collect *two* or more items of information about each individual, such as length *and* width of tree leaves, your data will be useful also for practice in the theory of correlation in Chapter 9.)

5.   THE CHOICE OF CLASS INTERVAL

In the instructions given above, no mention has been made of the problem of choosing a class interval of proper size. This is a complex question for which there is no single answer. Let us begin by inspecting the results of an experiment in which a tabulation is repeated with widely different class intervals. The experiment has been carried out with the data in Table 2-3-1, and the results of the experiment are shown in Figure 2-5-1. At the top of the figure is a histogram with class interval 0.1. It is obviously of little use because it fails to accomplish the function of a histogram, namely, that of organizing the data so that the properties of the distribution are apparent upon inspection. As presented in this upper histogram, the data are nearly as disorganized as they were in the original list of forty temperatures! In the second histogram the interval has been increased to 0.2, and the histogram shows a little more structure, although the frequencies still jump up and down in an erratic fashion as we go from

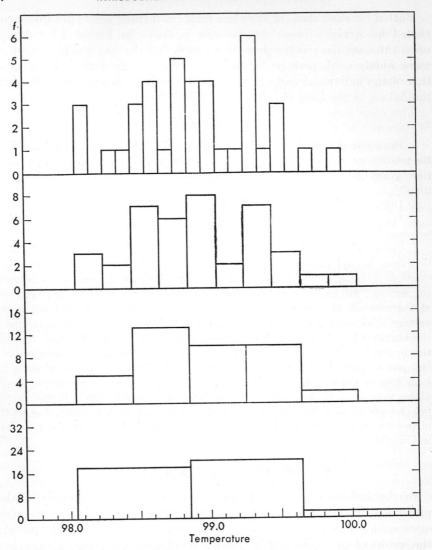

Figure 2-5-1. Effect of Varying Class Interval.

one class to the next. In the third histogram, the interval is 0.4, and the frequencies no longer oscillate, but climb steadily to a maximum and then decline again, indicating a well-defined structure for the distribution. In the fourth histogram, the interval is 0.8, and the histogram now consists of three large classes. The classes are now so wide that it becomes important to know where the variates are located inside each class, but the histogram does not tell us. We feel intuitively that the third of these four histograms contains more useful information than the others.

But in exactly what sense is the third histogram more "informative" than the others? It certainly does not contain more factual information about the original forty numbers in Table 2-3-1. As a description of these numbers, the first histogram is better than any of the others, since it locates the variates more exactly, and the set of original data is better still!

This question can be answered if we define our objective more exactly. We are not so much interested in describing this particular set of forty temperatures of malarial patients as we are in describing *the distribution of temperatures to be expected from such malarial patients in general.* The third histogram shows the general structure of the distribution, which we would expect to find in any group of patients similar to these and which we could use in predicting the percentage of future patients whose temperatures will reach various levels. The first histogram, on the other hand, contains accidental ups and downs which are probably characteristic only of the experimental group of forty patients and which we would not expect to see repeated for future patients. The fact that we intuitively regard the third histogram as superior to the first indicates that our intuitive objective is to go beyond our particular data and draw conclusions about the larger body of data from which it came.

This important distinction is customarily described by the formal terms "universe" and "sample." The *universe* is the sometimes hypothetical collection of all possible measures, real or potential, of the phenomenon in question, while the *sample* is a relatively small group of actual observations selected by some random process from the universe. A little reflection will show that the objective of the investigator is almost always *to draw conclusions about the universe rather than about the sample.* Doctors who perform autopsies upon dead cancer patients are not primarily interested in drawing conclusions about dead patients; they are more likely to be looking for information which is true of all cancer patients, so that it can be used in diagnosis or treatment. The agricultural research man who studies the yield of an experimental new variety of corn is interested in drawing conclusions which will also be true about all of the corn of this variety which might in future be grown in any comparable agricultural region.

From this point of view, the purpose of forming a frequency tabulation and drawing a histogram is to remove the special accidental peculiarities of the sample and to leave for demonstration the more stable properties which we believe to be characteristic of the universe. In the light of this objective let us formulate a rule-of-thumb for selecting an optimum class interval: We should choose for the class interval the *smallest* value which will give us a fairly smooth histogram, without excessive jumps from one frequency to the next. It is obviously good strategy, if you are in doubt, to use a small class interval in the initial tabulation, for if you decide later that it is too small, you can simply add your frequencies in pairs and thus obtain a tabulation with an interval twice as large without retabulating the original data.

In anticipation of a more detailed discussion of this topic later in the book, it is profitable to consider here the form which our histogram would take if an infinite universe were available for study, instead of only a relatively small sample. We could then make the class interval as small as we pleased, and we would still be assured that there would be enough variates in each class so that its frequency in comparison with the neighbor-

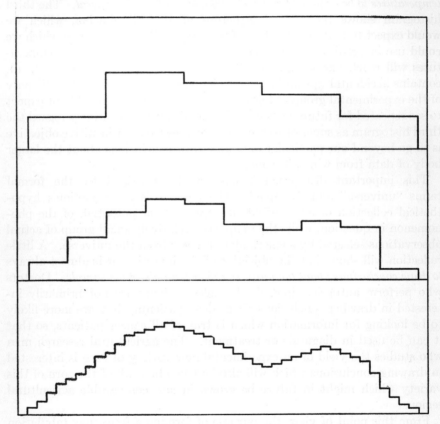

Figure 2-5-2.   Effect of Increasing Sample Size.

ing classes would be fairly stable, that is, that it would not be affected much by the accidental "give-and-take" of a few cases. As we made the class interval smaller and smaller, the tops of the rectangles would become narrower and narrower, and the contours of the histogram would approach closer and closer to a smooth, rounded curve, as shown in Figure 2-5-2. Carrying this argument to its limit, we see that an infinite universe could be represented by a smooth curve. From this point of view, we can state our conclusions in another way: In forming a histogram, we should choose a class interval of such a size that the general trend of the tops of the rectangles gives us the best possible approximation to the hypothetical smooth curve which would represent the universe. In many cases the investigator, after constructing a histogram, sketches a smooth curve over it in order to show what he believes the distribution of the universe to be like. Such sketches are shown in Figures 1-4-1, 1-4-2, and 1-4-3, page 10.

PROBLEMS

1. Table 2-5-1 is based upon admissions of dementia praecox patients to the Philadelphia General Hospital. Construct several histograms, using a different

TABLE 2-5-1.   Ages of 199 Dementia Praecox Patients upon Admission*

Age	No.	Age	No.	Age	No.	Age	No.
15	1	24	12	33	2	42	3
16	3	25	15	34	8	43	0
17	3	26	7	35	5	44	4
18	6	27	9	36	10	45	4
19	6	28	8	37	5	46	2
20	9	29	10	38	2	47	1
21	8	30	11	39	5	48	1
22	8	31	10	40	4	49	2
23	5	32	7	41	2	50	1

*Based upon data from *Practical Clinical Psychology* by Dr. Edward Strecker and Dr. Franklin Ebaugh, by permission of P. Blakiston and Son. Copyright by P. Blakiston and Son.

class interval for each. Which class interval, in your opinion, is best for the purpose of demonstrating the relationship between the age of the patient and the incidence of dementia praecox?

6.   OGIVES AND THEIR USES

The purpose of forming a histogram or a frequency polygon is primarily illustrative. Both are used to demonstrate, to the investigator or to the public, information already contained in the frequency tabulation, rather than to secure further information. Now we will describe another kind of graphical representation, called an *ogive*, which is occasionally used for purposes of illustration, but which has for its primary purpose the securing of additional information about the distribution.

The need for this new kind of representation arises when the investigator wishes to present the data in such a way that it will make clear the relative position of any individual in the group. Suppose that an applicant for employment tells you that he made a score of 72 in a mathematics examination which was given to his high school class just before graduation. With this information alone, you will have no more than a hazy notion of his ability. For all you know, the test may have been so easy that only the poorest men made scores as low as 72, or it may have been so difficult that a score of 72 indicates high ability. However, if the candidate gives you the further information that 83 per cent of the men in the class made lower scores than he did, you now have a definite basis for judgment. It is the purpose of this section to show how such relative rankings can be quickly computed for any frequency tabulation.

In describing the details of constructing an ogive, let us use the following specific problem. A civil service examination was given and it was announced that the highest 30 per cent of the examinees could expect immediate employment and that the next 40 per cent could expect positions to open up for them, in the order of their standing, during the next twenty-four months. The results of the examination are given in Table 2-6-1.

TABLE 2-6-1. Examination Scores

Boundaries	Limits	f	cum f	% cum f
69.5		↙ 0	0	
	70–72	2 ↘		
72.5		↙ 2	4	
	73–75	5 ↘		
75.5		7	13	
	76–78	14		
78.5		21	38	
	79–81	8		
81.5		29	53	
	82–84	15		
84.5		44	80	
	85–87	3		
87.5		47	85	
	88–90	6		
90.5		53	96	
	91–93	2		
93.5		55	100	

What is the most effective way of converting each examination score into a score showing the applicant's standing within the group?

First let us define the *cumulative frequency* (cum f) as the total number of variates which are below any given value of x, and the *percentage cumulative frequency* (% cum F) as the cumulative frequency reduced to a percentage basis by dividing by N. We compute these quantities as follows.

(1) List the boundaries, limits, and frequencies, with the boundaries staggered with respect to the limits and frequencies as shown in Table 2-6-1.

(2) Write a zero for the cumulative frequency of the lower boundary of the first class. Find the cum f for each other boundary by adding each f to the preceding cum f, as shown by the arrows. For example, the cum f of 72.5 is $0 + 2 = 2$; that at 75.5 is $2 + 5 = 7$; that at 78.5 is $7 + 14 = 21$, and so forth. Notice that the values of cum f are written *between* the classes, *opposite* the boundaries.

(3) The last number in the cum f column is N, the total number of variates (55 in the example). Divide each entry in the cum f column by N in order to obtain the percentage cumulative frequencies. These may be expressed as percentages, as shown in the example, or they may be left in the form of fractions or decimals.

(4) Plot an ogive or a percentage ogive of the data. An *ogive* is a graph of the cum f values plotted against the corresponding boundaries, and a *percentage ogive* is a similar graph in which percentage cumulative frequencies are used. Examples of each are shown in Figures 2-6-1 and 2-6-2. Notice particularly that each cum f or $\%$ cum f is plotted against a boundary, and not against a class mark.

Let us illustrate the use of an ogive by determining the standing of an examinee who made a score of 78. We enter the graph at 78 on the horizontal scale, go vertically up to the graphed line, and then horizontally to the cum f scale, as indicated by the arrows in Figure 2-6-1. We find that the value of cum f corresponding to 78 is 18, and this tells us that of the fifty-five examinees, only eighteen had scores lower than 78. If we perform the same operation on the percentage ogive (Figure 2-6-2), we obtain the same information in a more useful form: 34 per cent of the examinees made lower scores than 78. The examinee who made 78 is therefore not quite out of the running, but will have to wait almost twenty-four months for an opening.

The information described above can be conveyed in a very succinct way by expressing the examinee's standing in "percentile" form. The percentile rating of an individual within a group is the percentage of the membership of a group who have a lower standing than his. The examinee who made a score of 78 is at the *thirty-fourth percentile*, or, to state it more briefly,

$$78 = P_{34}$$

A percentage ogive is also useful for the inverse problem of finding the score corresponding to a given percentile. If, for example, it is found that there are supervisory positions open for the top 25 per cent of the examinees, then the qualifying score for such a position can be read immediately from the ogive by entering it at 75 per cent on the vertical scale and reading the

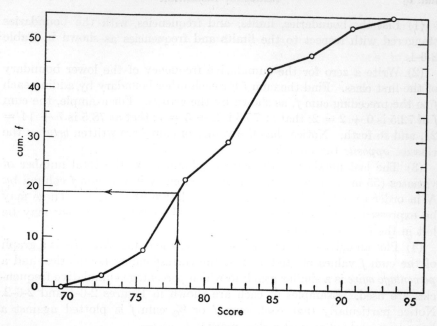

Figure 2-6-1.   An Ogive.

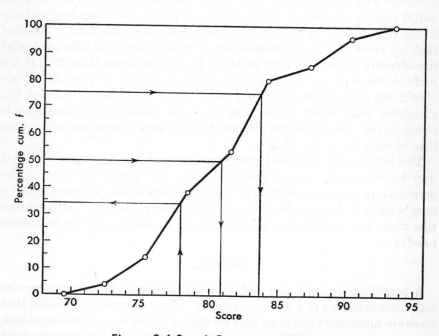

Figure 2-6-2.   A Percentage Ogive.

corresponding examination score, 84, as shown by the arrows in Figure 2-6-2. In addition to percentiles there are several other standard measurements of relative standing, as follows:

Quartile: The *first quartile* (Q_1) is the value of x such that one-fourth of the variates lie below it; it is in other words the twenty-fifth percentile. Similarly, Q_3 is the seventy-fifth percentile.

Deciles, octiles, and so forth, are defined similarly. For instance, the third decile is the value of x such that three-tenths of the variates lie below it, and the seventh octile is the value of x such that seven-eighths lie below it.

Median: The *median* (M) is the fiftieth percentile. From the arrows in Figure 2-6-2 we see that for this data, M is 81.2.

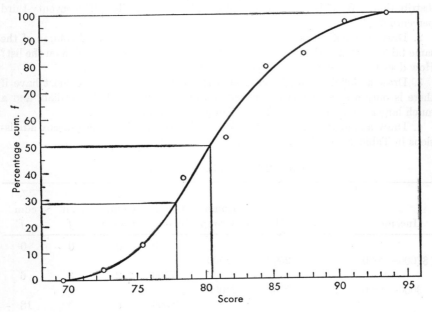

Figure 2-6-3.   A Smoothed Percentage Ogive.

If the ogive is to be used for estimating the percentile ratings of *future* examinees, then it may be well to draw a smoothed curve through the points, making the best possible compromise with all of them, but not necessarily going through them, as shown in Figure 2-6-3. In this way we avoid the local irregularities and retain only the general shape of the ogive. In doing this we assume that the small irregularities are characteristic only of the particular sample of fifty-five examinees and cannot be expected to recur in future samples. In using a smoothed ogive in this way, we are again estimating the properties of the universe from which the sample was taken. More exact methods of making such estimates will be discussed in later chapters.

It should be noted that percentile ratings can be used either to give information about the standing of an individual within the distribution, or to give information about the distribution itself. We learn something about the distribution of incomes in a given community if we are told that the fiftieth percentile, or median, is $3300; we learn more about the distribution if we find also that the first quartile is $3100 and the third quartile is $3900. The distribution could be described completely by listing all the percentiles.

PROBLEMS

1. Draw a smoothed percentage ogive for the data in Table 1-4-4, second column, using classes 45 to 49, 50 to 54, and so forth. What is the median of this distribution? What is the first quartile? The ninth decile? The seventy-third percentile?

2. Draw a smoothed percentage ogive of the grades in the third column of the same table. What is the percentile rating in language of the fifth man on the list? How does this compare with his percentile rating in mathematics?

3. Draw a sketch showing the general shape which a histogram must have if there is only a small interval between the first quartile and the median, and a much larger interval between the median and the third quartile.

4. Draw a smoothed percentage ogive of the ages of dementia praecox admissions in Table 2-5-1. Retain this ogive for future use.

TABLE 2-7-1.   The Lorenz Curve

Income	f	CM	Income of Group	Cum. Income	% Cum. Income	cum f	% cum f
				0	0	0	0
$2000– 3000	3	2500	7500				
				7500	2	3	6
3000– 4000	6	3500	21000				
				28500	6	9	18
4000– 5000	8	4500	36000				
				64500	13	17	34
5000– 7000	15	6000	90000				
				154500	32	32	64
7000–10000	7	8500	59500				
				214000	44	39	78
10000–15000	5	12500	62500				
				276500	57	44	88
15000–25000	3	20000	60000				
				336500	70	47	94
25000–45000	1	35000	35000				
				371500	77	48	96
45000–65000	2	55000	110000				
				481500	100	50	100

7. LORENZ CURVE

For the special purpose of displaying the degree of inequality of distribution of income, wealth, or property, a particular sort of graphical representation has been devised. It is called a *Lorenz curve* and it can be described most quickly by means of an example.

Table 2-7-1 shows the incomes of a sample of fifty men in a given profession. To form a Lorenz curve we begin by multiplying the *class mark* of each class by the *frequency* of that class, which gives us the *total income* of the class (column 4); we then form the cumulative values of these total incomes (column 5); and, finally, we reduce these cumulative frequencies to percentage values (column 6) by dividing them all by the total income, which in this case is $481,500. These cumulative values are staggered with respect to the original classes, to indicate that they refer to boundaries between classes. Next we form the cumulative *frequencies* at each boundary (column 7); and finally, we reduce these cumulative frequencies to per-

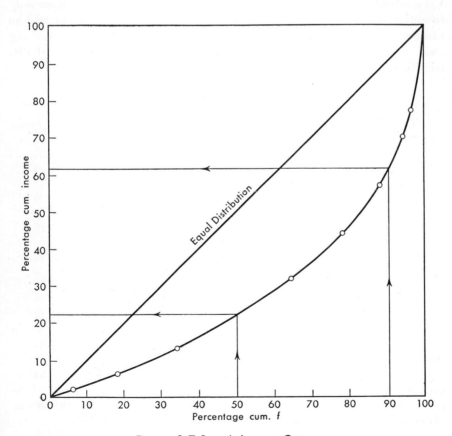

Figure 2-7-1.   A Lorenz Curve.

centage values (column 8) by dividing them all by the total frequency, which in this case is 50. A Lorenz curve of this data, shown in Figure 2-7-1, consists of a graph of the percentage cumulative income (column 6) plotted against the percentage cumulative frequency (column 8).

The reading of a Lorenz curve is illustrated by the arrows in Figure 2-7-1. If we wish to know what fraction of the total income goes to the lower paid half of the people, we find 50 per cent on the horizontal scale, find the corresponding point on the curve, and carry this over to the left-hand scale, as shown by the arrows. In this way we find that the lower 50 per cent of the earners receive only 23 per cent of the total salary. A simple variation of this technique will tell us about the upper fractions. For example, if we wish to know the percentage of the total income which is received by the upper 10 per cent of the earners, we enter the curve at 90 on the horizontal scale and read the result on the vertical scale. Since the lower 90 per cent of the earners receive 62 per cent of the total income, it follows that the upper 10 per cent receive 38 per cent of the total income.

To interpret the general appearance of the Lorenz curve, we have only to notice that if the total income were divided uniformly among all the earners, the curve would become a straight line. Thus the amount of sag away from the straight line is a measure of the non-uniformity of distribution.

PROBLEMS

1. The following table shows the distribution of property ownership in a certain community:

Property Value per Owner	Number of Owners
$000– $500	10
$500– $1000	12
$1000– $2000	4
$2000– $5000	7
$5000–$10000	4
$10000–$15000	3
$15000–$20000	1
$20000–$30000	4
$30000–$40000	3
$40000–$50000	2

Construct a Lorenz curve of this data.

2. Using the Lorenz curve which you constructed for Problem 1, find the following: the fraction of the total property owned by (a) the upper 10 per cent of the owners, (b) the lower 40 per cent of the owners, (c) the lower half of the owners. (d) Find the fraction of the owners who own half of the total property.

8. SUMMARY

The primary objective of the methods described in this chapter is to condense long tables of data into summarized forms which will (a) bring out the important characteristics of the distribution and (b) facilitate further work on the data. This objective is accomplished by sorting the data into groups according to size. The following terminology is used.

(1) *Variate.* Each of a set of tabulated numbers which form the statistician's raw material is called a variate. The symbol x is used to mean "any one of the variates."

(2) *Frequency tabulation.* A table showing the abundance, or frequency of occurrence, of variates of various sizes.

(3) *Histogram.* A graph presenting the data contained in a frequency tabulation.

(4) *Ogive.* A graph showing the total number, or the percentage, of variates falling below any given value of x.

(5) *Class.* Each group of variates in a frequency tabulation.

(6) *Upper limit and lower limit* (UL and LL). The largest and the smallest values of x which are to be included in a given class.

(7) *Upper boundary* and *lower boundary* (UB and LB). The dividing points between classes. The boundary between any two classes can be found by adding the upper limit of the preceding class to the lower limit of the following class and dividing by two.

(8) *Class mark* (CM). The midpoint of any class. It can be found by adding the upper limit of the class to the lower limit of the class and dividing by two.

(9) *Class Interval* (C). The width of each class. It can be found by subtracting the lower boundary of any class from the upper boundary of the class. Do *not* subtract the lower *limit* from the upper *limit*.

(10) *Frequency* (f). The number of variates in any class.

(11) *Cumulative frequency* (cum f). The total number of variates below any given value of x.

(12) *Percentage cumulative frequency* (% cum f). The percentage of variates which lie below any given value of x.

The procedure for forming a frequency tabulation is as follows.

(1) Choose an appropriate class interval. The interval is generally chosen in such a way as to divide the entire range of values of x into ten or fifteen equal intervals, but there is considerable latitude in the choice, depending upon the purpose of the tabulation. A detailed discussion of the optimum size will be found at the end of Article 5.

(2) Choose an appropriate set of class limits. The limits should be chosen in such a way as to facilitate the procedure of tabulation. The limits 20 to 29, 30 to 39, and so forth, are obviously more convenient than the limits 21 to 30, 31 to 40, and so forth, since in the former case it is

necessary to look at only the first digit in each number in order to assign it to its proper class.

(3) Go through the list of variates in the raw data and for each variate place a check mark in the appropriate class, as shown in Table 2-2-2.

(4) Count the number of check marks in each class and enter the total for each class under the f column of the tabulation.

The procedure for constructing a histogram is as follows.

(5) Choose a horizontal scale such that your graph will cover conveniently the range from the smallest to the largest of your variates. Choose a vertical scale such that your graph will extend from zero to the largest single frequency in your table.

(6) Locate on the horizontal scale the points corresponding to the class *boundaries*. These points divide the line into a number of segments, each of which corresponds to one of the classes.

(7) Upon each such segment, construct a column whose height corresponds to the frequency of the class which it represents.

The procedure for constructing a percentage ogive is as follows.

(8) Assign a cum f of zero to the lower boundary of the first class. Starting with this cum f, obtain the cum f of each of the other boundaries by adding to the preceding cum f the frequency of the intervening class, as described in Article 6.

(9) Divide each entry in the cum f column by the value of N (the total number of variates), and enter the result in the $\%$ cum f column.

(10) Construct a graph in which the horizontal scale is x and the vertical scale is $\%$ cum f. Plot each $\%$ cum f against the x of the corresponding boundary between classes, as shown in Figure 2-6-2.

(11) Connect the points in this graph by straight lines, if you are interested primarily in conclusions concerning the sample alone. Draw a smooth curve through the points if you are interested primarily in conclusions concerning the universe from which the sample was taken.

The procedure for using a percentage ogive is as follows.

(12) The percentile rating of an individual variate is found by locating its value of x on the horizontal scale, following a vertical line from this point up to the curve, following a horizontal line from this point on the curve over to the $\%$ cum f scale, and reading the corresponding value on this scale. This procedure is illustrated in Figures 2-6-2 and 2-6-3.

(13) The value of x corresponding to a given percentile rating is found by the reverse of the procedure just described. Locate the percentile rating on the $\%$ cum f scale, follow a horizontal line from this point over to the curve, follow a vertical line from this point down to the x scale, and read the value of x corresponding to this point. The procedure is demonstrated in Figures 2-6-2 and 2-6-3.

(14) *Deciles, quartiles, octiles,* and the *median* are special cases of percentiles and can be found by the procedure in (13) of this list. Definitions of these quantities are found in Article 6.

If the frequency tabulation describes the number of individuals owning various amounts of money, property, or income, and if the objective is to illustrate the degree of inequality of distribution of wealth among the individuals, then a Lorenz curve should be constructed. Detailed directions for constructing and using a Lorenz curve are given in Article 7.

CHAPTER
• 3 •
SOME MATHEMATICAL TOOLS

1. INTRODUCTION

Solving problems in statistics is likely to become very laborious if the
work is done by primitive methods. It is recommended that you master
the use of logarithms and learn to use a slide rule, so that you can reduce
the labor of computation and free your mind for the mastery of basic
principles. This chapter contains instructions for the use of these and
other mathematical tools. Articles 2 to 8, inclusive, deal with the elementary properties and uses of logarithms and slide rules, while the remaining
articles deal with mathematical symbols of special usefulness in statistics.
*If you are already familiar with the uses of logarithms and slide rules, go
directly to Article 9.*

2. LOGARITHMS

"A logarithm of a number is the power to which the base must be raised
in order to produce that number." This is the formal definition of a
logarithm, but unless you are well grounded in mathematics this definition
may be meaningless or vague to you. Perhaps a better approach is to
inspect an actual primitive logarithm table and study its properties. In
the first column of Table 3-2-1 are listed the values of two squared (4),
two cubed (8), and so on up to 2^7, or 128. In the second column are listed
the exponents, or powers, to which 2 was raised in order to give the numbers
in the first column. *The numbers in the second column are the logarithms
of the numbers in the first column, relative to the base 2.* For example, the

TABLE 3-2-1. Some Logarithms of Base 2

N	Log N
4	2
8	3
16	4
32	5
64	6
128	7

statement that *the logarithm of 32 to the base 2 is 5* means simply that *it is necessary to raise 2 to the fifth power in order to obtain 32*. This statement is commonly written in the abbreviated form

$$\log_2 32 = 5$$

where the subscript indicates the base being used. If we had chosen the number 3 instead of 2 for a base, the first column of Table 3-2-1 would have consisted of the numbers 3^2, 3^3, 3^4, and so forth. The choice of a base is governed by convenience, and the number 10 is generally chosen because it is also the base of our number system.

The antilogarithm is the inverse of the logarithm.* Thus, the statement that 32 is the antilog of 5 is equivalent to the statement that 5 is the log of 32.

Now notice that with the aid of Table 3-2-1 we can multiply numbers together by *adding* their logs and finding the antilog of the result. For instance, if we wish to multiply 4 by 8, we can proceed as follows: The log of 4 is 2, and the log of 8 is 3. The sum of these logs is 5. The antilog of 5 is 32, which is the answer to the problem. This relationship can be stated in the form

$$\log AB = \log A + \log B \tag{3-2-1}$$

Similarly, an inspection of the table will show that division of two numbers is accomplished by subtraction of their logs:

$$\log A/B = \log A - \log B \tag{3-2-2}$$

Thus to divide 128 by 16, we subtract 4 (the log of 16) from 7 (the log of 128), and obtain 3. Opposite 3 in the table we find its antilog, 8, which is the answer to the problem.

To square a number, or cube it, or raise it to any power, we multiply its log by that power:

$$\log (A^n) = n \log A \tag{3-2-3}$$

For example, to find the value of 4^3, we multiply 2 (the log of 4) by 3 (the power to which we wish to raise 4), obtaining 6. The antilog of 6 is 64, which is the required answer.

PROBLEMS

1. Using Table 3-2-1, find the values of the following: (a) $\log_2 128$, (b) $\log_2 8$, (c) antilog$_2$ 5.

2. Evaluate the following logs and antilogs: (a) $\log_5 25$, (b) $\log_3 27$, (c) antilog$_3$ 2, (d) antilog$_5$ 3.

---

*For the sake of brevity, these are most frequently called simply the "log" and the "antilog."

3. Complete the following computations with the aid of Table 3-2-1 and the laws of logarithms:

(a) $8^2 =$ (d) $4^3 =$

(b) $4 \times 16 =$ (e) $8 \times 16 =$

(c) $32/4 =$ (f) $128 \div 32 =$

3. LAWS OF EXPONENTS

Table 3-2-1 is of course of little use in its present form, because it contains the logs of only a few numbers. It does not, for example, tell us the logs of any numbers between 4 and 8, or of any fractional or decimal numbers. To see how the table can be extended to give us the log of any number, we must study the properties of exponents a little further.

The basic equations governing operations with exponents are as follows:

$$A^x A^y = A^{x+y} \tag{3-3-1}$$

$$A^x / A^y = A^{x-y} \quad (A \neq 0) \tag{3-3-2}$$

$$(A^x)^y = A^{xy} \tag{3-3-3}$$

For example, equation 3-3-1 tells us that 2^2 times 2^3 equals 2^5; equation 3-3-2 tells us that 2^7 divided by 2^4 equals 2^3; and equation 3-3-3 tells us that the square of 2^3 is 2^6. It will be noticed that these three equations contain the same information as those in the preceding article, but that here the information is expressed in the language of exponents rather than in the language of logs.

These relationships have a simple meaning so long as the exponents are integers. But, in order for our table of logarithms to be useful, we must include cases in which the exponent takes on any value whatever, including fractional or negative values. The expression 3^4 means 3 multiplied by itself four times, or $3 \times 3 \times 3 \times 3$. But what meaning can we assign to $3^{4.5}$, or to 3^{-4}, so that the three basic relations of exponents or logs will continue to be valid?

We can obtain an answer to this question by examining the three equations themselves. To assign a meaning to 2^1, for example, let us put A equal to 2, x equal to 4, and y equal to 3 in equation 3-3-2:

$$2^4 / 2^3 = 2^1$$

But $2^4 / 2^3$ is 16/8, or 2, and therefore 2 to the first power must equal 2 itself. In general,

$$A^1 = A \tag{3-3-4}$$

To assign a meaning to 2^0, let us put x equal to 4 and y equal to 4 in equation 3-3-2:

$$2^4 / 2^4 = 2^{4-4} = 2^0$$

From this we see that 2 to the zero power must equal one. In general,

$$A^0 = 1 \quad (A \neq 0) \tag{3-3-5}$$

To assign a meaning to expressions containing negative exponents, we can put x equal to 0 and y equal to n (where n means "any number whatever") in equation 3-3-2:

$$A^0/A^n = A^{0-n} = A^{-n}$$

Since A^0 is 1, this tells us that

$$A^{-n} = 1/A^n \quad (A \neq 0) \tag{3-3-6}$$

To assign a meaning to expressions like $2^{1/3}$, let x equal 1/3 and let y equal 3 in equation 3-3-3:

$$(2^{1/3})^3 = 2^1 = 2$$

In other words, $2^{1/3}$ is a number which, when cubed, is equal to 2. It is therefore the cube root of 2. To generalize this result, let x equal $1/n$ and let y equal n in equation 3-3-3:

$$(A^{1/n})^n = A$$

Now let us take the nth root of both sides of the equation:

$$A^{1/n} = \sqrt[n]{A} \tag{3-3-7}$$

By means of combinations of these equations, we can assign a meaning to any power of any number, whether the power is a positive or negative number, and whether it is a whole number or a fraction. For example, we can evaluate $2^{-3.5}$ as follows:

$$2^{-3.5} = 1/(2^{3.5}) = 1/(2^3 \times 2^{1/2}) = 1/(8\sqrt{2}) = 0.08838 \cdots$$

PROBLEMS

1. Evaluate the following, using the laws of exponents: (a) 3^{-2}, (b) $4^{2.5}$, (c) 17^0, (d) 9^1, (e) $9^{-1.5}$.

2. Evaluate the following logs: (a) $\log_2 1/8$, (b) $\log_9 3$, (c) $\log_4 1/32$.

4. CHOICE OF BASE 10

From the preceding article we can see that it is possible, although sometimes laborious, to compute the log of any number to any chosen base. It would be possible, for example, to extend Table 3-2-1 to include the logs of all numbers between 1 and 100, or between 1 and 1000, or any other range. But however long we made the table, there would be other numbers beyond its range, and the usefulness of the table for computing purposes would be limited. To avoid this limitation we must find a method by which we can tabulate the logs of only a few numbers and use these to find the logs of other numbers when needed. This can be accomplished in a particularly simple manner if we choose 10 as the base of the logarithm system, as we will show below. For this reason the base 10 is used universally whenever the logarithm table is to be used primarily as a computing aid. Such logs are usually called "common logs."

From the definition of a logarithm in Article 2, we see that

$$\log_{10} N = L \quad \text{if} \quad 10^L = N$$

Since $10^2 = 100$, for instance, we see that

$$\log 100 = 2*$$

Similarly,

$$\log 1000 = 3$$

and

$$\log \tfrac{1}{10} = -1$$

and

$$\log \sqrt{10} = 0.5000$$

Tables of common logarithms are widely used in many branches of applied mathematics. The various tables differ chiefly in the number of significant figures retained. In a "six-place" table, for example, the log of 7 is given as 0.845098, while in a "five-place" table it is given as 0.84510, and in a "four-place" as 0.8451. A six-place table is accurate to about one part in a million, and is used only where high precision is needed. Five-place tables (which give an accuracy of about one part in 100,000) are much more widely used. Where high accuracy can be sacrificed for the sake of speed, four-place or even three-place tables may be used. All such tables are used in the same way, and if you master the use of one table you can readily adapt your technique to other tables when greater accuracy or higher speed is desired. In this book we will use a four-place table, which is accurate to about one part in 10,000, or to about one part in 5000 if the "proportional parts" section of the table is used.

A table of four-place common logs is given in Appendix I. This table contains the logs of 900 numbers, from 1.00 to 9.99 inclusive, rounded off to four decimals. To find the log of a number not lying between these limits, we express the number as the product of two factors, one of which can be found in the table, and the other of which is a power of 10. We then find the log of the number by adding the logs of the two factors, according to equation 3-2-1. For example, the log of 2000 could be found as follows:

$$\log 2000 = \log (2 \times 1000) = \log 2 + \log 1000 = 0.3010 + 3 = 3.3010$$

Or, to find the log of 0.02,

$$\log 0.02 = \log 2 \times \tfrac{1}{100} = \log 2 + \log \tfrac{1}{100} = 0.3010 + (-2)$$

---

*It is customary to omit the subscript when 10 is used as the base. Following this convention, log 100 is understood to mean $\log_{10} 100$.

The value of this logarithm is 0.3010 minus 2, or -1.6990. It is convenient, however, not to combine the positive and negative parts in this way, but to keep them separate throughout the computation. For convenience, it is customary to subtract and add enough so that the negative part is 10 or a multiple of 10:

$$\log 0.02 = 8.3010 - 10$$

The preceding paragraph explains the principle of finding logs of numbers not in the table, but in practice it is more convenient to operate in accordance with a set of rules which embody the necessary principles. Such a set of rules is given below in detail.

TO FIND THE LOG OF A NUMBER

1. Insert an arrow after the first non-zero digit in the number. This arrow marks what we will call the "standard position." Round the number off, if necessary, so that it contains only three digits after the standard position. For example, if we need the log of 342.68, as given by four-place log tables, we write

$$\log 342.7 =$$
$$\uparrow$$

2. Count the number of digits between the standard position and the decimal point. Record this number, leaving space for a decimal to follow:

$$\log 342.7 = 2.$$
$$\uparrow$$

If the decimal point happens to be exactly at the standard position, this whole number is zero:

$$\log 3.427 = 0.$$

If the decimal point is to the *left* of the standard position, this whole number is negative. For example, in the number 0.003427 the decimal point is three spaces to the left of the standard position, and the whole number is therefore minus three, which we write as follows:

$$\log 0.003427 = 7. \qquad\qquad -10$$

3. Read the four-digit number beginning with the digit preceding the standard position (in our example, 3427). Find the first two of these (34) in the left-hand column under N in the log table (see a in Table 3-4-1); find the next digit (2) in the column headings under "Logarithms" (see b); and find the last digit (7) in the column headings under "Proportional Parts" (see c).

4. Step 3 identifies two columns and one row. Locate the two numbers which are in this row and in these two columns. Add these two numbers and write the result in the space reserved for the decimal part of the log.

TABLE 3-4-1.   Using a Table of Logarithms

	Logarithms							Proportional Parts			
			(b)						(c)		
N	0	1	2	3	—	—	6	7	8	—	
33 —				(d)					(e)		
(a) →34	5315	5328	5340	5353	— —	—	8	9	10	—	
35 —	—	—	—	— —	—	— —	—	—	— —		

In our example the two numbers are 5340 (see d) and 9 (see e); the sum of these is 5349. The final result then is

$$\log 342.7 = 2.5349$$

For the other examples in item two, the completed logs are

$$\log 3.427 = 0.5349$$

and

$$\log 0.003427 = 7.5349 - 10$$

TO FIND THE ANTILOG OF A NUMBER

1. Read the decimal part of the logarithm and find the next smaller number in the body of the table. For example, if we wish to find the antilog of $6.5338 - 10$, we find the number in the table which is just smaller than 5338; this "next smaller number" is 5328 (see Table 3-4-1).

2. Compute the difference between these two numbers, and find this difference (or the nearest number to it) which is in the same row and under "Proportional Parts." In the example, the difference is 5338 minus 5328, or 10, which we find in "Proportional Parts" opposite the row in which we are working.

3. The first two digits of the required antilog are found under N at the left-hand side of the row; the third digit is found under "Logarithms" at the top of the column containing the "next smaller number"; the fourth digit is found under "Proportional Parts" at the top of the column containing the difference. In the example, the first two digits are 34, which we find to the left of 5328, the third digit is 1, which we find above 5328, and the fourth digit is 8, which we find above 10 in the proportional parts section.

4. Place an arrow after the first of these digits; this marks the standard position. Read the whole number in the original logarithm, and locate the decimal point this many places to the right of the standard position. (If the whole number is *negative*, then locate the decimal point this many places to the *left* of the standard position.) In the example, the standard position is between the 3 and the 4, and the whole number in the logarithm is 6 minus 10, or minus 4. We therefore locate the decimal point four places to the left of the standard position. Our final result is

$$\text{antilog } 6.5338 - 10 = 0.0003418$$
$$\uparrow$$

In looking up logs or antilogs, you may find that your required number falls exactly halfway between two digits. In such cases it is customary, for the sake of uniformity, always to choose the even digit. For example, the antilog of 0.3307 is exactly halfway between 2.141 and 2.142, and we write

$$\text{antilog } 0.3307 = 2.142$$

With a little practice all these operations can be carried out rapidly and accurately, without writing down any of the intermediate numbers. Skill in the use of logarithms can be acquired only by practice, and it is recommended that you drill on these operations until you can carry them out rapidly and without hesitation. The time which you spend on drill in this way will be saved many times over in increased speed in later work.

You may prefer to interpolate directly in Appendix I, without using the proportional parts section. If you do so, your results will be accurate to within one part in 10,000. If you use the proportional parts table your results will be accurate to within one part in 5000.

PROBLEMS

1. Find the logs of the following numbers:

(a) 3497	(e) 3.841
(b) 296,400	(f) 146,300,000
(c) 0.000284	(g) 2.973
(d) 0.000,009,772	(h) 0.8160

2. Find the antilogs of the following numbers:

(a) 3.5872	(e) 6.2887
(b) 5.1775 − 10	(f) 0.9824
(c) 0.4087	(g) 9.4679 − 10
(d) 8.9739 − 10	(h) 7.5072 − 10

5. USES OF LOGARITHMS

The basic operations for which logarithms are useful are those of multiplication, division, and the finding of powers and roots of numbers, or any combination of these operations. The details of such computations can be learned most readily through the study of examples.

I. Multiplication

A press in a factory stamps out an average of 1463 metal parts per working hour. How many will it turn out in a year of 49 operating weeks, if the factory operates 42.5 hours per week?

To solve this problem, we must multiply 1463 times 49 times 42.5, and equation 3-2-1 tells us that we must add the logs of these three numbers, then look up the antilog of the result. We begin by arranging a framework, or plan, for the computation:

$$
\begin{aligned}
\log 1463 \; &= \\
\log 49 \; &= \\
\log 42.5 \; &= \underline{\hspace{3cm}} \;(+)\\
\log \text{answer} \; &= \\
\text{Answer} \; &=
\end{aligned}
$$

We next look up the logarithms of the three numbers, insert them in the framework of the computation, add them, and then look up the antilog of the result. The completed computation looks as follows:

$$
\begin{aligned}
\log 1463 \; &= 3.1653 \\
\log 49 \; &= 1.6902 \\
\log 42.5 \; &= \underline{1.6284} \;(+)\\
\log \text{answer} \; &= 6.4839 \\
\text{Answer} \; &= 3{,}047{,}000
\end{aligned}
$$

This number is accurate only to four significant figures, since we used four-place logs. The first three digits can be relied upon absolutely, and the fourth may contain a small error due to the accumulation of "rounding off" errors. In other words, the output per year will probably be between 3,046,000 and 3,048,000. If the stamping machine turned out exactly 1463 parts per hour, and the factory always operated exactly 42.5 hours per week for exactly forty-nine weeks, then it might be worth using five-place logs to obtain a more accurate answer, but it is more likely that the original numbers can be relied upon to only four significant figures or less, and in this case it would be wasteful and misleading to carry out the computation with higher accuracy.

II. Division

The distance from the earth to the sun is 92,900,000 miles. Light travels at the rate of 186,000 miles per second. How long does it require sunlight to reach us after it leaves the sun?

Here we must divide 92,900,000 by 186,000. Equation 3-2-2 tells us that we must subtract the log of 186,000 from the log of 92,900,000, and look up the antilog of the result. The computation is as follows:

$$\log 92,900,000 = 7.9680$$
$$\log \quad\ 186,000 = \underline{5.2695} \ (-)$$
$$\log \text{answer} \quad = 2.6985$$
$$\text{Answer} \quad\ = 499.4$$

Thus the time required is 499 seconds, or a little over 8 minutes.

III.   Powers

A meteorological sounding balloon is to be 8.23 feet in radius. How many cubic feet of gas will be required to fill it?

The formula for the volume of a sphere is $4/3\ \pi r^3$, where r is the radius of the sphere and π is 3.1416 . . . . To obtain the log of r^3, we must find the log of r and multiply it by 3, according to equation 3-2-3. The complete computation is as follows:

$$\log 8.23 \quad = 0.9154$$
$$\underline{\qquad 3} \ (\times)$$
$$\log 8.23^3 \quad = 2.7462$$
$$\log 3.142 \quad = 0.4972$$
$$\log 4 \qquad = \underline{0.6021} \ (+)$$
$$3.8455$$
$$\log 3 \qquad = \underline{0.4771} \ (-)$$
$$\log \text{answer} = 3.3684$$
$$\text{Answer} \quad\ = 2336$$

The required volume, rounded to three figures, is 2340 cubic feet.

IV.   Roots

A sunken storage tank is to be constructed in the form of a cube large enough to hold 3500 cubic feet of liquid. What should the dimensions of the tank be?

Since the volume of a cube is obtained by cubing the length of one side, we must find the cube root of 3500. If we rewrite equation 3-3-7 in the language of logs, we have

$$\log \sqrt[n]{A} = \frac{1}{n} \log A \qquad\qquad (3\text{-}5\text{-}1)$$

Thus, to find the cube root of 3500, we must find the log of 3500, divide it by 3, and look up the antilog of the result. The computation is as follows:

$$\log 3500 \quad = \quad 3.5441$$
$$3\overline{)3.5441}$$
$$\log \text{answer} = \quad 1.1814$$
$$\text{Answer} \quad\ = \quad 15.19 \text{ ft.}$$

V.   Operations with Negative Logarithms

All the operations described above proceed in much the same way when the whole number in the logarithm is negative.   The details are illustrated by the following examples:

(a) Multiply 0.008917 times 38.41 times 0.0868.   The computation is as follows:

$$
\begin{aligned}
\log 0.008917 &= 7.9502 - 10 \\
\log 38.41 &= 1.5844 \\
\log 0.0868 &= \underline{8.9385 - 10} \; (+) \\
\log \text{answer} &= 18.4731 - 20 \\
\text{Answer} &= 0.02972
\end{aligned}
$$

The whole number in the final log is 18 minus 20, or minus 2, and we insert the decimal point two spaces to the left of the standard position.

(b) Divide 0.00287 by 0.746.   The computation is as follows:

$$
\begin{aligned}
\log 0.00287 &= 17.4579 - 20 \\
\log 0.746 &= \underline{9.8727 - 10} \; (-) \\
\log \text{answer} &= 7.5852 - 10 \\
\text{Answer} &= 0.003848
\end{aligned}
$$

The first log would normally be written $7.4579 - 10$, but we add and subtract 10 in order to yield a positive number when we subtract the second log.   In the second column, $-20 - (-10) = -20 + 10 = -10$.

(c) Find the cube of 0.8745.   The computation is as follows:

$$
\begin{aligned}
\log 0.8745 &= 9.9418 - 10 \\
&\qquad\qquad\quad \underline{\hphantom{29.8254 - 3}3} \; (\times) \\
\log \text{answer} &= 29.8254 - 30 \\
\text{Answer} &= 0.6690
\end{aligned}
$$

The whole number is 29 minus 30, or -1.

(d) Find the cube root of 0.0004692.   The computations are as follows:

$$
\begin{aligned}
\log 0.0004692 &= 6.6714 - 10 \\
&\quad 3\underline{|26.6714 - 30} \; (\div) \\
\log \text{answer} &= 8.8905 - 10 \\
\text{Answer} &= 0.07772
\end{aligned}
$$

The first log would normally be written $6.6714 - 10$, but since we must divide by 3 we add and subtract enough so that the negative part will equal minus 10 after the division is performed.

PROBLEMS

Perform the following computations by means of the log table in Appendix I. For comparison, the times required by a moderately skilled computer for some of the problems are shown at the right.

1. 384×19600
2. 0.004173×41.38 (Time: 55 seconds)
3. $8468 \div 617$
4. $0.003282 \div 0.000176$ (Time: 60 seconds)
5. $0.00624 \div 0.08718$
6. $(1.572)^6$ (Time: 35 seconds)
7. $\sqrt{40.91}$
8. $\sqrt[3]{32150}$ (Time: 45 seconds)
9. $\sqrt[3]{0.0005281}$
10. $\sqrt[3]{\dfrac{8040 \times 91.6 \times 0.00264}{3.21 \times (0.0793)^2}}$ (Time: 2 minutes 55 seconds)

6. POPULATION AND INTEREST PROBLEMS

Logarithms are particularly useful in problems involving any quantity which varies at a rate which is proportional to the quantity itself. For example, if any colony of living organisms is provided with adequate food and space, the number of new organisms per unit of time will be proportional to the number of organisms already present. In particular, if a bacteriological culture contains one million bacteria, and is growing at the rate of 50,000 bacteria per hour, then it is reasonable to believe that in another culture containing three million bacteria, the rate of increase will be 150,000 per hour, since each million of the three millions will produce an increase of 50,000. We can describe this by stating that the hourly rate of increase is 5 per cent of the population.

Now let us suppose that a bacteriologist has estimated the population of such a culture, on the basis of sample counts, to be 850,000, and that he wishes to estimate the number which will be present after 40 hours if the bacteria continue to increase in the same way.

We might obtain a rough idea as follows. The population increases 5 per cent per hour; therefore in 40 hours it will increase 40×5 per cent or 200 per cent. The increase during 40 hours would therefore be 1,700,000, making a total of 2,550,000 at the end of 40 hours. This argument is however inaccurate, because it assumes that the rate of increase is always 42,500 per hour, whereas in fact the rate of increase will change as the population grows. A more accurate procedure would be to use the fact that at the end of any given hour the population is 105 per cent of what it was at the beginning of the hour; that is, that the hourly *ratio* of increase is 105 per cent or 1.05. We could then proceed as follows.

$$\begin{array}{ll} \text{Original population} & 850,000 \\[4pt] & \underline{\times 1.05} \\ \text{Population after 1 hour} & 892,500 \\[4pt] & \underline{\times 1.05} \\ \text{Population after 2 hours} & 937,125 \end{array}$$

and by continuing this through thirty-eight more steps we could find accurately the population to be expected after 40 hours.

This procedure can be greatly accelerated by the use of logs. If we start with the log of 850,000 and add the log of 1.05, we will have the log of the population after one hour; if we again add the log of 1.05, we will have the log of the population after two hours, and so forth. To solve our problem we must add the log of 1.05 forty times, which of course we can do in a single step:

$$\begin{array}{ll} \log 1.05 & = 0.0212 \\ & \underline{\quad 40 \quad} (\times) \\ 40 \times \log 1.05 & = 0.8480 \\ \log 850,000 & = \underline{5.9294} (+) \\ \log \text{answer} & = 6.7774 \\ \text{Answer} & = 5,990,000 \end{array}$$

We can formulate this procedure verbally as follows: The log of the population at any time is the log of the original population, plus the log of the *ratio of increase per interval* times the number of intervals which have elapsed. Or, if we let P_o stand for the original population, R the ratio of increase in a given time interval, n the number of such intervals which have elapsed, and P_n the population at the end of this time, then the equation for P_n is:

$$\log P_n = \log P_0 + n \log R$$

Any quantity which increases according to this equation is said to increase geometrically. The use of the formula is illustrated by the following examples:

(1) A city had a population of 58,900 in 1940 and a population of 61,700 in 1950. The owners of a department store plan to erect a new building in this city, which must be used for at least twenty years in order to repay its cost. In planning the size of the building, they wish to allow for expansion of the population of the city in future years. What population is to be expected by 1970?

To solve this problem, we must first find the annual ratio of increase, or its log. The following computation is self-explanatory:

$$\log 61,700 = 4.7903$$
$$\log 58,900 = \underline{4.7701} \;(-)$$

Increase in log in 10 years = 0.0202
Increase in log per year = 0.00202

$$\frac{20}{} \;(\times)$$

Increase in log in 20 years = 0.0404
$$\log \text{ of } P \text{ in } 1950 = \underline{4.7903} \;(+)$$

$$\log \text{ of } P \text{ in } 1970 = 4.8307$$
Population in 1970 = 67,720

The best estimate for the 1970 population, made from the data given here, is thus seen to be 67,700, rounded off to three significant figures.

(2) The conditions for geometric increase are fulfilled exactly in the increase of a sum of money lent at compound interest. We can use equation 3-6-1 directly for this problem if we let n be the number of interest periods, R the ratio of increase of the principal per interest period, and P_o and P_n the original and final principal. For example let us consider the following problem.

A sum of $2300 is deposited in a bank, and draws interest at 5 per cent, compounded semiannually. What will the principal be after twelve years?

Since the interest is compounded semiannually, there will be twenty-four interest periods during the twelve-year interval; therefore n is 24. Five per cent interest per year is equivalent to $2\frac{1}{2}$ per cent in six months, therefore the *ratio of increase* during each interest period is 1.025. The computations are as follows:*

$$\log R = 0.010724$$
$$\frac{24}{} \;(\times)$$
$$n \log R = 0.257376$$
$$\log P_o = \underline{3.3617} \;(+)$$

$$\log P_n = 3.6191$$
$$P_n = \$4160$$

3. A man wishes to purchase an endowment policy to educate his children. If he wishes to receive $10,000 from the policy fifteen years from now, how much should he pay, now, for the policy in full if his money will draw interest at 4% compounded annually?

This problem differs from the previous one only in that we know P_n

---

*This computation requires logarithms of more than four-place accuracy for R, since this log is to be multiplied by so large a number. We therefore use Appendix II, which contains a few six-place logs for interest problems.

and wish to obtain P_o. If we solve equation 3-6-1 for P_o we obtain

$$\log P_o = \log P_n - n \log R$$

We insert $P_n = \$10,000$, $n = 15$, and $R = 1.04$; we find that $\log P_o$ is 3.7445 and P_o is $5552.

PROBLEMS

1. If the interest rate is 3 per cent, compounded annually, what should be the present cost of an endowment policy if the beneficiary is to receive $10,000 at the end of twenty years?

2. In the preceding problem, how much should the beneficiary receive if he elects to cash the policy at the end of only fifteen years?

3. A Roman coin, estimated to be 2300 years old, was recently found near Naples. It is estimated to have been worth about 5¢. How much would it have been worth now if it had been deposited in a bank during the last 2300 years, drawing interest at 3 per cent compounded annually?

7. SLIDE RULE

A slide rule is a device for adding or subtracting logs mechanically. It has the great advantage of high speed, but it is limited in accuracy to about one part in a thousand. Since most of the computations to be made in statistical problems require no more accuracy than this, a slide rule is a very helpful tool for the statistician. It is recommended that you purchase a slide rule* and master its elementary uses before proceeding to the next chapter.

The principle of a slide rule can be grasped most readily as follows. Let us suppose that we wish to multiply two numbers (say 2 and 3) together by means of logarithms. We must add the log of 2 (which is 0.301) to the log of 3 (which is 0.477) and find the antilog of the sum. We could perform this addition mechanically by laying off 0.301 unit on a ruler, then laying off 0.477 unit on another ruler, and then laying the two lengths end to end and measuring the total length.

If the rulers used in the above process were to be used only for adding logs, we could save time by printing "2" at a point 0.301 unit from the end of each rule, "3" at a point 0.477 unit from the end, and so forth. In this way we would avoid the necessity for looking up the logs which are to be added. A slide rule actually consists of two rules printed in this way, as shown in Figure 3-7-1. It will be noticed that the divisions on the slide rule become closer and closer together as we go to the right; this is a consequence of the fact that the logs increase more and more slowly as we go to larger numbers.

---

*A satisfactory rule can be purchased at any price from 35¢ to $15.00. The Keuffel and Esser Student's Slide Rule at about $3.50 is recommended for all-round use.

The use of such a rule for multiplication is shown in Figure 3-7-1. If we place the left end of the upper rule opposite "2" on the lower rule (see a), then find "3" on the upper rule (see b), then read off the number

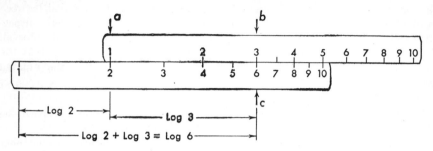

Figure 3-7-1. The Slide Rule.

opposite this on the lower rule (see c), the result must be the number whose log is log 2 plus log 3; it must in other words be the product of 2 times 3.

In practice the difficulty of using a slide rule lies chiefly in the reading of the scales. The following example will be useful in mastering the technique.

Illustrative Problem. Multiply 1.28 by 2.24. The successive steps (illustrated in Figure 3-7-2) are as follows:

1. Locate 1.28 on the D scale. We find by inspecting the rule that the space between the numbers 1 and 2 is separated into ten major divisions, labeled "1," "2," and so forth. These therefore must stand for 1.1, 1.2, 1.3, and so forth, up

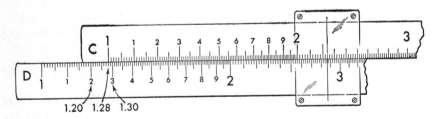

Figure 3-7-2. Multiplication with a Slide Rule.

to 1.9. The number 1.28 is therefore between the small 2 and the small 3. We see that the space between the small 2 and the small 3 is divided into ten sub-divisions; these must represent 1.21, 1.22, 1.23, and so forth up to 1.29. Our number is therefore on the eighth dividing line in this interval.

2. Slide scale C along until 1 on the C scale is opposite 1.28 on the D scale.

3. Find 2.24 on the C scale and place the runner, or movable vertical marker, on it. Upon inspection of scale C, we see that the interval between 2 and 3 is divided into ten major subdivisions, which must represent 2.1, 2.2, 2.3, and so forth. The

interval between 2.2 and 2.3 is divided into five subdivisions, and the fine dividing lines must therefore represent 2.22, 2.24, 2.26, and 2.28. We place the runner upon the second of these dividing lines, as shown in Figure 3-7-2.

4. Read the number on scale D which is now underneath the runner. We find by an inspection of the subdivisions that the runner lies in the interval between a dividing line representing 2.86 and one representing 2.88, and a careful inspection will show that it lies approximately one-fourth of the way along this interval. The entire interval represents 0.02, and one-fourth of this is 0.005, so that the number represented by the position of the runner is 2.865, which is the required answer, with some uncertainty in the final digit.

The computation described above takes far longer to describe than to perform. With a little practice you should be able to perform such a computation in full within fifteen or twenty seconds. The only pitfall in mastering this skill by yourself will lie in misinterpretations of the meanings of the subdivisions on the scales, and this pitfall can be avoided by careful inspection of the scales during your learning period.

PROBLEMS

Perform the following multiplications with a slide rule:

1. 3.81×1.92	4. 2.792×3.28
2. 1.745×4.85	5. 1.147×1.269
3. 1.019×9.17	6. 1.26×2.965

8. OTHER SLIDE RULE OPERATIONS

In the preceding section the use of a slide rule was illustrated only for numbers lying between 1 and 10. For other numbers, a slight modification of the procedure is necessary:

Example 1. Multiply 1972 by 316. Here we ignore the decimals, and multiply 1.972 by 3.16 in the usual way, obtaining 6.23. Next we round off both numbers and mentally estimate their product, as follows. The first number is approximately 2000, and the second is approximately 300, so that the answer should be approximately 600,000. With this information we see that the answer must be 623,000.

Example. 2. Multiply 0.000278 by 1,392,000. Again we ignore the decimals and multiplying 2.78 by 1.392, obtaining 3.87. Here, however, the estimation of the answer is more difficult, and it is better to rewrite the original numbers in the following forms: 1,392,000 is equal to 1.392 times one million, which is ten raised to the 6th power:

$$1{,}392{,}000 = 1.392 \times 10^6$$

Similarly, $$0.000278 = 2.78 \times 10^{-4}$$

These exponents can be found quickly by counting the number of spaces that the decimal is removed from the "standard position" referred to in Article 4. Now to complete our problem it is only necessary to multiply 10^6 by 10^{-4}, and this is equal (by 3-3-1) to 10^{6-4}, or 10^2. Our answer is therefore 3.87 times 10^2, or 387.

It is obvious that the operation of division can be performed by means of a simple modification of the procedure described above. For convenience, a set of specific rules for this and other operations are given in Table 3-8-1.

TABLE 3-8-1.   Use of the Slide Rule

MULTIPLICATION: Place 1 on C opposite first factor on D; find second factor on C and set runner on it; read answer under D. (If the second factor lies beyond the end of the D scale, start over, using the 1 at the *right* end of C instead of the 1 at the *left* end.)

DIVISION: Find numerator on D and place runner on it. Slide C until denominator on C is under runner. Read answer on D opposite 1 on C.

SQUARING: Find number on D and place runner on it; square of number is found on A under runner.

SQUARE ROOTS: Find number on A and place runner on it; square root is found on D under runner. (To decide whether to use the left or the right half of A, first make a mental estimate of about how large a number is to be expected.)

These operations are illustrated by the following examples:

1. Multiply 317 by 38.2. We place 1 on the C scale opposite 3.17 on the D scale, and then locate 3.82 on the C scale. We find that this number falls *beyond* the right-hand end of the C scale, so that the answer cannot be found in this way. We therefore begin again, placing the 1 which is at the extreme *right*-hand end of the C scale opposite 3.17 on the D scale. From here we proceed as usual, finding 3.82 on the C scale and reading the answer opposite it on the D scale. The required answer is 12,110.

2. Divide 0.00416 by 0.0000237. We find 4.16 on the D scale and place the runner on it. We then slide the C scale until 2.37 is under the runner. We read the number on the D scale which is opposite 1 on the C scale; this number is 1.755. To locate the decimal, we rewrite the problem in powers of 10. We wish to find 4.16 times 10^{-3}, divided by 2.37 times 10^{-5}. Since 10^{-3} divided by 10^{-5} is $10^{-3-(-5)}$ or 10^2, the answer is 1.755 times 10^2 or 175.5.

3. Find the square of 0.00796. We find 7.96 on D and place the runner upon it. Under the runner on scale A we find the number 634. To locate the decimal, we write 0.00796 in the form 7.96 times 10^{-3}. The square of 10^{-3} is 10^{-6} (equation 3-3-3), and the square of 7.96 is 63.4. Our result is therefore 63.4 times 10^{-6}, or 0.0000634.

4. Find the square root of 4.95. Here we find 4.95 on the *left* half of the A scale (the corresponding point on the right half indicates 49.5), place the runner upon it, and read the result under the runner on the D scale; it is 2.225.

5. Find the square root of 42,900,000. Here we can rewrite the number either as 4.29 times 10^7 or as 42.9 times 10^6. The second form is better for our purposes since it is easier to take the square root of 10^6 than of 10^7. We therefore find the square root of 42.9 (using the *right* half of scale A). This square root is 6.55, and the square root of 10^6 is 10^3. Our answer is therefore 6.55 times 10^3, or 6550.

PROBLEMS

Perform the following operations with a slide rule:

1. 417×3.92
2. 5680×0.00291
3. $847 \div 15.28$
4. $0.000642 \div 17920$
5. $58,900 \div 0.00895$
6. 7.97^2
7. $(0.000588)^2$

8. $\sqrt{184}$
9. $\sqrt{1840}$
10. $\sqrt{278,000}$
11. $\sqrt{0.00278}$
12. $\dfrac{352 \times 19.74}{11.48}$
13. $\sqrt{\dfrac{5.93 \times 64.2}{247 \times 0.0985}}$

9.   SUMMATION SYMBOL

A very useful symbol in statistics is the Greek capital letter sigma (Σ), which means "the sum of the following variates." For example, Σx means "the sum of all the x's," and Σxy means "the sum of all the products of x times y." For the data given in Table 3-9-1, for example,

TABLE 3-9-1.   Data for Five Children

	1	2	3	4	5	6	7	8	9
	Height	Age	IQ	Grade	Height Plus Age	Height Minus Age	Grade Times Height	Height Times Age	Age Squared
	x	y	z	C	$x + y$	$x - y$	$4x$	xy	y^2
	53	10	80	4	63	43	212	530	100
	63	11	115	4	74	52	252	693	121
	51	9	95	4	60	42	204	459	81
	50	8	120	4	58	42	200	400	64
	58	12	75	4	70	46	232	696	144
Σ	275	50	485	20	325	225	1100	2778	510
Σ/N	55	10	97	4	65	45	220	555.6	102

Σx means the sum of the heights of the five children, or 275, while Σy means the sum of their ages, or 50. In the same way, we see that $\Sigma(x + y)$ is the sum of the terms in the fifth column, or 325. From the remaining columns, we see that $\Sigma 4x$ is 1100, Σxy is 2778, and Σy^2 is 510.

In the derivations of formulas, it is frequently desirable to rewrite these composite sums in simpler forms. If, for example, we require the value of $\Sigma(x + y)$, and know already the values of Σx and Σy, it would be advantageous to be able to compute the former sum directly from the latter two, without computing the separate values of $x + y$. To see that this is possible, let us write out the meaning of these sums in equation form. The symbol Σx means "the first value of x plus the second value of x plus . . . and so forth":

$$\Sigma x = x_1 + x_2 + x_3 + \cdots + x_N \qquad (3\text{-}9\text{-}1)$$

where N is the number of variates. Similarly,

$$\Sigma y = y_1 + y_2 + y_3 + \cdots + y_N$$

and $\qquad \Sigma(x + y) = (x_1 + y_1) + (x_2 + y_2) + \cdots + (x_N + y_N)$

If we rearrange the terms on the right-hand side of the above equation, we have

$$\Sigma(x + y) = (x_1 + x_2 + x_3 + \cdots + x_N) + (y_1 + y_2 + \cdots + y_N)$$

or, replacing the two parts of the right-hand side by their equivalents in summation notation,

$$\Sigma(x + y) = \Sigma x + \Sigma y \qquad (3\text{-}9\text{-}2)$$

The validity of this equation can be observed experimentally by noting that in Table 3-9-1 the sum of the $x + y$ column (325) is equal to the sum of the x column (275) plus the sum of the y column (50).

A similar equation, the proof of which will be left to the student, is

$$\Sigma(x - y) = \Sigma x - \Sigma y \qquad (3\text{-}9\text{-}3)$$

This equation can be experimentally verified by noting that the sum of column 6 in Table 3-9-1 is equal to the sum of column 1 minus the sum of column 2.

The next of this series of equations is

$$\Sigma Cx = C\Sigma x \qquad (3\text{-}9\text{-}4)$$

where C stands for any number which does not change as we go from one entry to the next in our table. Such a number is called a *constant*. An example is shown in the fourth column of Table 3-9-1, which gives the grade in which each child is enrolled. Since all are in the fourth grade, this value is a constant. We can verify equation 3-9-4 by observing that the sum of column 7 is equal to four times the sum of column 1.

The last equation of this series is

$$\Sigma C = NC \qquad (3\text{-}9\text{-}5)$$

For example, we see that the sum of column 4 is 5 (the number of variates) times 4 (the constant which we are summing).

Upon a first reading of the four equations above, the student is likely to feel that they contain only trivial information which is obviously true.

As a warning against too uncritical an acceptance of them, let us point out that we cannot apply the same procedure to the sum of a set of products. Column 8 of Table 3-9-1 contains the products of x times y, and the sum of these products is 2778. If we add the x and y columns first and then multiply the results together we have 275 times 50, or 13,750. In other words, it is *not* true that $\Sigma xy = (\Sigma x) \times (\Sigma y)$.

If the var.ates are grouped into a frequency tabulation, then it is necessary in finding Σx to multiply each value of x by the number of times which it occurs, that is, by its frequency. For example, in Table 3-9-2,

TABLE 3-9-2. Summation of a Frequency Table

x	f	fx
4	3	12
7	4	28
10	9	90
13	8	104
16	1	16
Σ	25	250
Σ/N		10

we obtain Σx by first multiplying each entry in the x column by the corresponding number in the f column, entering the result in the fx column, and adding the results. We see that Σx for this table is 250. This convention will be used throughout the book, and you should remember that *the summation symbol, when applied to a frequency tabulation, implies that each variate is to be multiplied by its frequency before adding.*

PROBLEMS

1. Write a detailed proof of equation 3-9-3.
2. Write a detailed proof of equation 3-9-4.
3. Write a detailed proof of equation 3-9-5.
4. Find the value of $\Sigma(2x - 3y)$, in Table 3-9-1, and check your result by equations 3-9-4 and 3-9-3.
5. Compute the value of Σx^2 in Table 3-9-1.
6. Compute the value of $(\Sigma x)^2$ in Table 3-9-1, and compare it with the value of Σx^2 obtained in the preceding problem.
7. Find the value of Σx^2 in Table 3-9-2.

10. SYMBOL FOR ARITHMETIC MEAN

In statistics the term *average* is used rather loosely to indicate any single value which is selected because it is in some way representative of its group, and there are several ways of selecting such a representative value. The term *arithmetic mean* is used to indicate a specific kind of average, namely, that which is obtained by adding the variates and dividing the sum by the number of variates. The arithmetic mean of a variate x is denoted by the symbol $\bar{x}$, and is defined by the equation

$$\bar{x} = \Sigma x/N \qquad\qquad (3\text{-}10\text{-}1)$$

where N is the total number of variates. For the data in Table 3-9-1 there are five variates, so that $\bar{x}$ is equal to 275 divided by 5, or 55. In Table 3-9-2 there are twenty-five variates, as we see by adding the frequency column, and $\bar{x}$ is equal to 250 divided by 25, or 10.

The symbol can be used to indicate the mean of any variate or any combination of variates. For example, we can obtain the value of $\overline{x + y}$ by dividing the sum of the fifth column of Table 3-9-1 by 5. In this way we see that $\overline{x + y} = 65$; and, similarly, $\overline{x - y} = 45$, $\overline{xy} = 555.6$, and $\overline{y^2} = 102$.

When we need an arithmetic mean of a composite quantity it is sometimes possible to obtain it by combining the means of the components. To prove that $\overline{x + y}$ can be obtained in this way, let us write it in summation form by applying equation 3-10-1:

$$\overline{x + y} = \Sigma(x + y)/N$$

This sum can be separated by applying equation 3-9-2;

$$\overline{x + y} = \Sigma x/N + \Sigma y/N$$

and these two sums can be expressed as arithmetic means by applying equation 3-10-1, giving us, finally,

$$\overline{x + y} = \bar{x} + \bar{y} \qquad\qquad (3\text{-}10\text{-}2)$$

By applying this technique to equations 3-9-3, 3-9-4, and 3-9-5, we obtain the following set of rules for manipulating the symbol for arithmetic mean. The detailed proofs are left to the student.

$$\overline{x - y} = \bar{x} - \bar{y} \qquad\qquad (3\text{-}10\text{-}3)$$

$$\overline{Cx} = C\bar{x} \qquad\qquad (3\text{-}10\text{-}4)$$

$$\overline{C} = C \qquad\qquad (3\text{-}10\text{-}5)$$

The row labeled Σ/N in Table 3-9-1 will show you what these equations mean in practice. We see that $\bar{x}$ is 55 and $\bar{y}$ is 10. From the fifth column we see that $\overline{x + y}$ is 65, as required by equation 3-10-2; and from the sixth column we see that $\overline{x - y}$ is 45, as required by equation 3-10-3. From the seventh column we see that $\overline{4x}$ is 220, as required by equation 3-10-4; and from the fourth column we see that $\overline{4}$ is 4, as required by equation 3-10-5.

These four equations will be used frequently in the derivations of later formulas, and they should be studied carefully. You may prefer to remember them in verbal form, as follows:

Equation 3-10-2. The mean of a sum of two variates is the sum of their means.

Equation 3-10-3. The mean of the difference of two variates is the difference of their means.

Equation 3-10-4. The mean of a constant times a variate is the constant times the mean of the variate.

Equation 3-10-5. The mean of a constant is that constant.

The reader should be cautioned against careless use of the symbol for the arithmetic mean, since expressions which look almost alike may have totally different values. The following specific examples may be noted:

1. The mean of the square of a variate is written $\overline{x^2}$, and the square of the mean of a variate is written $\bar{x}^2$, and the two are *not in general equal*. In Table 3-9-1, for example, $\bar{y}$ is 10, and therefore $\bar{y}^2$ is 100. The value of $\overline{y^2}$, on the other hand, is 102, as we can see from the last column of the table.

2. The mean of the product of x and y is written $\overline{xy}$, while the product of the means of x and y is written $\bar{x}\bar{y}$. Again the two are not in general equal. In Table 3-9-1, for example, $\bar{x}\bar{y}$ is 55 times 10, or 550, while $\overline{xy}$ is 555.6.

PROBLEMS

1. Write a formal proof of equation 3-10-3.
2. Write a formal proof of equation 3-10-4.
3. Write a formal proof of equation 3-10-5.

4. Find the value of $\bar{z}$, $\overline{x+z}$, and $\overline{yz}$ in Table 3-9-1. How does $\overline{yz}$ compare in size with $\bar{y}\bar{z}$?

11.   USES OF SUMMATION SYMBOL

In order for you to follow the derivations of formulas later in the book, it will be necessary for you to develop some skill in the manipulation of these symbols. The purpose of this article is to provide you with an opportunity to develop this skill, and at the same time to derive some auxiliary formulas which will be useful in later developments.

Example 1. If n is a variate which takes on the values 1, 2, 3, 4, and so forth, up to N, what is the value of $\bar{n}$? To solve this problem we begin by writing the definition of Σn in expanded form as follows:

$$\Sigma n = 1 + 2 + 3 + \cdots + N$$

Now let us rearrange these terms in pairs, pairing the first term with the last term, the second term with the next to last term, and so forth:

$$\Sigma n = [1 + N] + [2 + (N - 1)] + [3 + (N - 2)] + \cdots$$

Now notice that if N is even there are $N/2$ of these pairs, and that each pair has the same total value, namely $N + 1$. We can therefore write the sum in the form

$$\Sigma n = (N/2)(N + 1)$$

The mean of n is equal to Σn divided by the number of variates, which is N. Upon dividing by N, we obtain:

$$\bar{n} = (N + 1)/2 \qquad\qquad (3\text{-}11\text{-}1)$$

For example, the mean of the numbers 1 to 100 is $(100 + 1)/2$, or $50\frac{1}{2}$. The proof for odd values of N is left to the student as an exercise.

 Example 2. If n is a variate which takes on the values 1, 2, 3, 4, and so forth, up to N, what is the mean value of $\overline{n^2}$? This apparently simple problem can be solved only by an indirect approach. We begin by observing that $n^3 - (n - 1)^3 = 3n^2 - 3n + 1$, as we can verify by multiplying out the cube on the left. Now if we sum both sides of this equation we will have

$$\Sigma[n^3 - (n - 1)^3] = \Sigma[3n^2 - 3n + 1]$$

The sum on the left can be evaluated by inspection, since it consists of the series of terms $1^3 - 0^3$, $2^3 - 1^3$, $3^3 - 2^3$, and so forth, up to $N^3 - (N - 1)^3$. When we sum these terms, the last part of each term cancels the first part of the preceding term, leaving only N^3 for the sum of the series. Inserting this value for the sum of the left-hand side, we have

$$N^3 = \Sigma(3n^2 - 3n + 1)$$

or, dividing both sides by N,

$$N^2 = \Sigma(3n^2 - 3n + 1)/N$$
$$= \overline{3n^2 - 3n + 1} \quad \text{(by 3-10-1)}$$
$$= \overline{3n^2} - \overline{3n} + \overline{1} \quad \text{(by 3-10-2)}$$
$$= 3\overline{n^2} - 3\bar{n} + 1 \quad \text{(by 3-10-4 and 3-10-5)}$$

Our objective is to find $\overline{n^2}$, so that we must now solve for this quantity. The result is

$$\overline{n^2} = (N^2 + 3\bar{n} - 1)/3$$

or, if we insert the value of $\bar{n}$ from equation 3-11-1 and simplify,

$$\overline{n^2} = (2N^2 + 3N + 1)/6 \qquad\qquad (3\text{-}11\text{-}2)$$

PROBLEMS

 1. Find the arithmetic mean of all the numbers from 1 to 11, inclusive. From one to 5299, inclusive.

 2. Find the mean of the squares of the numbers from 1 to 9, inclusive. From 1 to 45, inclusive.

3. Derive an equation for $\overline{n^3}$, using the methods of the preceding proof. (Hint: begin with the expression $n^4 - (n - 1)^4$; expand this expression and sum the resulting equation.)

4. Derive equation 3-11-1 for odd values of N.

12.   SUMMARY

Chapter 3 consists of two primary topics: first, the use of logs and slide rules as computing aids; second, the presentation of some basic operational rules of mathematics for later use throughout the book. These topics will be reviewed separately in the following outline:

I.   Computing Aids

(1) LOGARITHMS.   A common logarithm is defined by the equation

$$\log A = L \quad \text{if } 10^L = A$$

The basic laws of logarithms are given by equations 3-2-1, 2, and 3; and 3-5-1:

$$\log AB = \log A + \log B$$
$$\log A/B = \log A - \log B$$
$$\log A^n = n \log A$$
$$\log \sqrt[n]{A} = (1/n) \log A$$

The uses of these laws for rapid computation are illustrated in Articles 5 and 6.

(2) SLIDE RULE.   All the various manipulations with logs can be performed with a slide rule with an accuracy of about one part in a thousand.   The operational procedures are summarized in Table 3-8-1.

II.   Basic Mathematical Tools for Statistics

(1) MANIPULATIONS OF EXPONENTS.   The basic laws are given by equations 3-3-1 to 3-3-7:

$$A^x A^y = A^{x+y}$$
$$A^x/A^y = A^{x-y}$$
$$(A^x)^y = A^{xy}$$
$$A^1 = A$$
$$A^0 = 1 \quad (A \neq 0)$$
$$A^{-n} = 1/A^n \quad (A \neq 0)$$
$$A^{1/n} = \sqrt[n]{A}$$

These equations are illustrated in Article 3.

(2) SUMMATION SYMBOL.   This symbol is defined by equation 3-9-1:

$$\Sigma x = x_1 + x_2 + x_3 + \cdots + x_N$$

or, for a frequency tabulation,

$$\Sigma x = f_1 x_1 + f_2 x_2 + f_3 x_3 + \cdots + f_N x_N$$

The operational rules governing the use of the symbol are given by equations 3-9-2 to 3-9-5:

$$\Sigma(x + y) = \Sigma x + \Sigma y$$

$$\Sigma(x - y) = \Sigma x - \Sigma y$$

$$\Sigma(Cx) \quad = C\Sigma x$$

$$\Sigma C \qquad = NC$$

(3) BAR SYMBOL FOR THE ARITHMETIC MEAN. This symbol is defined by equation 3-10-1:

$$\bar{x} = \Sigma x/N$$

The operational rules governing its use are given by equations 3-10-2 to 3-10-5:

$$\overline{x + y} = \bar{x} + \bar{y}$$

$$\overline{x - y} = \bar{x} - \bar{y}$$

$$\overline{Cx} \quad = C\bar{x}$$

$$\overline{C} \quad = C$$

Examples of the uses of these symbols are given in Article 11.

CHAPTER

• 4 •

ARITHMETIC MEAN AND STANDARD DEVIATION

1. INTRODUCTION

In Chapter 2 we studied methods by which a large body of data can be expressed in a concisely summarized form by means of a frequency tabulation and a histogram. In this chapter we will introduce an alternative form of description, which is mathematical instead of graphical. In this new kind of description, we compute a few key numbers which describe or measure various properties of the distribution. A complete discussion of these numerical measurements will be given in Chapter 7; but two of them must be introduced now because of the role which they play in the development of the theory to come. These two are the arithmetic mean and the standard deviation.

2. ARITHMETIC MEAN

The definition of this quantity has already been given in equation **3-9-1,** which tells us that the arithmetic mean is the sum of all the variates divided by the number of variates. For ungrouped data, the arithmetic mean can be computed directly from this definition, as shown in Article 9 of the preceding chapter.

For grouped data, we proceed as follows. The average value of the variates in any single class is likely to be in the neighborhood of the class mark, and, lacking more exact information, we proceed as if all the variates had exactly the value of the class mark. We introduce a column headed "x," in which we list the class marks, and a column headed "fx," in which each x is multiplied by the frequency of the class, as shown in Table 4-2-1. We sum this last column (giving 585 in the example), and divide by N (which is 45 in the example, as we see by summing the f column), giving 585/45 or 13 for the value of $\bar{x}$. For reference purposes we will describe this operation by means of a standard equation:

$$\bar{x} = \Sigma fx/N \quad \text{(for grouped data)} \tag{4-2-1}$$

TABLE 4-2-1.   Arithmetic Mean from Definition

Limits	f	x	fx
4– 6	1	5	5
7– 9	7	8	56
10–12	12	11	132
13–15	14	14	196
16–18	8	17	136
19–21	3	20	60
	45		585

$$\bar{x} = 585/45 = 13$$

In general, this method of finding $\bar{x}$ is far too slow for practical computations and should be used only when the frequency tabulation is very short or when the class marks are whole numbers and not very large. More rapid methods will be presented in Articles 4 and 5.

PROBLEMS

1. Find the mean of the forty temperatures in Table 2-3-2. How does this compare with the mean of the same temperatures as obtained from the original data in Table 2-3-1? How do you account for the difference?

2. Find the arithmetic mean for Table 2-2-2. Would you expect the same mean for the data in Table 2-2-1?

3.   STANDARD   DEVIATION

Before defining the standard deviation, let us define an intermediate quantity. The deviation of a variate is the difference between the variate and the arithmetic mean. It is denoted by the symbol d:

$$d = x - \bar{x} \tag{4-3-1}$$

For example, the deviation of the second variate in Table 4-3-1 is 5 minus 7, or minus 2. The *standard deviation* is a special kind of average of the deviations; it is the square root of the arithmetic mean of the squares of the deviations. It is denoted by the Greek letter small sigma:

$$\sigma = \sqrt{\overline{d^2}} = \sqrt{\overline{(x - \bar{x})^2}} \tag{4-3-2}$$

The notation in this equation is very compact, and it requires careful reading. The equation tells us that the standard deviation is to be found by computing the deviations of all the variates, squaring each of these deviations, adding these squares, dividing by the number of variates, and finding the square root of the result.

The standard deviation can be computed directly from this defining equation for both grouped and ungrouped data. For ungrouped data, the procedure is shown in Table 4-3-1. We begin by computing the

TABLE 4-3-1. Standard Deviation of Ungrouped Data

x	d	d^2	
7	0	0	$\Sigma x = 42$
5	-2	4	$N = 6$
2	-5	25	
11	4	16	$\bar{x} = 7$
8	1	1	$\Sigma d^2 = 50$
9	2	4	
			$\overline{d^2} = 50/6 = 8.33$
42		50	$\sigma = \sqrt{8.33} = 2.89$

arithmetic mean, which we find to be equal to 7. We subtract 7 from each of the variates in the x column (obtaining a negative result whenever the value of x is less than 7) and enter the results in the column headed d. We then square each value of d and enter the results in the column headed d^2. We next sum this column (obtaining 50 in the example) and then divide the result by the number of variates (6), which gives us $\overline{d^2}$ (8.33 in the example). We then take the square root of $\overline{d^2}$, obtaining 2.89, which is the standard deviation.

For grouped data, the procedure is shown in Table 4-3-2. We begin by finding $\bar{x}$ in the usual way (in this case $\bar{x}$ is 13, as we found from Table

TABLE 4-3-2. Standard Deviation for Grouped Data

x	f	d	d^2	fd^2	
5	1	-8	64	64	$\Sigma d^2 = 576$
8	7	-5	25	175	
11	12	-2	4	48	$N = 45$
14	14	1	1	14	
17	8	4	16	128	$\overline{d^2} = 576/45 = 12.8$
20	3	7	49	147	
	45			576	$\sigma = \sqrt{12.8} = 3.58$

4-2-1), and we then subtract this value of $\bar{x}$ from each value of x and enter the result under the d column. We square each of these values of d, and multiply each such square by f, and enter the result in the fd^2 column. We next sum this column (obtaining 576 in the example), and divide by

N (which is 45). This gives us 12.8 for $\overline{d^2}$. Finally we take the square root of this, giving us 3.58 for σ.

This direct method is not to be recommended for general use. It is included here to familiarize you with the basic definition of the standard deviation, but unless the set of data is particularly simple, more rapid methods are to be preferred.

It might appear to some readers that we are wasting time in first squaring the deviations, averaging them, and then taking the square root, thereby undoing what we did in the first place. A little reflection, however, will show that this is not quite the same as simply averaging the deviations. In Table 4-3-1, for example, the absolute* deviations are 0, 2, 5, 4, 1, and 2, and the mean of these is 2.33, which is a little smaller than the standard deviation. The standard deviation is a kind of average of the deviations, but it is an average in which the large deviations are given somewhat more weight than the smaller ones.

PROBLEMS

1. Compute the standard deviation of the following set of numbers: 14, 17, 12, 10, 19, and 18.

2. Compute the standard deviation of the following data:

x	f
13–15	2
16–18	5
19–21	9
22–24	5
25–27	2

4. RAPID METHODS FOR UNGROUPED DATA

The methods in the preceding sections would be excessively lengthy if applied to most of the bodies of data encountered in practical problems. The material with which a statistician deals usually consists of far more variates than do the illustrative problems used in this book, and the variates themselves are likely to be more complicated numbers. In this and the following section we will develop rapid methods for computing the mean and the standard deviation.

The variates, or the class marks, are usually rather simple numbers, while the arithmetic mean is usually a lengthy decimal, and therefore so is each of the deviations. The computations can be shortened, therefore, if we avoid the use of the deviations and work directly with the variates themselves. To see how this is possible, let us square out the right-hand side of equation 4-3-2, as follows:

$$\sigma = \sqrt{\overline{(x - \bar{x})^2}} = \sqrt{\overline{(x^2 - 2x\bar{x} + \bar{x}^2)}}$$

---

*The absolute value of any number is its numerical value with the plus or minus sign ignored.

Now, by equation 3-10-2, we can rewrite the mean of the sum as the sum of the means:

$$\sigma = \sqrt{\overline{x^2 - 2x\bar{x} + \bar{x}^2}}$$

In the middle term of this equation, both 2 and $\bar{x}$ are constants, and equation 3-10-4 tells us that they can be written in front of the averaging sign:

$$\sigma = \sqrt{\overline{x^2} - 2\bar{x}\bar{x} + \bar{x}^2}$$

The middle term is now seen to be simply $2\bar{x}^2$, and it can be combined with the right-hand term:

$$\sigma = \sqrt{\overline{x^2} - \bar{x}^2} \qquad\qquad (4\text{-}4\text{-}1)$$

In words, this equation tells us that the standard deviation is the square root of the mean of the squares of the variates minus the square of the mean of the variates. Its use is demonstrated in Table 4-4-1, which you will find to be self-explanatory.

TABLE 4-4-1.　　Use of Equation $\sigma = \sqrt{\overline{x^2} - \bar{x}^2}$

x	x^2	
2	4	
9	81	$\overline{x^2} = 320/10 = 32$
7	49	
8	64	$\bar{x} = 50/10 = 5$
3	9	
4	16	$\bar{x}^2 = 5^2 = 25$
8	64	
5	25	$\sigma = \sqrt{32 - 25} = 2.65$
2	4	
2	4	
50	320	

Another possibility for saving time arises when the variates are large numbers which do not differ very much from one another, such as those in the left-hand column of Table 4-4-2. In such cases a great deal of time can be saved by first subtracting a fixed number from all of the variates in order to reduce them to a more manageable size. Let x_0 stand for such a fixed number, or *zero point*, chosen at the investigator's convenience. Our objective is then to express $\bar{x}$ and σ in terms of $x - x_0$ rather than in terms of x alone. To do so, let us observe that $x = x_0 + (x - x_0)$, and then let us take the mean of both sides of this equation. The result is:

$$\bar{x} = \overline{x_0 + (x - x_0)}$$

The right-hand side of this equation can be separated into two means by applying equation 3-10-2, giving us

$$\bar{x} = x_0 + \overline{(x - x_0)} \qquad (4\text{-}4\text{-}2)$$

In words, this equation tells us that the mean of any variate is the mean of its deviations from any arbitrary zero point, plus that zero point. Its use is illustrated in the left hand side of Table 4-4-2, in which 10842.0 has

TABLE 4-4-2.   Change of Zero Point

Arithmetic Mean		Standard Deviation
x	$x - x_0$	$(x - x_0)^2$
10842.3	0.3	0.09
10842.7	0.7	0.49
10843.1	1.1	1.21
10842.1	0.1	0.01
10842.8	0.8	0.64
10842.2	0.2	0.04
	3.2	2.48

$x_0 = 10842.0$

$\overline{x - x_0} = 3.20/6 = 0.533$

$\bar{x} = 10842.0 + 0.533$

$\quad = 10842.533$

$\overline{(x - x_0)^2} = 2.48/6 = 0.413$

$\overline{(x - x_0)}^2 = 0.533^2 = 0.284$

$\sigma = \sqrt{0.413 - 0.284}$

$\quad = 0.359$

been chosen for the zero point. The mean of the deviations from this starting point is found to be 0.533, and the mean of the original numbers is therefore 10842.0 plus 0.553, or 10842.533.

To see how the standard deviation can be computed in terms of these deviations from the zero point, let us express $\overline{x^2}$ and $\bar{x}^2$ in terms of $x - x_0$, and insert the results in equation 4-4-1. Starting with $\overline{x^2}$, we have

$$\overline{x^2} = \overline{[(x - x_0) + x_0]^2} = \overline{(x - x_0)^2 + 2(x - x_0)x_0 + x_0^2}$$

By applying equation 3-10-2 we can separate this into three terms;

$$\overline{x^2} = \overline{(x - x_0)^2} + \overline{2(x - x_0)x_0} + \overline{x_0^2}$$

and since 2, x_0 , and x_0^2 are all constants, we can apply equations 3-10-4 and 3-10-5, giving us

$$\overline{x^2} = \overline{(x - x_0)^2} + 2x_0\overline{(x - x_0)} + x_0^2$$

Now let us leave this result for a moment and find the value of $\bar{x}^2$:

$$\bar{x}^2 = \overline{(x - x_0)} + x_0{}^2 = \overline{(x - x_0} + x_0)^2$$

or

$$\bar{x}^2 = \overline{x - x_0}{}^2 + 2x_0\overline{(x - x_0)} + x_0^2$$

Inserting these values for $\overline{x^2}$ and $\bar{x}^2$ in equation 4-4-1 and simplifying, we have

$$\sigma = \sqrt{\overline{(x - x_0)^2} - \overline{(x - x_0)}^2} \qquad (4\text{-}4\text{-}3)$$

The use of this equation is demonstrated in the right-hand column of Table 4-4-2.

PROBLEMS

1. Find the standard deviation of the numbers in Table 4-3-1, using the method of equation 4-4-1.

2. Find the arithmetic mean and the standard deviation of the following set of numbers: 49638, 49644, 49632, 49637, 49641, 49640, 49639, 49645, 49631, and 49644. Which of the equations for $\bar{x}$ and σ are most suitable for this problem?

5.   RAPID METHODS FOR GROUPED DATA

If the data are in the form of a frequency tabulation, there is a further way in which we can effect a saving of time. Since each class mark is equal to the first class mark plus a multiple of the class interval, we can take out the class interval as a factor throughout and simplify the computations. Let us introduce the following notation:

x_0 = the class mark of any convenient class, usually the one containing the largest number of variates.

u = the serial number of any class, starting with $u = 0$ for the class labeled x_0 and increasing with increasing values of x.

$$\qquad (4\text{-}5\text{-}1)$$

An example of a choice of x_0 and an assignment of a set of values of u is shown in Table 4-5-1. Note that the values of u increase downward, following the values of x, and that negative values of u are assigned to classes with class marks smaller than x_0.

Our working equations have until now been expressed in terms of x, and we now wish to express them in terms of u. The first step is to write in mathematical form the relationship between the old and the new variables. This relationship can be obtained from an inspection of Table 4-5-1; it is

$$x = x_0 + Cu \qquad (4\text{-}5\text{-}2)$$

where C is the class interval, described in Chapter 2, Article 3. For example, x for the last class is 549.5 plus 20 times two, and x for the first class is 549.5 plus 20 times -3. If we wish to obtain the value of u corresponding to any given value of x, we can rewrite the above equation in the form

$$u = (x - x_0)/C \qquad (4\text{-}5\text{-}3)$$

TABLE 4-5-1.   Rapid Method for Grouped Data

Limits	x	f	u	fu	fu^2
480–499	489.5	3	-3	-9	27*
500–519	509.5	11	-2	-22	44
520–539	529.5	21	-1	-21	21
540–559	549.5 $(=x_0)$	27	0	0	0
560–579	569.5	14	1	14	14
580–599	589.5	5	2	10	20
		81		-28	126
		(N)		(Σu)	(Σu^2)

Computations

$$N = 81; \quad C = 20; \quad x_0 = 549.5$$
$$\bar{u} = -28/81 = -0.346$$
$$\overline{u^2} = 126/81 = 1.56$$
$$\bar{x} = 549.5 + 20(-0.346) = 542.6$$
$$\sigma = 20\sqrt{1.56 - (-0.346)^2}$$
$$= 20\sqrt{1.56 - 0.12} = 24.0$$

*This column is most quickly computed by multiplying u by fu.

To express the arithmetic mean in terms of u and x_0 , let us start with equation 4-4-2, and in it replace $x - x_0$ by Cu, according to equation 4-5-3:

$$x = x_0 + \overline{x - x_0} = x_0 + \overline{Cu}$$

Since C is a constant, we can move it outside of the bar symbol for the arithmetic mean, by equation 3-10-4:

$$x = x_0 + C\bar{u} \tag{4-5-4}$$

For the standard deviation, we begin with equation 4-4-3 and again replace $x - x_0$ by Cu:

$$\sigma = \sqrt{\overline{(x - x_0)^2} - \overline{(x - x_0)}^2} = \sqrt{\overline{(Cu)^2} - \overline{(Cu)}^2}$$

Since C is a constant we can again apply 3-10-4:

$$\sigma = \sqrt{C^2\overline{u^2} - C^2\bar{u}^2} = \sqrt{C^2(\overline{u^2} - \bar{u}^2)}$$

or, finally,

$$\sigma = C\sqrt{\overline{u^2} - \bar{u}^2} \tag{4-5-5}$$

If we use σ_u to denote the standard deviation in u, then by equation 4-4-1,

$$\sigma_u = \sqrt{\overline{u^2} - \bar{u}^2} \tag{4-5-6}$$

With this, equation 4-5-5 becomes simply

$$\sigma_x = C\sigma_u \tag{4-5-7}$$

where we have used σ_x to distinguish the standard deviation in x units from that in u units. The uses of these equations are demonstrated in Table 4-5-1, in which all the details of the computations are shown. These equations provide a very rapid method of obtaining the arithmetic mean and the standard deviation, even when the frequency tabulation is very lengthy.

PROBLEMS

Use equations 4-5-4 and 4-5-5 in all cases. It is suggested that in each problem you leave room for two additional columns at the right of the fu^2 column, for further computations upon these data to be described in future chapters.

1. Find the arithmetic means and the standard deviations of the two distributions of temperatures which you obtained in Problem 1, Article 3, Chapter 2. Does this additional information clarify the nature of the difference between the two distributions?

2. Find the arithmetic mean and the standard deviation of the distribution in Table 4-2-1.

3. Find the arithmetic mean and the standard deviation of the examination scores in Table 2-6-1.

4. Find the arithmetic mean and the standard deviation of the data which you gathered for Problem 4, Article 4, Chapter 2.

5. Find the arithmetic mean and the standard deviation of the ages of the dementia praecox patients in Table 2-5-1.

6. SUMMARY

The arithmetic mean ($\bar{x}$) and the standard deviation (σ) are useful for describing any distribution. They are also useful as intermediate quantities to be used in further analyses of the data by methods to be described later in the book.

The arithmetic mean is defined by equation 3-10-1:

$$\bar{x} = \Sigma x / N$$

or, for a frequency tabulation,

$$\bar{x} = \Sigma fx / N$$

and the standard deviation is defined by equation 4-3-2:

$$\sigma = \sqrt{\overline{(x - \bar{x})^2}}$$

In practice it is usually inconvenient to compute these quantities directly from their definitions, and the following rapid methods should be used instead:

I. For distributions consisting of relatively few ungrouped small variates, use equations 3-10-1 and 4-4-4:

$$\bar{x} = \Sigma x / N$$

$$\sigma = \sqrt{\overline{x^2} - \bar{x}^2}$$

The procedure is demonstrated in Table 4-4-1.

II. For distributions consisting of relatively few ungrouped large variates, use equations 4-4-2 and 4-4-3:

$$\bar{x} = x_0 + \overline{x - x_0}$$

$$\sigma = \sqrt{\overline{(x - x_0)^2} - \overline{(x - x_0)}^2}$$

where x_0 is any convenient zero point. The procedure is demonstrated in Table 4-4-2.

III. For distributions consisting of grouped data, use equations 4-5-4 and 4-5-5:

$$\bar{x} = x_0 + C\bar{u}$$

$$\sigma = C\sqrt{\overline{u^2} - \bar{u}^2}$$

where x_0 is the class mark of any class chosen at the convenience of the investigator (usually the largest class is chosen) and u is the serial number of any class, starting with $u = 0$ for the class labeled x_0, and increasing with increasing values of x. The method is demonstrated in Table 4-5-1.

CHAPTER

• 5 •

PROBABILITY

1. INTRODUCTION

The concept of probability is widely used and understood. We do not need a formal definition to understand the meaning of the statement that the probability of a snowfall in March is smaller than the probability of a snowfall in January, or that the probability that a man will be killed by a traffic accident is greater than the probability that he will be killed by lightning. We all indicate our opinions about the degree of probability of various events, by means of such expressions as "His chances of being elected are very small," or "The odds are against us," or even "The train has probably arrived by now."

Statements such as these convey useful information, but it is obvious that they would be much more useful if they could be expressed in quantitative terms. For example, a surgeon may tell a man who has undergone a cancer operation that there will "probably not be a recurrence." But the word "probably" covers a variety of meanings, and if the surgeon can instead make a quantitative statement which describes the *degree* of probability, the patient will have a much more reliable basis for planning his life. Our first task is to define the concept of probability in an exact numerical way.

2. PROBABILITY DEFINED

If we let s be the number of ways in which a given event E can succeed, and f the number of ways in which it can fail, then the probability that E will occur is

$$P(E) = s/(s + f) \qquad\qquad (5\text{-}2\text{-}1)$$

and the probability that E will not occur is*

$$P(\text{not } E) = f/(s + f) \qquad\qquad (5\text{-}2\text{-}2)$$

---

*These abbreviations for probabilities of events are customarily read "P of E" and "P of not E."

We see from these definitions that

$$P(\text{not } E) = 1 - P(E) \qquad (5\text{-}2\text{-}3)$$

To illustrate these equations, let us compute the probability that a card drawn at random from a standard deck will be a spade. Since there are thirteen spades in the deck, the event can occur in thirteen ways, and s is 13. There are thirty-nine non-spades in the deck, so that the event can fail to occur in thirty-nine ways, and f is 39. The probability that the card will be a spade is therefore $13/(13 + 39)$, or $1/4$, or 0.25; and the probability that it will not be a spade is $39/(13 + 39)$, or $3/4$, or 0.75.

It is obvious from the definition that the probability scale ranges from zero to one; *zero is the probability of an impossible event*, and *one is the probability of a certain event*, and all other probabilities lie between these limits. If the probability is $1/2$, or 0.50, then the event is exactly as likely to succeed as to fail.

In everyday language, it is customary to describe probabilities by stating the ratio of the favorable to the unfavorable cases, that is, by the ratio of s to f. "The chances are three to one in his favor" becomes, in our terms, "The probability that he will succeed is $3/4$."

In practice the method of finding s and f must depend upon the individual problem. For example, let us compute the probability that when two dice are thrown, the sum of the two numbers will be 7. The answer is obtained as follows: The first die can fall in any of six ways, and with *each* of these the second can fall in any of six ways, so that there are thirty-six ways in which the pair can fall, and $s + f$ is therefore 36. To find s, we must list and count the pairs which total 7; they are 1 and 6, 2 and 5, 3 and 4, 4 and 3, 5 and 2, and 6 and 1, where the first number of each pair refers to the first die and the second number to the second die. We see that s equals 6, and the required probability is therefore $6/36$, or 0.167.

PROBLEMS

1. If a card is drawn at random from a standard deck, what is the probability that it will be (a) a heart? (b) A black card? (c) Smaller than a 5?

2. A girl who is 5'8'' tall is offered a blind date with one of her roommate's brothers. If there are three brothers, and they are 5'7'', 5'10'', and 5'11'' in height, what is the probability that the girl will be taller than her escort? That she will be shorter?

3. If two dice are thrown, what is the probability that (a) their sum will be 2? (b) That their sum will be 5? (c) What is the most likely sum?

3. DISCUSSION OF DEFINITION

The fundamental definition of probability given in 5-2-1 is simple and easy to use in most cases, but there are some subtleties of reasoning in its application which are not apparent at first glance. The following remarks may help you to avoid ambiguities in applying the definition to practical problems.

(1) In counting the number of ways in which an event may happen, it is necessary to remember that these ways of happening must be equally likely.* If we ignore this requirement we can arrive at absurdities like the following. A given group of hospitalized soldiers included 105 patients suffering from malaria, 247 from typhus, 5 from pneumonia, 23 from gunshot wounds, and 2 from poison gas illness. Since there are three ways in which a soldier in the group might be ill from natural causes, and two ways in which he might be ill as a result of enemy action, it follow that the probability that a given soldier is ill from natural causes is 3/5, or 0.600! This result would of course be justified only in the event that all five types of illness were equally likely.

(2) A little reflection will show that a statement about probability is not a statement about a physical situation, but is instead a statement about a particular observer's knowledge of the situation. A given event can have one probability relative to the information in the possession of one observer, and a totally different probability relative to the information in the possession of another observer. To clarify this statement, let us picture a specific experiment.

Imagine that a deck of cards is shuffled and placed on a table, and that the top card is then removed and laid to one side. Three observers, *A*, *B*, and *C* are asked to state the probability that this card which was removed is a spade. Observer *A*, who has seen none of the cards, replies that the probability is 0.25. Observer *B* is permitted to examine the four *bottom* cards of the deck before giving his answer. He sees that these four cards include three spades and a diamond, so that from his point of view there are only 48 *unknown* cards left, of which 10 are spades and 38 are non-spades. He replies that the probability that the top card is a spade is 10/48, or 0.208 approximately. Observer *C*, however, has caught a glimpse of the top card as it was being removed, and he has seen that it was in fact the ten of diamonds. Relative to his information the probability that it is a spade is of course zero! The physical arrangement of the cards is unchanged; yet three different statements about the probability are all correct, each relative to a different body of information.

A statement about probabilities implies possession of incomplete information about a situation. A "correct" statement is simply a statement of the best possible guess in the light of this incomplete information.

PROBLEMS

1. Criticize the following computation. A given lake contains bluegills, black bass, white bass, perch, smallmouth bass, and catfish. Since there are six kinds

---

*We are thus forced to use the concept of *equal probability* in defining probability, and the definition is therefore partly circular.

of fish, of which three kinds are bass, the probability that a fish caught at random will be a bass is 0.50.

2. In a rummy game, two players are dealt the following hands:

	First Player	Second Player
Spades	A, 10, 9	K
Clubs	10	2,3,4,J
Diamonds	7,3	J
Hearts	K	9

What is the probability that the first card drawn from the remainder of the deck will be a club? Give three answers, relative to the information in the possession of (a) the first player, (b) the second player, and (c) a spectator who sees both hands. Which of the three probabilities do you think is most reliable?

3. A die is so weighted that a five turns up twice as often as any other face. (a) What is the probability that a five will turn up, relative to the information given above? (b) What is the probability for a man who does not know that the die is weighted? (c) What is it for a man who knows that the die is weighted, but does not know which face the weighting favors?

4. Compute the correct probability in the first illustrative example (about hospitalized soldiers) in the foregoing article.

4. EMPIRICAL PROBABILITIES

In practice, it is frequently more convenient to look upon the probability of an event as simply the percentage of cases in which the event can be expected to occur. It is then not necessary to enumerate the ways in which the event can succeed or fail; we can instead estimate the probability on the basis of past experience. In the absence of other information, the best estimate of the probability is simply the percentage of cases in which the event has occurred in the past. If, for example, we are asked the probability that a card drawn from an incomplete deck will be a spade and if we know that in previous experiments four cards out of ten drawn from this deck have turned out to be spades, then the best estimate of the probability that any card drawn in the future will be a spade is 0.40.

Probabilities which are estimated in this way are sometimes called "empirical probabilities." Empirical probabilities are widely used in life insurance work and in other applied fields. For instance, if we wish to estimate the probability that a boy who is now 10 years old will still be alive at age 30, we have only to consult the American Experience Mortality Tables (Appendix III in this volume), which shows us that out of every 100,000 Americans who are alive at the age of 10, 85,441 have survived until age 30. The probability that a given 10-year-old boy will survive until age 30 is therefore 0.85. In the same way, we see that of 92,637 people who are alive at age 20, 57,917 will be alive at age 60, and the probability that any given 20-year-old will survive until 60 is therefore 57,917/92,637 or 0.63.

It is perhaps worth emphasizing again the relationship between probability and knowledge. We saw in the preceding paragraph that the probability that a given 20-year-old will survive to the age of 60 is 0.63. This is the correct probability if we know only that he is American and 20 years old. If we know also that he is 54 pounds overweight, or that both of his parents lived beyond the age of 90, then the given probability would no longer be the correct one, and we would instead have to base the probability upon tables containing data about people comparable to himself. The most reliable probabilities are of course those which are based upon the most information. It is worth noting, for example, that life insurance companies find it worth while to collect a great deal of medical information about their clients before granting them insurance.

PROBLEMS

Problems 1, 2, and 3 should be solved with the aid of the American Experience Mortality Table given in Appendix III.

1. What is the probability that a man who is now 20 will still be alive at 40? At 60? At 80? At 95?

2. What is the probability that a man who is now 93 will survive at least one more year? Two more years?

3. What is the age which a man of 20 has a 0.5 chance of reaching?

4. Using the data in Table 2-2-2, find the probability that a wire chosen at random will have a breaking strength of (a) 207 pounds, (b) more than 204 pounds.

5. MATHEMATICAL EXPECTATION

The concept of probability can be illustrated very clearly in terms of the related concept of expectation, which is a measurement of the cash value of an uncompleted gambling operation. The expectation (Exp.) of a given venture is defined as the probability (P) that it will succeed, times the gain (G) which will result if it does succeed:

$$\text{Exp.} = P \times G \qquad (5\text{-}5\text{-}1)$$

If, for example, a man holds five lottery tickets out of a total of 100, and the prize is to be worth $200, then his expectation is $200 times 0.05, or $10. If the holder of the tickets should decide to sell his tickets before the drawing is held, this is the value which should·be placed upon them. In general, the decision about the advisability of entering any venture should depend upon a balancing of the cash cost of the venture against the expectation which is being purchased. If a poker player plans to call a bet of $1, which would increase the pot to $6, then his probability of winning should be at least 1/6 in order to justify his calling the bet; otherwise he will be spending his dollar for less than a dollar's worth of expectation and will in the long run lose.

A slightly different situation arises in the purchase of insurance. We can see from Appendix III that the probability that a man who is now 20 will die within a year is approximately 0.008. If such a man owns a life insurance contract for $1000, covering him for one year, then his expectation is obviously about $8. Since he must pay more than this for the contract, he is accepting a statistical loss on the transaction. The purchasers of insurance are willing to accept such a loss because the primary purpose of insurance is not to gain on the venture but to distribute the financial burden caused by individual catastrophes.

PROBLEMS

1. If a 30-year-old man has a one-year life insurance contract which will pay $5000 in case of his death, what is his expectation? What is his expectation if he is 90 years old?

2. The merchants in a given city promote Christmas shopping each year by giving away numbered lottery tickets with each purchase. At a later drawing, the holder of the winning ticket receives an automobile worth about $1800. The serial numbers on tickets issued late in the distribution period are larger than 700,000. About what is the expectation for the holder of a single ticket? If you were offered a block of 100 tickets for 50¢ just before the drawing, should you accept the offer?

3. A nursery operator observes that a given kind of seedlings survive to salable size about two times out of three. They sell for $2 apiece. If he plants 100 such seedlings, what is his total expectation?

6.   INDEPENDENT EVENTS

When we are discussing the probabilities of several events, it is necessary to use a notation which distinguishes between them. If we are discussing two events, called event A and event B, then it will be convenient to let $P(A)$ mean the probability of event A, and $P(B)$ the probability of event B. $P(A$ and $B)$ will then be understood to mean the probability that both events will happen, and $P(A$ or $B)$ the probability that one or the other will happen. It is the objective of this and the following sections to show how these composite probabilities can be computed from the probabilities of the separate events.

Let us first consider the probability that both of two events will occur. For clarity, we must make the following distinction: Two events are said to be *dependent* if the outcome of the first has an effect upon the probability that the second will occur, and *independent* if the outcome of the first has no effect upon the second. If, for example, we draw two cards from a deck and ask for the probability that both are spades, we must know whether or not the first card was replaced in the deck before the second card was drawn. If it was replaced, then the probability that the second card will be a spade is 1/4, whether the first card was a spade or not, and the two events are therefore *independent*. If, on the other hand, the first card was not replaced, then the probability that the second card will be a spade is either 12/51 or 13/51, depending upon whether the first card was a spade or not, and the two events are therefore *dependent*.

To find the probability that both of two independent events will occur, we must count the ways in which the composite event can succeed and the ways in which it can fail. The first event can happen in any of $s_1 + f_1$ ways, and following *any one of these* the second event can happen in any of $s_2 + f_2$ ways, so that the total number of ways in which the pair of events can take place is $s_1 + f_1$ times $s_2 + f_2$. By the same argument, the first event can succeed in any of s_1 ways, and following any of these the second event can succeed in any of s_2 ways, making a total of s_1 times s_2 ways in which both of the events can succeed together. The probability that both will succeed is therefore

$$\frac{s_1 s_2}{(s_1 + f_1)(s_2 + f_2)}$$

This can be written in the form

$$\frac{s_1}{(s_1 + f_1)} \times \frac{s_2}{(s_2 + f_2)}$$

or simply $P(A)$ times $P(B)$. We therefore have the following result: The probability that *both* of two independent events will occur is the product of their separate probabilities. For reference we will write this:

$$P(A \text{ and } B) = P(A) \times P(B) \quad (A \text{ and } B \text{ independent}) \qquad (5\text{-}6\text{-}1)$$

This can obviously be extended to any number of events.

To illustrate this equation, let us compute the probability that a 4 will turn up on all three successive throws of a die. The probability of a 4 on each throw is 1/6, and since the events are independent, the probability that a four will turn up on all the throws is $(1/6) \times (1/6) \times (1/6)$, or 1/216, or 0.0046.

PROBLEMS

1. Three construction firms are bidding for a contract. On the basis of past experience, the probability that A's bid will be higher than B's is 0.60, and the probability that C's will be higher than B's is 0.40. What is the probability that B will win the contract with the lowest bid?

2. If two dice are thrown, what is the probability that both will come up 5's? (Use equation 5-6-1.)

3. A student wishes to borrow $5 from his roommate. He knows that the roommate has exactly $5 in his possession, but the probability is 0.3 that the roommate will spend part of it for a movie during the day, and 0.4 that he will lend part of the $5 to another roommate. What is the probability that the $5 will remain intact?

4. On a particularly dangerous bombing mission, it is estimated that one-third of the planes will be lost. What is the probability that a given plane will survive three such missions?

7. DEPENDENT EVENTS

The argument used for the derivation of equation 5-6-1 can be used, with a slight modification, for the case in which the two events are dependent. In this case the total number of ways in which the pair of events can occur is $s_1 + f_1$ times $s_2 + f_2$, as before, but the total number of ways in which both can succeed must be reconsidered. The first of the two events can succeed in s_1 ways, and following any one of these there will be s_2 ways in which the second can succeed, and there are therefore s_1 times s_2 ways in which both will succeed. But s_2 must now obviously mean the number of ways that the second event can succeed after the first event has already succeeded. If, for example, we draw two cards from a deck and ask for the probability that both will be spades, then there are thirteen ways in which the first card can be a spade, but, corresponding to each of these, there are only twelve ways in which the second card can also be a spade. The derivation of 5-6-1 is obviously still valid if this change of meaning is kept in mind. We can state this result as follows. The probability that both of two dependent events will occur is equal to the probability that the first will occur multiplied by the probability that the second will occur, the latter probability being computed on the assumption that the first has already occurred. For reference we will put this in equation form:

$$P(A \text{ and } B) = P(A) \times P(B \text{ if } A \text{ has occurred})$$

$$(A \text{ and } B \text{ dependent)} \quad (5\text{-}7\text{-}1)$$

This can obviously be extended to any number of events. For example, if we are to draw three cards from a deck and wish to know the probability that all three will be spades, then we proceed as follows. The probability that the first card will be a spade is $1/4$. If the first card is a spade, then the probability that the second card will also be a spade is $12/51$. If both of these are spades, the probability that the third will also be a spade is $11/50$. The probability that all will be spades is the product of these three probabilities, or $11/850$, or approximately 0.0129. Similarly, the probability that the first will be a spade and the other two will be diamonds is $1/4$ times $13/51$ times $12/50$, or approximately 0.0153.

PROBLEMS

1. If two cards are drawn from a deck, what is the probability that both will be diamonds? That the first will be a diamond and the second a club? That neither will be diamonds?

2. The probability that a given candidate will be nominated is 0.3, and the probability that he will be elected if nominated is 0.4. What is the probability that he will hold the office?

3. In a given medical school, 28 per cent of the students drop out in their first

year, 13 per cent of those remaining drop out in their second year, and 9 per cent of the remainder drop out before graduating. What is the probability that a given entering student will graduate?

4. The probability that a given bombing plane will make a successful flight to the target area is 0.9, the probability that the navigator will locate the target is 0.7, and the probability that the bombardier will score a hit is 0.4. When the plane takes off, what is the probability that the target will be hit?

8.   MUTUALLY EXCLUSIVE EVENTS

If two events are alternative ways in which a single operation can turn out, that is, if the occurrence of one event means that the other event cannot occur, then the two events are said to be mutually exclusive. If, for example, we draw a single card from a deck and ask for the probability that it will be either a spade or a club, then these two possibilities are mutually exclusive; if it is a spade it cannot be a club, and vice versa. In this article we will discuss the probability that either one or the other of two mutually exclusive events will occur.

The number of ways in which the first event can occur is s_1, and the number of ways in which the second event can occur is s_2. Since the two events are mutually exclusive, there is no overlap between these two sets of ways, and the total number of ways in which one or the other can occur is simply $s_1 + s_2$. The probability that either one or the other will occur is therefore $(s_1 + s_2)/n$, where n is the total number of ways in which the event can turn out. We can rewrite this in the form s_1/n plus s_2/n. In other words, the probability that either one or the other of two mutually exclusive events will occur is the sum of their separate probabilities. For reference purposes, we will write this in equation form:

$$P(A \text{ or } B) = P(A) + P(B) \quad (A \text{ and } B \text{ mutually exclusive}) \quad (5\text{-}8\text{-}1)$$

For example, the probability that a single card drawn from a deck will be either a spade or a club is 1/4 plus 1/4, or 0.50.

PROBLEMS

1. If a die is thrown, what is the probability that either a 5 or 6 will come up?

2. If a card is drawn from a standard deck, what is the probability that it will be either a spade or a diamond?

3. If two dice are thrown, what is the probability that the two faces will not total 5? (Use equation 5-2-3.)

9.   PERMUTATIONS

In problems concerning the probability that several events will all occur, we can either multiply together the separate probabilities, according to equation 5-6-1, or we can list and count the number of ways in which the composite event can succeed or fail, and use equation 5-2-1. If we make the latter choice, the enumeration of the separate possibilities may become very lengthy. If we can instead set up formulas by means of which the number of possible ways can be computed, then this listing and counting will not be necessary. One such formula will be derived in this article.

A *permutation* is an arrangement or a sequence of a number of objects. There are, for example, six permutations of the letters A, B, and C; they are ABC, ACB, BAC, BCA, CAB, and CBA. Instead of listing and counting these six permutations, we could have deduced their number as follows. Each permutation is to contain three letters. To obtain any one permutation we must select a letter to fill the first place, and then, from the remaining letters, we must select one to fill the second place, and so forth. There are three ways to fill the first place (with an A, B, or C), and corresponding to each of these there are two ways to fill the second (if, for example, we fill the first space with B, then we can fill the second with either A or C). Thus there are three times two ways of filling the first two spaces, and, corresponding to each of these, there is only one way to fill the third space. The total number of permutations is therefore $3 \times 2 \times 1$, or 6. It is convenient to introduce the following abbreviation:

$$n! = 1 \times 2 \times 3 \times 4 \times 5 \cdots \text{ to } n \qquad (5\text{-}9\text{-}1)$$

This is read "n factorial." For example, "3 factorial," or 3!, is $1 \times 2 \times 3$, or 6, and 4! is 24. Using this notation, we can generalize the results of the preceding paragraph by the statement that the number of permutations of n objects is $n!$.

In statistics, we must frequently compute the number of permutations which can be made up from n objects when only r of them are used in any given permutation. We will call this "the number of permutations of n objects taken r at a time," and abbreviate it Perm(n,r). For example, the number of permutations of 4 objects taken two at a time is 12, as we can readily see by listing the possible two letter words which we can form from the letters A, B, C, and D. To obtain a general equation for the number of permutations of n objects taken r at a time, let us picture the process of forming a specific permutation of r letters from a pool containing n letters. We can choose, for the first of the r letters, any letter in the pool; that is, we can fill the first space in any of n different ways. Whichever one we choose, there will be only $n - 1$ letters remaining in the pool, and we can therefore fill the second space in any one of $n - 1$ ways. There are therefore $n \times (n - 1)$ ways of filling the first two spaces, or $n \times (n - 1) \times (n - 2)$ ways of filling the first three, or finally, $n \times (n - 1) \times (n - 2) \cdots (n - r + 1)$ ways of filling all r places.

This result can be written more simply if we multiply it by $(n - r)!$ and then divide it by the same amount. The effect of the multiplication is to supply the factors from $n - r$ down to one:

$$\text{Perm}(n, r) = \frac{[n(n - 1)(n - 2) \cdots (n - r + 1)](n - r)!}{(n - r)!}$$

or, combining the factors in the numerator:

$$\text{Perm}(n,r) = \frac{n!}{(n-r)!} \qquad (5\text{-}9\text{-}2)$$

For the special case of n objects taken all at a time, we must use the result obtained earlier, which we can now formulate as follows.

$$\text{Perm}(n,n) = n! \qquad (5\text{-}9\text{-}3)$$

For example, Perm(5,2) is $(5\times4\times3\times2\times1)/(3\times2\times1)$, or 20. It is suggested that you list the two-letter permutations to be made up from the letters A, B, C, D, and E and verify this conclusion.

To illustrate the use of these formulas for probability problems, let us compute the probability that a given player in a bridge game will receive a hand consisting of thirteen spades. To find this we may proceed as follows. There are Perm(52,13), possible different bridge hands (counting each permutation as a different hand), so that $s + f$ in equation 5-2-1 is Perm (52,13). Included among these there are Perm(13,13) hands which consist of all spades, and s is therefore Perm(13,13). The required probability is Perm(13,13)/Perm(52,13), or

$$\frac{13!}{52!/39!}$$

or approximately 0.0000000000016. If we imagine that an inveterate bridge player plays thirty hands per evening, 365 days per year, then we can readily compute that he should expect an all-spade hand about once in every sixty million years!

The problem in the preceding paragraph is given to illustrate the use of permutations in probability computations, but it would have been possible to obtain the same result by means of equation 5-7-1, as follows: The probability that the first card of the thirteen will be a spade is $13/52$. On the assumption that the first card was a spade, the probability that the second card will also be a spade is $12/51$. Continuing, we see that the probability that all thirteen will be spades is $(13/52) \times (12/51) \times (11/50)$ $\cdots \times (2/41) \times (1/40)$, which gives us the same result as before.

PROBLEMS

1. Work out the details of the computation of the probability that a random bridge hand will consist of thirteen spades. (It is suggested that you collect powers of 10 as suggested in Article 8 of Chapter 3.)

2. A hostess is planning a luncheon with eight guests to be seated around a table, and she is trying to find a seating arrangement which will be most congenial for everyone. How many seating arrangements must she consider, if (a) any person may occupy any seat? (b) the hostess seats herself at the head of the table? (c) guest A must not be seated next to guest B or guest C? (d) there are four men and four women, and men and women must be seated alternately?

3. A fraternity containing fifteen members wishes to elect a president, a vice president, a treasurer, a recording secretary, a corresponding secretary, and a sergeant-at-arms. In how many different ways is it possible to select such a slate of officers?

10. PERMUTATIONS WITH SOME IDENTICAL OBJECTS

If some of a set of n objects are identical with each other, the number of different permutations which can be formed is obviously smaller than it would be if the objects were all distinct. For example, an experiment will readily show that we can form only twelve different four-letter permutations from the letters A, A, B, and C, although we can form twenty-four from the letters, A, B, C, and D. To arrive at this result without listing and counting the twelve permutations, we can instead reason as follows. If we temporarily identify the two identical objects separately by calling them A_1 and A_2, then there are 4! or 24 separate permutations, according to equation 5-9-2. But this count includes BA_1CA_2 and $BA_2 CA_1$ (for example) as two different words, when they are in fact identical if we drop the subscripts. We can correct for this duplication if we divide our preliminary result by 2. If there had been three identical letters, it would obviously have been necessary to divide by 3!, or 6. If k_1 objects are identical, then Perm(n,n) is $n!/k_1!$, and if k_2 others are also identical, then we must divide this result by $k_2!$. In general,

$$\mathrm{Perm}(n,n;k_1,k_2,\cdots) = \frac{n!}{k_1!k_2!\cdots} \qquad (5\text{-}10\text{-}1)$$

where k_1 objects are identical, k_2 others are also identical, and so forth. For example, let us compute the number of five-letter "words" which can be formed from the letters $AAABB$. Here n is 5, k_1 is 2, and k_2 is 3. Equation 5-10-1 then gives us Perm$(5,5;2,3) = 5!/(2!\times3!)$, or 10.

The usefulness of this equation is illustrated by the following problem. If each of two parents has one gene for blue eyes and one for brown eyes, then according to the laws of genetics, the probability that their child will have blue eyes is 1/4, and the probability that he will have brown eyes is 3/4. If the parents have five children, what is the probability that three of them will have brown eyes and two will have blue eyes?

To answer this question, we proceed as follows. The probability that the first child will have brown eyes is 3/4, and the probability that the second child will have brown eyes is 3/4; therefore, by equation 5-6-1, the probability that both will have brown eyes is 9/16. Continuing in this way, the probability that the first three children will have brown eyes and that the last two will have blue eyes is $(3/4)^3 \times (1/4)^2$.

Obviously the result will be the same if we ask for the probability that there will be three brown-eyed children and two blue-eyed children in some other order; for example, the probability that the first and fourth children will have blue eyes and the others brown eyes is also $(3/4)^3 \times (1/4)^2$. Since all these various possible sequences are mutually exclusive, we can obtain the probability that one or another of them will occur by adding their separate probabilities. In other words, we must multiply $(3/4)^3 \times (1/4)^2$ (which is the probability for a given sequence) by the number of possible sequences. The number of possible sequences is obtained directly from 5-10-1, with $n = 5$, $k_1 = 3$, and $k_2 = 2$. The required probability is therefore

$$P = \left(\frac{3}{4}\right)^3 \left(\frac{1}{4}\right)^2 \frac{5!}{3! \times 2!} = 0.26$$

It is desirable to include a standard reference equation for problems of this type. Stated in general terms, the problem is this: If the probability that a given event will succeed is p, and the probability that it will fail is q, then, in n such events, what is the probability that there will be exactly s successes? To answer this, we need only to generalize our results: The probability that there will be exactly s successes and $n - s$ failures in a given order is $p^s q^{n-s}$, and the number of possible orders is $\dfrac{n!}{s!(n - s)!}$. The total probability is therefore

$$P(s) = \frac{n!}{s!(n - s)!} p^s q^{n-s} \tag{5-10-2}$$

For example, let us solve the following problem: If six dice are thrown, what is the probability that there will be exactly two 5's? To apply 5-10-2, we will call a 5 a success, so that p is $1/6$ and q is $5/6$. Upon inserting these values in 5-10-2, with $n = 6$ and $s = 2$, we find that the probability of exactly two 5's is $\left(\dfrac{6!}{2!4!}\right)\left(\dfrac{1}{6}\right)^2\left(\dfrac{5}{6}\right)^4$, or approximately 0.20.

PROBLEMS

1. Using equation 5-10-2, compute the probability that the parents in the illustrative problem will have (a) three blue-eyed children and two brown-eyed children; (b) four brown-eyed and one blue-eyed; (c) five blue-eyed children.*

2. If five dice are thrown, what is the probability that there will be three 1's and two 6's?

3. How many six-letter "words" can be formed from the letters $AAABBC$?

4. If six coins are tossed, what is the probability that there will be (a) four heads and two tails? (b) Five heads and one tail? (c) Six heads?

11. COMPOSITE PROBABILITY PROBLEMS

Many problems can be solved most effectively by means of a combination of the equations demonstrated in this chapter. It is the purpose

---

*In part c the quantity 0! must be evaluated. Since $n! = \dfrac{(n + 1)!}{n + 1}$ we can see that 0! must equal $1!/1$ or 1 for consistency of meaning.

of this article to bring together these methods by means of a set of representative problems in probability.

(1) If six dice are thrown, what is the probability that there will be at least two 6's? Answer: Equation 5-10-2 can be used to discover the probability that there will be *exactly* two 6's, but there is no simple equation which will tell us the probability that there will be *at least* two 6's. We must therefore assemble the answer as follows. The probability of exactly two 6's is 9375/46,656; of exactly three, 2500/46,656; of exactly four 375/46,656; of exactly five, 30/46,656; and of exactly six, 1/46,656. Since these are mutually exclusive, we can add them to obtain the probability that one or another of these events will take place, in other words, that there will be at least two 6's. The required probability is therefore 12,281/46,656 or 0.263.

We could have shortened the labor of this computation by computing first the probability that there will *not* be at least two 6's. The probability that there will be only one 6 is 0.402, and the probability that there will be no 6's is 0.335, so that the probability that our event will *not* take place is 0.737. From 5-2-3, we see that the probability that it *will* take place is 1 minus 0.737, or 0.263, as before.

(2) A man plans to take an examination to qualify for a promotion. The examination consists of five problems and in order to qualify he must solve the first three problems, and he must also solve either the fourth or fifth, or both. In preparing for the examination, he has tested himself on comparable problems, and he believes that the probability that he can solve the first problem is 0.8, and for the others 0.6, 0.9, 0.75, and 0.3, in that order. What is the probability that he will qualify? Answer: Let us begin by computing the probability that he will solve either the fourth or the fifth, or both. We can obtain this by adding the probabilities that he will solve the fourth but not the fifth (0.75×0.7), the fifth but not the fourth (0.25×0.3), and both the fifth and the fourth (0.75×0.3). This gives us a total probability of 0.825. (Alternatively, we could compute the probability that he would fail on both (0.25×0.7) and then subtract this from one to find the probability that he would succeed on at least one.) The problem is now resolved into finding the probability that all four events will take place, and the four probabilities are 0.8, 0.6, 0.9, and 0.825. Following equation 5-5-1, we multiply these together and find that the required probability is 0.356.

(3) Suppose that you were offered the following wager: Two cards are to be drawn from a deck at random; if there is at least one spade, you win 50¢ from your opponent; if there are no spades, he wins 50¢ from you. Is this a fair wager? Answer: At first glance this game appears to be evenly matched, since the probability of drawing a spade is 1/4 and you have two chances at it. This is however incorrect. The probability that two cards drawn at random will both be *non*-spades is $(39/52) \times (38/51)$, or 0.56,

so that your opponent should expect to win in about fifty-six trials out of a hundred. He would therefore win twelve times oftener than you, and could expect to win about six dollars in one hundred plays.

(4) A widely played gambling game consists of the following wager: The player bets any sum of money on any number from 1 to 6; let us say that he bets one dollar on 5. Three dice are then thrown. If there is one 5, he wins a dollar, if there are two 5's, he wins two dollars, and if there are three 5's, he wins three dollars. Is this a fair wager? If not, how much should the player expect to win or lose on a hundred plays? Answer: The probabilities that there will be no 5's, one 5, two 5's, and three 5's, respectively, are 125/216, 75/216, 15/216, and 1/216. In 216 plays, therefore, he can expect to lose one dollar 125 times, win one dollar 75 times, win two dollars 15 times, and win three dollars once. He should therefore expect to lose seventeen dollars per 216 plays, and the operator of the game should therefore expect to show a profit of about 7.9 per cent of the money wagered.

(5) A doctor finds that a patient has three characteristic symptoms which are always present in a given disease. None of the symptoms is, however, an absolute basis for a diagnosis, because not all people having the symptoms have the disease. In particular, 4 per cent of the people who do not have the disease nevertheless have the first symptom, 12 per cent have the second symptom, and 5 per cent have the third symptom. If $1\frac{1}{4}$ per cent of all men in the patient's age group have the disease and if the symptoms are independent of each other for patients not having the disease, what is the probability that the patient in question has the disease? Answer: If N is the total number of men in the patient's age group, then the number of these who do not have the disease is $(1-0.0125)$ N or $0.9875N$. For any one of these, the probability that he will have all three symptoms is 0.04 times 0.12 times 0.05 or 0.00024. The number of men who do not have the disease but have all three symptoms is therefore 0.00024 times $0.9875N$, or $0.000237N$. The number of people who have all three symptoms and do have the disease is $0.0125N$. The total number of people with all three symptoms is therefore $0.000237N$ plus $0.0125N$ or $0.01274N$, and since $0.0125N$ of them have the disease, the probability that the patient has the disease is $0.0125N/0.01274N$ or 0.98. Thus the *combination* of symptoms forms a very powerful diagnostic tool, even though the occurrence of the symptoms separately means very little.

PROBLEMS

1. If four dice are thrown, what is the probability that there will be at least two 5's? (Work this in two different ways.)

2. In the second illustrative problem in this article, what is the probability that the man will solve the first and second problems correctly, plus at least one of the last three?

3. Answer Problem 9, Chapter 1, Article 4, with the following additional in-

formation: About 2 per cent of the men in the patient's age group have the disease in question.

4. A boy and his father, aged 11 and 56, are to share equally in an inheritance of $40,000 at the end of ten years if both survive, and if only one survives he will receive the entire inheritance. If neither survives, the inheritance will be given to a specified college. What are the mathematical expectations of the son, the father, and the college?

5. A man is 50 and his wife is 41. What is the probability that both will be alive at the end of twenty years? That he will be living and she will be dead? That she will be living and he will be dead? That both will be dead?

6. In Problem 4, Article 7, what is the probability that the target will be struck if ten planes are assigned to the mission?

7. A man has three different pairs of socks in a drawer. If he enters the room in the dark and takes two socks at random, what is the probability that they will be a pair?

8. From a committee of eight men and three women, a subcommittee of four is to be chosen by lot. What is the probability that it will consist of two men and two women? That the men on the subcommittee will outnumber the women?

9. Cards in a box are numbered from 1 to 100 inclusive. If two are drawn at random, what is the probability that their sum will be an odd number? An even number?

12. SUMMARY

The *probability* of an event A is defined (equation 5-2-1) as the number of ways in which the event can succeed (s) divided by the total number of ways in which the event can succeed or fail ($s + f$):

$$P(A) = \frac{s}{s + f}$$

where all the $s + f$ ways in which the event can occur must be equally likely. The probability scale runs from zero (for an impossible event) to one (for a certain event).

The *empirical probability* of an event is the fraction of cases in which the event has occurred in the past. Examples of its use are given in Article 4.

The *mathematical expectation* of any venture is the probability that the venture will succeed, times the gain which will result if it does succeed. It is useful for evaluating the present cash value of an incomplete venture, the outcome of which is in doubt. Examples are given in Article 5.

The probabilities of composite events can be computed by means of the following laws:

I. The probability that both of two independent events will take place is the product of their separate probabilities. (Two events are independent if the outcome of the first does not affect the probability that the second will occur.)

II. The probability that both of two dependent events will occur is the probability of the first multiplied by the probability which the second will have if the first has already occurred.

III. The probability that one or the other of two mutually exclusive events will take place is the sum of their probabilities. (Two events are mutually exclusive if it is impossible for both to take place.)

These three laws are proved and illustrated in Articles 6, 7, and 8.

In computing probabilities, and for other purposes in statistics, the concept of a permutation is very useful. A permutation is a sequence of a set of objects; thus ACB is one permutation of the first three letters in the alphabet, and CAB is another. The number of permutations which can be made from n objects, when only r of the objects are used in any given permutation, is denoted by Perm(n,r) and is read "the number of permutations of n objects taken r at a time." It is given by equation 5-9-2,

$$\mathrm{Perm}(n,r) = \frac{n!}{(n-r)!}$$

where $n!$ is defined by equation 5-9-1:

$$n! = 1 \times 2 \times 3 \times 4 \cdots n$$

If n is zero, then the special definition $0! = 1$ applies instead.

If all of the n objects are used in each permutation, then we must use equation 5-9-3:

$$\mathrm{Perm}(n,n) = n!$$

The above equations require that the n objects are all distinguishable from each other. If instead, k_1 of the objects are identical with each other, and k_2 others are identical with each other, and so forth, then we must use equation 5-10-1:

$$\mathrm{Perm}(n,n;k_1,k_2,\cdots) = \frac{n!}{k_1!k_2!\cdots}$$

Examples of the uses of these equations are given in Articles 9 and 10.

If the probability that an event will succeed is p and the probability that it will fail is q, then the probability that it will succeed exactly s times in n trials is given by equation 5-10-2:

$$P(s) = \frac{n!}{s!(n-s)!} p^s q^{n-s}$$

The use of this equation for probability problems is shown in Article 10. Its further use in the development of statistical theory will be explained in the following chapter.

Practical problems in probability are likely to require some ingenuity in fitting the theory to the problem, and many problems require a combination of the principles here developed. Some examples of such composite probability problems are discussed in Article 11.

CHAPTER

. 6 .

NORMAL CURVE

1. INTRODUCTION

In Chapter 1 it was pointed out that many of the distributions occurring in practical investigations show a remarkable similarity to each other. In particular, it was pointed out in Article 4 that a histogram of the distances which a group of high school girls can throw a baseball is very similar in general appearance to that of the percentage of dry matter in mangel roots, or to the egg sizes of a certain marine snail in Greenland, or to the scores of a group of freshmen on an intelligence test. In this chapter we will attempt to isolate and describe the factors which account for the remarkable similarities in these apparently unrelated distributions and to show what conclusions can be drawn from the assumption that these factors are operative in any given distribution.

2. HISTOGRAM AS PROBABILITY GRAPH

The first obstacle which arises in a comparison of distributions from different sources is the fact that irrelevant differences may be present which have been introduced by the investigators and which are not intrinsic to the distributions. Our first task is to express the data in such a form that these irrelevant differences disappear. The simplest such difference arises from the fact that different investigators may have chosen different sample sizes and different class intervals for the same investigation.

The effect of different sample sizes is easily removed if we shift our attention away from the *frequency* per class and direct it instead to the *probability* per class, which we can obtain by dividing the frequency for each class by N. From the data in Table 6-2-1, for example, we see that eight patients out of forty had temperatures between 99.15 and 99.45, and therefore the probability that a patient chosen at random from the same universe will have a temperature between these limits is 8/40 or 0.200. The probabilities, computed in this way, are listed in the fourth column of Table 6-2-1. Obviously these probabilities will be the same, or nearly the same, for any two investigators working on the same problem, regardless of the sample sizes which they may choose.

The effect of choice of class interval is easily removed if we shift our attention from the probability per *class* to the probability per *x unit*. If

TABLE 6-2-1. Probability per x Unit

Limits	x (CM)	f	Prob. per class (f/N)	Prob. per degree (f/NC)
98.0– 98.2	98.1	2	0.050	0.167
98.3– 98.5	98.4	5	0.125	0.417
98.6– 98.8	98.7	10	0.250	0.833
98.9– 99.1	99.0	10	0.250	0.833
99.2– 99.4	99.3	8	0.200	0.667
99.5– 99.7	99.6	4	0.100	0.333
99.8–100.0	99.9	1	0.025	0.083
		40		

the probability is 0.200 that a patient chosen at random will have a temperature between 99.15 and 99.45, then the probability per degree is 0.200/0.3 or 0.667. In general, we can obtain the probability per x unit by dividing f/N by C:

$$P(x) = f/NC \qquad (6\text{-}2\text{-}1)$$

The probabilities per x unit are shown in the last column of Table 6-2-1 and are represented graphically in Figure 6-2-1. Obviously these probabilities are independent of the choice of class interval as well as sample size. A smooth curve has been drawn through these points to indicate that it is likely that the probability per degree changes steadily rather than abruptly as we go from one temperature to another. The use of such a probability graph is demonstrated by the following examples:

(1) On the basis of the data in Figure 6-2-1, what is the probability that a patient chosen at random from the same group will have a temperature between 98.3 and 98.4? Answer: Since the interval here is only 0.1 degree wide, the probability does not change much within the interval, and we can read the probability per degree from the midpoint of the interval, at 98.35. We find this probability per degree to be about 0.37, as shown by the left-hand arrow in the figure. Since the interval is 0.1 degree wide, and the probability per degree is 0.37, the total probability for the interval is 0.1 times 0.37 or 0.037. Therefore, about 37 patients per thousand should have temperatures within this interval.

It should be noted that in multiplying the base times the average height of this vertical strip we have obtained its area. In general, *the probability that a variate chosen at random will lie between two limits is simply the area under the probability curve between these two limits.*

(2) What is the probability that a patient chosen at random will have a temperature between 98.77 and 99.42? Answer: The interval is now so

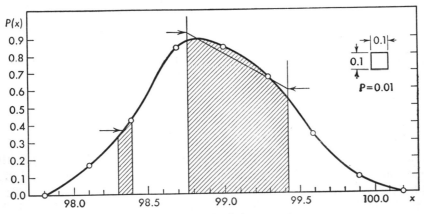

Figure 6-2-1.   Probability per Degree.

wide that the probability changes considerably within the interval, and the method used for the first problem is not accurate. We must instead deduce the probability from a direct measurement of the area under the curve between these two limits. This can be done conveniently and accurately by means of a simple instrument called a planimeter, but if such an instrument is not available, the area can be measured with sufficient accuracy by either of the following procedures.

(a) If the curve is on graph paper, count the squares under the curve and between the two limits, estimating the areas of the incomplete squares. The probability equivalent of each square is obtained by multiplying the base of any square by its height, in the units given by the graph. For example, in Figure 6-2-1, the base of each square is 0.1 degree and the height of each square is 0.1 probability unit per degree. One square therefore represents a probability of 0.01, as indicated on the graph.

(b) A slightly less accurate but more rapid procedure is the following. Draw vertical lines at each of the limits, and then lay a transparent ruler down along the top of the area in such a way that it makes the best possible compromise with the curved top boundary, as shown in Figure 6-2-1. Compute the area under the resulting trapezoid as follows. The height of the trapezoid is 0.93 at the left boundary and 0.60 at the right boundary, as shown by the arrows. The average height is therefore 0.765. The width of the base is 99.42 minus 98.77 or 0.65. The area is therefore 0.765 times 0.65 or 0.497. The required probability of an occurrence between these limits is therefore 0.497; in other words, 497 patients out of a thousand should have temperatures between these limits.

(3) The following tabulation* shows the number of accidents reported on Ohio highways in 1950, subdivided into groups according to the age of the driver:

Age	Number
Under 16	483
17	663
18	1253
19	1364
20	1318
21 to 24	6617
25 to 44	19669
45 to 64	7879
Over 64	1485

What is the probability that the driver in any given accident is (a) 19 years old? (b) That he is 40 years old? (c) That he is between 17 and 22, inclusive? (d) What age has the highest probability? Answer: The difficulty in dealing with this data arises from the fact that the class width differs from one class to the next, so that the frequencies cannot be compared directly with each other. This difficulty arises frequently in practice, since statistical data is often tabulated in this way. The difficulty is immediately overcome by converting the data into probability per x unit. The details are left to the student as an exercise.

PROBLEMS

1. Convert the data in Table 2-2-2 to probability per pound. Plot the data and draw a smooth curve, and read from it the following: the probability that a given wire will have a breaking strength (a) between 205.3 and 206.1 pounds, (b) above 205.8 pounds.

2. Reread illustrative problem (3) above. Convert the data to probability per year, plot, and answer the questions asked in the problem.

3. Convert the data in Table 2-7-1 to probability per thousand dollars of income, plot, and draw a smooth curve. What income has the highest probability?

3.   THE PROBABILITY GRAPH IN t UNITS

We have seen that it is possible to compare any two distributions of similar variates, in spite of differences in class interval and sample size, by expressing them in terms of probability per x unit, which we have called $P(x)$. If the two distributions are concerned with variates which are measured in totally different units, then we must reconcile these units in order to compare the distributions with each other. For example, if we

---

*Reprinted from "Summary of Motor Vehicle Traffic Accidents in Ohio," State of Ohio, 1950, by permission.

wish to investigate the properties which a distribution of intelligence quotients has in common with a distribution of men's heights, then it is obviously foolish to try to compare the probability per IQ unit to the probability per inch of height. We need a new common unit in which both IQ and height can be measured, so that the resulting probabilities per unit will be comparable.

For this purpose we define a new unit of measurement called a t unit. The size of the new unit is simply the standard deviation of the distribution, and the starting point is the arithmetic mean:

$$t = (x - \bar{x})/\sigma \qquad (6\text{-}3\text{-}1)$$

If, for example, the arithmetic mean of a distribution of IQ's is 95, and the standard deviation is 20, then an x score of 135 becomes a t score of $+2$, and an x score of 65 becomes a t score of -1.5. The fourth column of Table 6-3-1 shows a set of x's reduced to t units.

If we change the horizontal scale of the probability graph from x units to t units, then we must also change the vertical scale from probability per x unit to probability per t unit. This is readily done by multiplying the probability per x unit by the number of x units in a t unit, that is, by the standard deviation. We will use the symbol $P(t)$ for the probability per t unit:

$$P(t) = P(x) \times \sigma = f\sigma/NC \qquad (6\text{-}3\text{-}2)$$

TABLE 6-3-1.   Reduction to $P(t)$*

Boundaries in Feet	f	$x - \bar{x}$	$\dfrac{x - \bar{x}}{\sigma}$ (t)	$f\sigma/NC$ $P(t)$	
15– 25	1	−60.63	−2.89	0.007	$N = 303$
25– 35	2	−50.63	−2.42	0.014	$C = 10$
35– 45	7	−40.63	−1.94	0.048	$\bar{x} = 80.63$
45– 55	25	−30.63	−1.46	0.173	$\sigma = 20.95$
55– 65	33	−20.63	−0.99	0.228	$\sigma/NC = 0.00691$
65– 75	53	−10.63	−0.51	0.366	
75– 85	64	− 0.63	−0.03	0.442	
85– 95	44	+ 9.37	+0.45	0.304	
95–105	31	+19.37	+0.92	0.214	
105–115	27	+29.37	+1.40	0.187	
115–125	11	+39.37	+1.88	0.076	
125–135	4	+49.37	+2.36	0.028	
135–145	1	+59.37	+2.83	0.007	

*Reprinted by permission of Prentice-Hall, Inc., from *Applied General Statistics* by Croxton and Cowden. Copyright 1939 by Prentice-Hall, Inc.

If we now plot $P(t)$ against t, it is obvious that we will remove any effect of the nature of the units in which the variates were originally measured and leave for comparison only the basic pattern of the distribution.

To illustrate the procedure of reducing a frequency tabulation to a graph showing the frequency per t unit plotted against t units, let us use the data in Figure 1-4-1, showing the distances which 303 freshmen high school girls in Gary, Indiana, could throw a baseball. The procedure (illustrated in Table 6-3-1) is as follows: First we subtract $\bar{x}$ from each class mark (column 3) and divide each of the resulting numbers by σ (column 4). The resulting numbers are, by definition, the distances expressed in t units. To obtain $P(t)$ we first compute σ/NC (which is 0.00692) and then multiply it by each value of f (column 5). The values of $P(t)$ are plotted against t (filled circles in Figure 6-3-1), and a smooth curve has been drawn by eye to fit the points as well as possible. If we apply the same procedure to the data concerning the percentage of dry matter in mangel roots, (Figure 1-4-2), we obtain the set of points which are

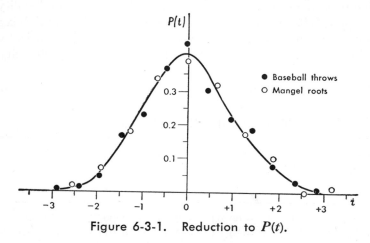

Figure 6-3-1.   Reduction to $P(t)$.

shown by open circles in Figure 6-3-1. The differences between the two distributions are no greater than we might expect from the random variations between one sample and another.

PROBLEMS

1. Convert the data in Table 4-3-2 to the $P(t)$ form and plot. How does the value of $P(t)$ for $t = -1$ compare with the corresponding value in Figure 6-3-1?

2. Write a summary of all the advantages of expressing data in the form of probability per t unit instead of frequency per class.

4.   BINOMIAL DISTRIBUTION

In the preceding article we saw that many distributions, when expressed in terms of probability per t unit, reach a maximum of about 0.4 at the point where t is zero, fall to about 0.25 when t is ± 1, and drop to less than 0.1 when t reaches ± 2.   Beyond this the curves diminish more gradually, generally reaching zero by the time t is $\pm 2\frac{1}{2}$ or ± 3.   The objective of this article is to investigate the possibilities of explaining this characteristic shape on theoretical grounds.   There are two basic questions to be answered:

(1) What hypotheses must we make about the nature of the causes governing the sizes of the variates in order to show theoretically that the probability curve should have the properties described above?

(2) Having accepted these postulates on the grounds of their success in predicting the shape of a large number of observed probability curves, what additional information can we extract from them?

Let us begin with the following preliminary assumptions about the factors which determine the size of any variate.   Later we will investigate the possible modifications of these assumptions:

(1) Each variate consists of a fixed ingredient (x_0) which is the same for all variates, plus a variable ingredient.   The size of the variable ingredient is not determined by a single cause, but by a very large number of small causes, each of which makes only a small contribution to the total.

(2) The small causes all act independently of each other.

(3) All the contributions made by these causes are equal in size, but may be positive or negative.

(4) The probability that a given contribution will be positive is $1/2$, and the probability that it will be negative is $1/2$.

In practice, it is not necessary for the statistician to know the nature of the small contributing causes, but it will perhaps be instructive to try to identify some of them in a specific example.   The following is an account of the work of an astronomer in measuring the output of light from each of a set of stars.   He begins by photographing the unknown stars, and then, on the same plate, he makes a second exposure, this time using a field of stars whose brightnesses are already known.   After developing the plate, he sends a beam of light through the image of each unknown star and then into a photoelectric cell, where its intensity is measured exactly. He makes a similar measurement upon each of the stars of known brightness, and from the resulting data he constructs a graph showing the relationship between the photocell reading and the brightness of the star which produced the image.   Then, using the photocell reading of each unknown star, he reads off the brightness of the unknown star.   Each unknown star is measured twice, and the difference between the two measures is computed for each.   A frequency tabulation formed from these differences displays the characteristic bell shape which we are trying to investigate.* In this case some of the contributing causes have been identified and listed by the investigator.

---

*See for example the *Astronomical Journal*, Volume 51, No. 6, page 170.

(1) The transparency of the sky in the region of the comparison stars probably differed a little from that of the unknown star.

(2) The comparison exposure may have been a little longer or shorter than the exposure on the unknown star.

(3) The photographic plate is not exactly uniform in sensitivity, and the star image may have fallen on a spot of slightly higher or lower than average sensitivity.

(4) The developer may not have circulated exactly evenly over the plate.

(5) The temperature of the photographic plate might have changed slightly between the star exposure and the comparison exposure, thus changing its sensitivity slightly.

(6) The moisture content of the plate may have changed between the two exposures, thus altering its sensitivity.

(7) The sensitivity of the photocell is not uniform over its surface, and the star image may have fallen a little to the left or right of its usual position, thus striking a region of slightly different sensitivity.

(8) The voltage applied to the photocell may have varied slightly between the unknown star reading and the comparison star readings.

(9) Small errors are introduced in rounding off the photocell readings.

These contributing causes at first glance fail to fulfil the postulates on two counts: first, they do not constitute a "large number" of causes; and second, they do not all make contributions of equal size. In the above investigation, for example, it was shown that the differences of transparency of the sky far outweighed any other cause. It is possible, however, to surmount both of these difficulties by assuming that the large contributions made by these identifiable causes are themselves made up of numerous smaller contributions, each too small to be separately identifiable.

To approach this problem on a mathematical basis, let us introduce the following notation:

x_0 = the fixed ingredient which is present in all the variates.

e = the size of each of the small contributions made by the various causes. We will call each of these contributions an element.

n = the number of elements present in each variate.

s = the number of these elements which are positive.

$n - s$ = number of elements remaining which are negative.

$P(s)$ = the probability that there will be exactly s positive elements in a given variate.

N = the number of variates.

If you are not accustomed to operating with so large a number of symbols, you will probably find the mathematical treatment difficult to follow. If this is the case, you might find it useful to construct an imaginary situation in which the various quantities are illustrated. The following is offered as an example. A merchant has been offering for sale an article for 75¢, but, upon finding that his customers prefer to gamble on the transaction, he offers instead to toss eight coins and to determine the selling price as follows. For each head which turns up, the price is increased 5¢ above the original price, and for each tail it is decreased 5¢. Let us suppose that 256 customers accept these terms and that the merchant then studies the distribution of the actual charges for these customers. In this case, e is 5¢, n is 8, x_0 is 75¢, N is 256, x is the actual charge to any customer, s is the number of heads in any given throw, and $P(s)$ is the probability that there will be this many heads. For example, $P(3)$ is the probability that any given customer will throw three heads, and it is therefore also the probability that any given customer will pay 65¢.

To investigate the probability of occurrence of an x of a given size, we must find how many positive contributions are necessary to produce an x of this size. Each variate will consist of x_0 , plus s positive contributions of size e, plus $n - s$ negative contributions of size e:

$$x = x_0 + s \times e + (n - s)(-e)$$

or
$$x = x_0 + 2es - en \tag{6-4-1}$$

If we solve this for s, we have

$$s = (x - x_0 + ne)/2e \tag{6-4-2}$$

For example, for the charge to be 95¢, it is necessary that there must be $(95 - 75 + 8 \times 5)/(2 \times 5)$, or 6 heads.

The probability of occurrence of an x of a given size can now be found by computing the probability that there will be exactly s heads, where s is related to x by 6-4-2. We can use equation 5-10-2 to obtain this probability by inserting $\frac{1}{2}$ for p and $\frac{1}{2}$ for q:

$$P(s) = \frac{n!}{s!(n - s)!} \left(\frac{1}{2}\right)^s \left(\frac{1}{2}\right)^{n-s} \tag{6-4-3}$$

TABLE 6-4-1.   Computation of $P(s)$

s	$P(s)$	x	$NP(s)$
0	1/256	$0.35	1
1	8/256	0.45	8
2	28/256	0.55	28
3	56/256	0.65	56
4	70/256	0.75	70
5	56/256	0.85	56
6	28/256	0.95	28
7	8/256	1.05	8
8	1/256	1.15	1

The use of this equation is illustrated in Table 6-4-1, where the probability of occurrence is tabulated for each value of s in the illustrative example. In the third column are shown the values of x which result from the various values of s, and in the fourth column are given the theoretical number of occurrences of each value of s when the number of variates is 256. Equation 6-4-3 gives us the probability of occurrence of one specific value of x. If we can rewrite it in the form of a probability per x unit, and then convert the result to probability per t unit, we will have a theoretical distribution which we can compare directly with any observed distribution which is expressed in the same way. To avoid confusion we will make these transformations separately.

A. CONVERSION TO x UNITS. Equation 6-4-3 gives us the probability of occurrence of a single value of s, that is, the probability per s unit. To obtain the probability per x unit we must multiply by the number of s units in one x unit. An inspection of equation 6-4-2 shows that if we increase x by one unit, s will increase by $1/2e$ units; there are therefore $1/2e$ units of s in one x unit. The probability per x unit is therefore

$$P(x) = \frac{1}{2e} \frac{n!}{s!(n-s)!} \left(\frac{1}{2}\right)^n$$

To complete the transformation to x units we must now replace s by the corresponding value of x, from equation 6-4-2:*

$$P(x) = \frac{1}{2e} \frac{n!}{\left(\dfrac{x - x_0 + ne}{2e}\right)!\left(n - \dfrac{x - x_0 + ne}{2e}\right)!} \left(\frac{1}{2}\right)^n \qquad (6\text{-}4\text{-}4)$$

where we must choose the values of x in such a way that the terms in the denominator are positive integers. This gives us the probability per x unit, expressed in x units. For example, if we insert 95¢ for x, we obtain $7/640$ for $P(x)$, which is the probability per penny in the neighborhood of 95¢.

B. CONVERSION TO t UNITS. We now wish to express our results in terms of t units, which are defined by equation 6-3-1. For our purpose it is convenient to solve this for x:

$$x = \bar{x} + \sigma_x t \qquad (6\text{-}4\text{-}5)$$

We see that if we change t by one unit, x will change by σ_x units, and there are therefore σ_x units of x in one t unit. To change equation 6-4-4 to probability per t unit we must therefore multiply by σ_x :

$$P(t) = \sigma_x P(x)$$

To change our variable from x to t we must substitute for x its value in terms of t, as given by 6-4-5. Upon making this substitution, we have

---

*If you find that this treatment takes you beyond your depth mathematically, it is suggested that you omit the remainder of Article 4 and go directly to Article 5.

$P(t)$

$$= \sigma_x \left(\frac{1}{2e}\right) \frac{n!}{\left(\dfrac{\bar{x} + \sigma_x t - x_0 + ne}{2e}\right)! \left(n - \dfrac{\bar{x} + \sigma_x t - x_0 + ne}{2e}\right)!} \left(\frac{1}{2}\right)^n \quad (6\text{-}4\text{-}6)$$

C. EVALUATION OF $\bar{x}$ AND σ_x IN TERMS OF $\bar{s}$ AND σ_s . We cannot yet use equation 6-4-6 for a direct comparison with observed distributions because of the presence of the two unknown quantities $\bar{x}$ and σ_x . To evaluate these, let us begin by taking the mean of both sides of equation 6-4-1:

$$\bar{x} = \overline{x_0 + 2es - en} = x_0 + 2e\bar{s} - en \quad (6\text{-}4\text{-}7)$$

The value of σ_x is, by definition, $\sqrt{(x - \bar{x})^2}$. From equations 6-4-1 and 6-4-7 we see that $x - \bar{x} = 2es - 2e\bar{s}$, and σ_x becomes

$$\sigma_x = \sqrt{(2es - 2e\bar{s})^2} = 2e\sqrt{(s - \bar{s})^2} = 2e\sigma_s$$

Substituting these values for $\bar{x}$ and σ_x in 6-4-6, we have

$$P(t) = \sigma_s \frac{n!}{(\bar{s} + \sigma_s t)!(n - \bar{s} - \sigma_s t)!} \left(\frac{1}{2}\right)^n \quad (6\text{-}4\text{-}8)$$

D. EVALUATION OF $\bar{s}$ AND σ_s . Our final objective has not yet been accomplished; we have merely shifted the problem from that of finding $\bar{x}$ and σ_x to that of finding $\bar{s}$ and σ_s . To find $\bar{s}$ we must multiply each value of s by the number of times which it occurs, add the results, and divide by the total number of occurrences. Since we are interested in theoretical rather than observational results, we must use the expected number of occurrences, which is simply the number of variates times the probability that any variate will have the given value of s; it is in other words $N \times P(s)$. We can either proceed directly with these expected occurrences, as shown in the last column of Table 6-4-1, or we can shorten the work a little by cancelling the N as follows:

$$\bar{s} = \Sigma s N P(s)/N = \Sigma s P(s)$$

By the same argument, we can find σ_s as follows:

$$\sigma_s = \sqrt{(s - \bar{s})^2} = \sqrt{\Sigma(s - \bar{s})^2 N P(s)/N} = \sqrt{(s - \bar{s})^2 P(s)}$$

The computation of $\bar{s}$ and σ_s for $n = 8$ is shown in Table 6-4-2, from which we see that $\bar{s}$ is 4 and that σ_s is $\sqrt{8}/2$. If we repeat the experiment for other values of n (the computations are left to the student as an exercise), we obtain the following:

n	$\bar{s}$	σ_s
8	4.0	$\sqrt{8}/2$
7	3.5	$\sqrt{7}/2$
6	3.0	$\sqrt{6}/2$
5	2.5	$\sqrt{5}/2$

From this result we generalize as follows:*

$$\bar{s} = n/2 \qquad (6\text{-}4\text{-}9)$$

$$\sigma_s = \sqrt{n}/2 \qquad (6\text{-}4\text{-}10)$$

E. The Final Equation.   If we now substitute $n/2$ for $\bar{s}$ and $\sqrt{n}/2$ for σ_s in equation 6-4-8 we will obtain

$$P(t) = \frac{n!\sqrt{n}}{\left(\dfrac{n - \sqrt{n}\,t}{2}\right)!\left(\dfrac{n + \sqrt{n}\,t}{2}\right)!2^{n+1}} \qquad (6\text{-}4\text{-}11)$$

This equation now expresses our theoretical distribution in exactly the same form as the actual distributions shown in Figure 6-4-1, and it is possible to compare them directly and to see how closely the actual distributions come to the theoretical one for any assumed value of n.   Follow-

TABLE 6-4-2.   Computation of $\bar{s}$ and σ_s for $n = 8$

s	$P(s)$	$sP(s)$	$s - \bar{s}$	$(s - \bar{s})^2 P(s)$
0	1/256	0/256	−4	16/256
1	8/256	8/256	−3	72/256
2	28/256	56/256	−2	112/256
3	56/256	168/256	−1	56/256
4	70/256	280/256	0	0
5	56/256	280/256	1	56/256
6	28/256	168/256	2	112/256
7	8/256	56/256	3	72/256
8	1/256	8/256	4	16/256
		1024/256		512/256

$$\bar{s} = 1024/256 = 4.0$$

$$\sigma_s = \sqrt{512/256} = \sqrt{8}/2$$

ing the assumptions listed at the beginning of this article, we are primarily interested in the case in which the number of elements is very large.   Accordingly, let us begin by studying equation 6-4-11 with small values of n, and then see what changes will occur when n becomes progressively larger.   If we begin with $n = 9$, equation 6-4-11 predicts the following values of $P(t)$:

---

*A proof of these equations can be found in Chapter 1 of the second volume of Kenney's *Mathematics of Statistics*, D. Van Nostrand Company, 1939.

t	$P(t)$
0.333	0.369
1.000	0.246
1.667	0.105
2.133	0.026
3.000	0.0029

The resulting probability curve is shown by the solid circles and the curve in Figure 6-4-1. We see that the curve reaches a maximum of about 0.39, that it changes curvature between $t = 1$ and $t = 2$, that it begins to level off beyond $t = 2$, and that it has almost reached zero by $t = 3$. In short, it resembles very closely the curve shown in Figure 6-3-1.

If we go to $n = 16$, we find the following values of $P(t)$:

t	$P(t)$
0.0	0.393
0.5	0.349
1.0	0.244
1.5	0.133
2.0	0.056
2.5	0.017
3.0	0.0037
3.5	0.0005
4.0	0.00003

When plotted, these values give us a probability curve which differs very little from the $n = 9$ curve, as shown by the open circles in Figure 6-4-1. The only perceptible differences in the $n = 16$ curve as compared with the $n = 9$ curve are these: first, the central value is a little higher; and second, the wings of the curve extend out a little farther. If we choose still larger values of n, the central value builds up a little farther, and the wings extend farther and farther to the left and to the right, but otherwise the general shape of the curve differs extremely little from that in Figure 6-4-1.

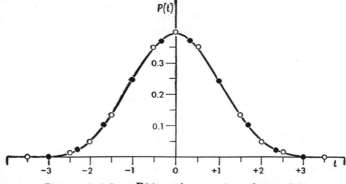

Figure 6-4-1. $P(t)$ with $n = 9$ and $n = 16$.

The agreement between the theoretical curve (Figure 6-4-1) and the observational curves (6-3-1 and others) is sufficiently good to indicate that the assumptions listed at the beginning of this article may apply to many distributions occurring in various fields. It would, however, be faulty logic to accept this as positive evidence of the correctness of the postulates. In particular, if we can predict the observed distributions successfully by using only some of the assumptions, then it would be unnecessary and logically faulty to accept the remaining ones. The problem of reducing to a minimum the number of assumptions which we must make in this derivation is an important one, and we will return to it in Article 6.

PROBLEMS

1. Using equation 6-4-11, compute for $n = 4$ the values of $P(t)$ for $t = 0$ and for $t = 1$.

2. Write a complete derivation of equation 6-4-11, supplying all the steps which are omitted in the text.

5. NORMAL CURVE

In the preceding article we showed that equation 6-4-1 represents the probability curve which is to be expected when the deviation of each variate from the mean is composed of a large number of small equal contributions, independent of each other and each having a probability of $1/2$ of being positive; and we demonstrated the use of this equation for several values of n.

This procedure has two weaknesses: first, the computation of $P(t)$ becomes very laborious if n is large; second, the equation is applicable only for those values of t such that $(n \pm \sqrt{n}\, t)/2$ is a whole number.

The first difficulty is particularly inconvenient since it is precisely the large values of n in which we are interested; in fact, we would like to find what the distribution is like if n becomes larger and larger without limit.

Fortunately it is possible, by means of mathematical analysis involving calculus, to find what happens to $P(t)$ as n becomes indefinitely large. The result can be written in the following simple form:

$$P(t) = \frac{1}{\sqrt{2\pi}} e^{-t^2/2} \qquad (6\text{-}5\text{-}1)$$

where e is an abbreviation for the number $2.718 \cdots$.* The curve obtained by plotting equation 6-5-1 is called the *normal curve,* and any distribution which approximates this curve is called a normal distribution. To show

---

*The number e has a standard abbreviation because it is widely used in advanced mathematics. Some readers may be familiar with it in connection with its use as the base of the so-called Napierian or natural system of logarithms.

that it gives the limiting value of $P(t)$ as n becomes very large, a few specific values of $P(t)$ are shown in Table 6-5-1, computed for $n = 4, 9, 16, 25$, and 36. In the last column are shown the corresponding values obtained from equation 6-5-1. An inspection of the table shows that for large values of n the difference between the two equations becomes negligible. We therefore adopt equation 6-5-1 as the equation for the theo-

TABLE 6-5-1. $P(t)$ for Increasing Values of n

	Equation 6-4-11					Equation 6-5-1
t	$n = 4$	$n = 9$	$n = 16$	$n = 25$	$n = 36$	
0	0.3750		0.3928		0.3962	0.3989
1	0.2500	0.2461	0.2444	0.2435	0.2431	0.2420
2	0.0625		0.0555		0.0546	0.0540
3		0.0029	0.0037	0.0040	0.0041	0.0044

retical form to be expected for any distribution which fulfills the basic assumptions listed at the beginning of Article 4.

The computation of $P(t)$ by means of equation 6-5-1 can be performed by means of the principles described in Chapter 3. For example, to evaluate $P(t)$ for $t = 3$, we begin by evaluating the exponent, which is $-3^2/2$ or -4.5. To proceed from here, let us evaluate $e^{4.5}$ by means of equation 3-2-3, which tells us that $\log e^{4.5} = 4.5 \log e$. Log e is 0.4343, from which we see that $\log e^{4.5} = 1.954$. We look up the antilog of 1.954 and see that $e^{4.5}$ is equal to 90.0. From equation 3-3-6 we see that $e^{-4.5}$ must be $1/e^{4.5}$ or $1/90.0$. The remainder of the computation can be completed most quickly by slide rule, giving us $P(3) = (1/\sqrt{2 \times 3.1416}) \times (1/90) = 0.0044$.

PROBLEMS

1. Using equation 6-5-1, compute $P(t)$ for $t = 0$, $t = 1$, $t = 2$, $t = -2.5$, and $t = -4$.

6. APPLICABILITY OF NORMAL CURVE

The assumptions described in the preceding article are sufficient for the derivation of the equation of the normal curve, and we can assert that any distribution which fulfils these assumptions will have an approximately normal form. Actually, it is possible to derive the normal curve from still less restrictive assumptions and thus to broaden the scope of the cases in which we should expect normal distributions. The mathematical treatment required for these derivations is complex, and we will limit ourselves to summarizing their conclusions.

As a first step in generalizing our results, let us consider the effect of removing the fourth assumption listed in Article 4, and let us substitute the more general condition that the probability that an element is positive is some fixed number p, and the probability that it is negative is a fixed number q, where $q = 1 - p$. The mathematical treatment is similar to that in Article 4, and the conclusions are as follows.

(1) The mean of the resulting distribution is not x_0, but is now $x_0 + (p - q)en$.

(2) The standard deviation of the resulting distribution, in terms of s, is no longer $\sqrt{n}/2$, but is

$$\sigma_s = \sqrt{npq} = \sqrt{np(1 - p)} \tag{6-6-1}$$

or, in terms of x, $\sigma_x = 2e\sqrt{npq}$. Equation 6-6-1 is displayed for future reference in later chapters.

(3) The limiting form of the distribution, as n becomes larger and larger, is again the normal curve, regardless of the values of p and q.

To generalize still further, it is possible to remove the restriction that all the elements must have the same size. Instead we can picture the elements as having various sizes (as long as they are all very small) and assume only that the probability of occurrence of an element of a given size is a fixed number. Under these conditions it is still possible to derive the equation of the normal curve. In short, the only essential conditions are the first and second ones listed in Article 4.

These two important conditions can be mastered most quickly by studying some distributions which result from situations in which the conditions are violated. An example of such a distribution is shown in Figure 6-6-1, which shows the result of measuring the length of the glumes of 595 individual wheat plants. The histogram shows three well-defined maxima, and no resemblance whatever to the normal curve. The explanation for this is revealed by an examination of the source of the data. The wheat plants were a cross between Rivet wheat (with an average glume length

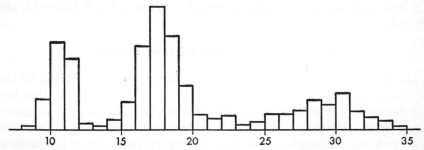

Figure 6-6-1. Lengths of Wheat Glumes. (Based upon data from "The Combination of Observations" by David Brunt, by permission of the Cambridge University Press.)

of 9 millimeters) and Polish wheat (with an average glume length of 28 millimeters). The sample shows marked maxima near these two points, and a third maximum intermediate between them. It appears highly likely that the first of the two conditions has been violated, namely that all the causes of differences between the variates should be small. Here there is obviously a very large cause at work, namely the differences in the inheritance factor, which enters on an all-or-nothing basis. Furthermore, we cannot escape from this first condition by supposing that such an inheritance factor (say, for example, the inheritance of the Rivet genes) is itself made up of a large number of contributing factors, because if we adopt this view then we violate the second condition, namely, that all the contributing factors must be independent. Obviously such hypothetical small contributing factors are not independent, since they are inherited all together or not at all.

Figure 6-6-2 shows the results of drawing sets of 15 cards at random from a deck and counting the number of aces in each set, each set being returned to the deck and mixed before the next set is drawn. The histogram shows a general resemblance to the normal curve, but is conspicuously unsymmetrical. Here the first condition is roughly fulfiled, but the second condition is violated, because the probabilities for the separate elements are not independent. On the contrary, the probability that any one of the fifteen cards will be an ace is strongly influenced by the number of aces already drawn in that set.

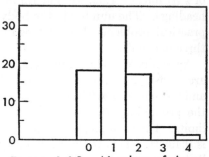

Figure 6-6-2.   Number of Aces.

The final justification for the use of the normal curve in any practical problem must lie in its success in predicting a distribution similar to the observed one. You should make an observational check, if possible, before adopting the hypothesis that a given distribution is normal, even though the causes operating upon the variates appear to fulfil the conditions for the normal curve.

PROBLEMS

1. Would you expect a normal distribution, approximately, for the number of heads obtained by tossing twenty coins a large number of times?

2. Would you expect a normal distribution for the heights of a large number of American students of both sexes? Of American men? Of mixed American and Japanese men? Explain.

3. If you counted the number of errors made each time by a rat in running a maze a large number of times, would you expect the resulting distribution to be normal? Explain in full.

7. NORMAL CURVE TABLES

The normal curve is used so widely in statistics that statisticians have found it to their advantage to precompute and tabulate a set of values of $P(t)$ for all values of t which are likely to be needed in practical problems. Such tables are widely available, and it is therefore not necessary in practice to compute $P(t)$ from equation 6-5-1. It is the purpose of this article to describe the standard normal curve tables and to explain their uses. The tables reproduced in the back of this book (Appendices IV and V) contain tables as follows.

Appendix IV: These numbers, labeled "Ordinates of the Normal Curve," are the values of $P(t)$ corresponding to each tabulated value of t. The whole number and the first decimal of t are found in the left-hand column, and the second decimal is found in the top row. The value of $P(t)$ is then found in the body of the table. For example, to find the value of $P(t)$ for $t = 1.52$, we find 1.5 in the left column and 0.02 in the column headings. The number in the body of the table is then 0.12566. For most practical problems these values of $P(t)$ should be rounded off to four or three decimals.

Appendix V: These numbers, labeled "Areas under the Normal Curve," are measures of the total area under the normal curve between *its center* and *the tabulated value of t*. As we showed in Article 2, these areas measure the probability that a variate chosen at random will lie between these limits. For example, we see from the table that the area given for $t = 2.93$ is 0.49831. This is the probability that a variate chosen at random will lie between $t = 0$ and $t = 2.93$. For convenience we will use the abbreviation $A(t)$ for these areas.

The normal curve tables can be used directly to find the probability that a variate chosen at random will fall between any given limits. The details are shown in the following illustrations.

(1) What is the probability of occurrence of a variate between $t = 1.0$ and $t = 1.2$? Answer: Since the interval is small, we can assume that the mean value of $P(t)$ over the interval is not perceptibly different from its value at the midpoint. Accordingly we read $P(t)$ from the tables for $t = 1.1$ and find it to be 0.2178. This is the probability per t unit, and we must multiply it by the number of t units in the interval, which is 0.2. The required probability is 0.2178 times 0.2, or 0.04356. In other words, about forty-four variates out of a thousand should fall within this interval if the distribution is normal.

(2) What is the probability that a variate chosen at random will lie between -1 and $+2$ in t units? Answer: Since the interval is wide, $P(t)$ will vary greatly from one side of the interval to the other, and we cannot use the method of the preceding problem. Instead we must find the area under the curve between these limits. We find that $A(1)$ is

0.3413; this is the probability of occurrence of a variate between $t = 0$ and $t = 1$. Since the curve is symmetrical, it is also the probability of occurrence of a variate between -1 and zero. We see also that the $A(2)$ is 0.4772; this is the probability of occurrence of a variate between zero and 2. The relationship of these two areas is shown in Figure 6-7-1. By adding the two probabilities we find that the required probability is 0.8185. In other words, about 82 per cent of the variates should lie between -1 and $+2$ for any distribution which is normal.

(3) What is the probability that a variate chosen at random will lie between $+1$ and $+2$ on the t scale? Here we find, as before, that $A(1) = 0.3413$ and $A(2) = 0.4772$, but now these are related as shown in Figure 6-7-2, and it is necessary to subtract the smaller from the larger in order to obtain the area between 1 and 2. The required probability is therefore 0.1359.

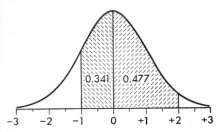 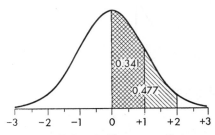

Figure 6-7-1. Sum of Areas.   Figure 6-7-2. Difference of Areas.

(4) What is the probability of occurrence of a variate more than three standard deviations away from the mean? Answer: We find from the tables that $A(3)$ is 0.4986; this is the probability that a given variate will lie between zero and 3 in t units. The probability that a variate will lie between -3 and $+3$ is twice as large, or 0.9972. The probability that a given variate will *not* lie between these limits is obtained by subtracting this from 1. This gives us 0.0028 for the probability that a given variate will fall outside of these limits.

PROBLEMS

1. Find the probability of occurrence of a variate between 2.4 and 3.0 in t units, using the $P(t)$ tables.

2. Repeat Problem 1, using the $A(t)$ tables, and compare the results. Is this a more or a less accurate procedure than that of Problem 1?

3. Use the $A(t)$ tables to find the probability of occurrence of a variate between 2 and 3 in t units.

8. PROPERTIES OF NORMAL CURVE

By using the tables as shown in the preceding article, the following properties of the normal curve can readily be demonstrated.

(1) Approximately 68 per cent of the variates lie within one standard deviation from the mean.

(2) Approximately 95 per cent of the variates lie within two standard deviations from the mean.

(3) Approximately 99.7 per cent of the variates lie within three standard deviations from the mean, and only 0.3 per cent lie beyond this range. These percentages are shown as areas in Figure 6-8-1.

(4) Half of the variates should lie within 0.6745 t unit from the mean.

(5) At 1 t unit from the center, the height of the normal curve is 0.2420/ 0.3989, or about 0.6 as high as it is at the center.

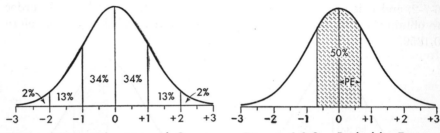

Figure 6-8-1.   The Normal Curve.   Figure 6-8-2.   Probable Error.

The fourth property is useful in connection with a measure of dispersion called probable error, which will be discussed briefly here. The probable error (PE) is that deviation from the mean such that the probability that a variate chosen at random will have a smaller deviation is one half. It is, in other words, the half-width of the range containing half of the variates. This meaning is demonstrated in Figure 6-8-2. From the normal curve tables we see that, if the distribution is normal, the probable error is related to the standard deviation by the simple relationship:

$$PE = 0.6745\sigma \qquad (6\text{-}8\text{-}1)$$

The probable error is widely used as a measure of the uncertainty of results in the exact sciences, and it is described here for the sake of those students who plan to work in these fields. In all other fields the same results are customarily described in terms of standard deviation. It is perhaps to be regretted that two such measures are in widespread use, when one would have served as well.

PROBLEM

1. Using the normal curve tables, verify the five properties of the normal curve listed in the above article.

9. FITTING NORMAL CURVE

Before accepting the hypothesis that a given distribution is normal, it is desirable to make an exact comparison between the distribution and the normal curve. This can be done in either of two ways: first, we can reduce the observed data to probability per t unit and plot it against t, as we did in Figure 6-3-1, and then plot the normal curve on the same diagram; second, we can compute the frequencies which would be expected if the distribution were exactly normal and plot these predicted frequencies on the histogram of the data. The second procedure will be adopted here. It can be learned most quickly by study of the illustrative example in Table 6-91, which contains the scores of 206 freshmen on the Thorndyke Intelligence Test.* The specific steps are as follows.

(1) Compute $\bar{x}$ and σ for the distribution. This step has been omitted from Table 6-9-1. For this data, $\bar{x}$ is 81.59 and σ is 12.14.

(2) List the boundaries (x_b) of all classes (third column). These should be staggered, so that each boundary comes between two classes, as shown.

(3) Convert the x values of these boundaries into t values. This is best accomplished in two steps: first, subtract $\bar{x}$ from each x_b (fourth column); second, divide the results by σ (fifth column).

(4) Read from the normal curve tables the values of $A(t)$ corresponding to each of these values of t (sixth column).

(5) Compute the probability for each class (seventh column). This is done by subtracting values of $A(t)$ in pairs. For example, the probability of occurrence of a variate between $t = 0$ and $t = -3.06$ is 0.4989, as we see from the first entry in the sixth column, and the probability of occurrence of a variate between $t = 0$ and $t = -2.64$ is only 0.4959, as we see from the second entry in this column. The probability of occurrence of a variate between -3.06 and -2.64 is obviously 0.4989 minus 0.4959, or 0.0030, which we enter in the seventh column. The only exception to this procedure occurs in the 80 to 84 class, in which t changes from a negative to a positive value. For this class we see that the probability between minus 0.17 and zero is 0.0675, while that from zero to plus 0.24 is 0.0948. The total probability for the class (0.1623) is obtained by adding these two. These probabilities in the seventh column should again be staggered as shown, since each represents the probability *between* two boundaries.

(6) In the last column are given the predicted frequencies (f_p). To compute these, we multiply the total number of variates (N) by the probability that any of these variates will fall in the given class. For example, the predicted probability that a variate will fall in the first class is 0.0030, and we find the predicted frequency by multiplying this by 206, obtaining 0.6.

---

*For source of data, see Figure 1-4-3.

TABLE 6-9-1.   Fitting Normal Curve

Limits	f	Boundaries (x_b)	$x_b - \bar{x}$	$(x_b - \bar{x})/\sigma$ (t)	$A(t)$	Prob.	$N \times$ Prob (f_p)
		44.5	-37.09	-3.06	0.4989		
45– 49	1					0.0030	0.6
		49.5	-32.09	-2.64	0.4959		
50– 54	2					0.0088	1.8
		54.5	-27.09	-2.23	0.4871		
55– 59	2					0.0215	4.4
		59.5	-22.09	-1.82	0.4656		
60– 64	10					0.0449	9.2
		64.5	-17.09	-1.41	0.4207		
65– 69	15					0.0794	16.4
		69.5	-12.09	-1.00	0.3413		
70– 74	27					0.1223	25.2
		74.5	$- 7.09$	-0.58	0.2190		
75– 79	37					0.1515	31.2
		79.5	$- 2.09$	-0.17	0.0675		
80– 84	30					0.1623*	33.4
		84.5	$+ 2.91$	$+0.24$	0.0948		
85– 89	34					0.1474	30.4
		89.5	$+ 7.91$	$+0.65$	0.2422		
90– 94	18					0.1132	23.3
		94.5	$+12.91$	$+1.06$	0.3554		
95– 99	13					0.0752	15.5
		99.5	$+17.91$	$+1.48$	0.4306		
100–104	10					0.0400	8.2
		104.5	$+22.91$	$+1.89$	0.4706		
105–109	4					0.0187	3.9
		109.5	$+27.91$	$+2.30$	0.4893		
110–114	2					0.0073	1.5
		114.5	$+32.91$	$+2.71$	0.4966		
115–119	1					0.0025	0.5
		119.5	$+37.91$	$+3.12$	0.4991		
	206		$\bar{x} = 81.59$		$\sigma = 12.14$		

*Where t changes sign, the values of $A(t)$ must be added.

(7) Plot the values of f_p on the original histogram, and connect them by means of a smooth curve, as shown in Figure 6-9-1.

The suitability of the normal curve is judged by the quality of the fit of the normal curve to the original histogram, or by the agreement between the predicted and the observed frequencies in the table. In Table 6-9-1, for example, we see that the normal curve predicts a frequency of **16.9**

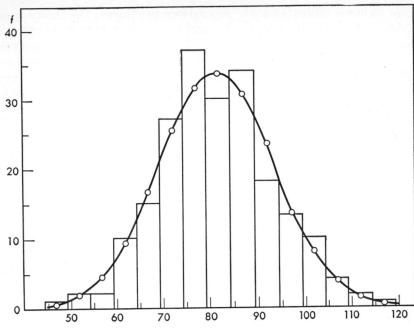

Figure 6-9-1.   A Fitted Normal Curve.

for the fifth class, while the class actually contains a frequency of 15. This difference could easily arise from accidents of sampling, and, in fact, all the observed frequencies are compatible with the hypothesis that the universe from which the sample came is distributed normally.   More exact tests to measure the probability that a given distribution is normal will be described in Chapter 11.

PROBLEMS

1. Fit a normal curve to the data in Table 4-3-2, and graph the results as shown in Figure 6-9-1.   For which class is the disagreement between the predicted and the observed frequencies the worst?

2. Fit a normal curve to the data in Table 4-5-1.

10.   USES OF NORMAL CURVE

After the investigator has tested a distribution by the methods of the preceding article, and has accepted the hypothesis that the universe from which it came is approximately normal, he is justified in using the normal curve tables to predict the probabilities or frequencies for any future samples from the same universe.   The practical utility of this procedure can be described most rapidly by means of a few illustrative examples:

I. A manager of a factory plans to establish a new plant, which will require eighteen skilled men for supervisory positions. He knows from experience that only those men who make a score of 115 or above on a given aptitude test are likely to succeed in these positions. He gives this test to the first twenty-five men who apply for employment in the new locality and finds the distribution of scores shown in Table 6-10-1. How many men should he plan to interview and test in order to be reasonably certain of finding at least eighteen who will score 115 or above?

TABLE 6-10-1.   Scores of Twenty-Five Applicants

Score	f
70– 79	2
80– 89	3
90– 99	9
100–109	8
110–119	2
120–129	1

For this problem, the obvious procedure would be to find what fraction of the sample had scores of 115 or above, and then divide 18 by this fraction to find the required number of applicants. This procedure is hopelessly weak because the sample is so small that this fraction is very poorly determined by the observations. As an alternative to this we proceed as follows.

(1) We assume that the distribution is normal, both on the grounds that a normal distribution is generally to be expected for variates of this nature and on the grounds that a normal curve fits the available observational data fairly well.

(2) We reduce the score of 114.5 to a t score. The mean of the sample is 97.7 and the standard deviation is 11.6, giving us $(114.5-97.7)/11.6$, or 1.45 for the score of 114.5 expressed in t units.

(3) We find that $A(t)$ for this t score is 0.4265. Therefore, 42.65 per cent of the applicants should be expected to have scores between 97.7 and 114.5, and of course 50 per cent should be expected to have scores lower than 97.7. This leaves 7.35 per cent whose scores should be above 114.5.

(4) We must now select a number N such that 7.35 per cent of N is greater than 18. N must therefore be greater than $18/0.0735$, or 245. It would be reasonable for the manager to be prepared to test about 250 or 300 applicants in order to be fairly confident that he would obtain the needed 18 men with scores of 115 or above.

II. A turkey raiser sells his turkeys on a sliding price basis, depending upon the weights of the turkeys. The price scale is shown in Table 6-10-2, which also shows the distribution of weights per hundred turkeys in his

TABLE 6-10-2. Distribution of Turkey Weights

Weight	No. per 100	Price per Pound
7– 9	0	$0.75
9–11	1	
11–13	5	0.65
13–15	23	
15–17	36	0.55
17–19	27	
19–21	6	0.49
21–23	2	

flocks. He is offered a new contract for his turkeys under which he will be paid as follows:

Weight	Price per Pound
6.0 to 8.5	80¢
8.5 to 11.0	70¢
11.0 to 13.5	60¢
13.5 to 16.0	55¢
16.0 to 18.5	53¢
18.5 to 21.0	51¢
21.0 to 23.5	49¢

Assuming that the distribution is normal, how many turkeys per 100 should he expect to fall into each of the new classifications? Would it be to his financial advantage to accept the new contract or to continue under the previous arrangement?

To solve this problem it is necessary to compute the arithmetic mean and the standard deviation of the distribution and then to compute the predicted frequencies in the new classes, using the procedure shown in Table 6-9-1. The values of the boundaries used should of course be the boundaries of the new classes, namely, 6.0, 8.5, 11.0, and so forth. The details are left to the student as an exercise.

The operation described in the above paragraph is called "graduation of frequencies," and is frequently performed in statistical work. Further important uses of the normal curve will be described in future chapters.

PROBLEMS

1. In illustrative problem I, answer the following further questions. (a) How many applicants would it be necessary to interview to be fairly certain of finding

five with a score above 128?   (b) If 800 applicants are to be examined, how many of them would you expect to have scores between 78 and 108?

2. Complete the illustrative problem concerning the turkey raiser.   Find the predicted frequency for each of the new classes and the total payment which he would receive per hundred turkeys under each contract.

3. For the data in Table 1-4-3, if a sample of 1000 wires were chosen to be tested from the same machine, how many would you expect to have breaking strengths under 200 pounds?   Under 195 pounds?   With this information in mind, answer Problem V, Article 4, Chapter 1.

11.   SUMMARY

The material in this chapter falls into three parts, as follows.   I.   The technique of expressing any distribution in a standard form, in which it can be compared with any other distribution expressed in the same form. II. A theoretical explanation of the similarity of many distributions when expressed in this standard form.   III.   Uses of the theoretical conclusions so reached.   The procedures and the central results are as follows:

I. Any distribution can be presented in a standard form in which it is independent of the choice of class interval, size of sample, and units of measurement of the variate.   The process of converting the data to this standard form consists of (1) converting the x values to t units, where t is defined as $(x - \bar{x})/\sigma$, and (2) converting the frequencies to probabilities per t unit, or $P(t)$, which is computed from equation 6-3-2:

$$P(t) = f\sigma/NC \quad (observed \text{ values of } P)$$

The procedure is illustrated in Table 6-3-1 and Figure 6-3-1.   The purposes of this procedure are as follows.

(1) To make comparisons between distributions which have different class intervals, sample sizes, or x units.

(2) To study and describe the properties which various distributions have in common, as a starting point for the theoretical study of these properties in part II.

(3) To make possible the estimation of the probability of an occurrence between various values of x or between various values of t.   This is accomplished by measuring the area under the probability curve, as shown in Figure 6-2-1, and as described in the accompanying text.

(4) To remove the distortion which is produced when data is tabulated in classes of different widths.

II. When we study a number of observed distributions in the standard form described above, we find that many of them have almost exactly the same shape, shown in Figure 6-3-1 and described in the opening paragraph of Article 4.   This characteristic shape can be explained theoretically if we adopt the following hypotheses concerning the causes of differences between the variates:

(1) Each variate differs from the mean not as a result of a single cause or a few large causes, but as a result of a large number of causes, each of which contributes only a relatively very small amount to the final value of the variate.

(2) Each of these small causes is independent of all the other small causes.

On the basis of these hypotheses, it is possible to show theoretically that the resulting distribution in $P(t)$ form should fulfil equation 6-5-1:

$$P(t) = \frac{1}{\sqrt{2\pi}} e^{-t^2/2} \quad (\textit{theoretical} \text{ values of } P)$$

where $e = 2.718 \cdots$. The curve obtained by plotting this equation is called the normal curve, and any distribution which approximates it is called a normal distribution. Properties of the normal curve are described in Article 8 and illustrated in Figures 6-8-1 and 6-8-2. In practical use of the normal curve, the values of $P(t)$ are not computed from the equation, but are instead read from precomputed tables. The use of such tables is described in Article 7.

III. A standard procedure in statistics is to fit a normal curve to a given set of data. The purpose of this is usually twofold: first, by comparing the distribution with the best fitting normal curve, it is possible to confirm or reject the hypothesis that the universe from which the sample came was distributed normally. Many further statistical conclusions depend upon this hypothesis, and it is important that it be tested in this way. Second, after the hypothesis has been confirmed, the normal curve tables can be used to predict the frequency of occurrence to be expected in any future samples to be taken from the same universe. The operational procedures in fitting a normal curve are described in steps 1 to 7 in Article 9, and the uses of the resulting information are described in Article 10.

CHAPTER

• 7 •

FURTHER DESCRIPTIVE DEVICES

1. INTRODUCTION

One of the purposes of statistics is that of describing a distribution in precise mathematical terms, in order that the investigator may compare it with other distributions. This function has been introduced in Chapter 3, with the arithmetic mean and the standard deviation (both of which are numerical descriptions of properties of distributions) and will be continued in this chapter.

This descriptive function is not the central purpose of statistics as it is treated in this book and is, furthermore, not necessary in the logical development of this central purpose. We have come, in other words, to a branching in the objectives of elementary statistics. The present chapter is one of the branches and is complete in itself, while in the following chapter we will return to the development of the primary objective. It is suggested, therefore, that if you do not have time to study all the topics, you should omit this chapter entirely and go at this point directly to Chapter 8.

2. PROPERTIES OF FREQUENCY DISTRIBUTIONS

We have seen in Chapter 6 that many distributions occurring in practice closely resemble the normal curve and that such distributions can be described by giving the arithmetic mean and the standard deviation. Many other distributions resemble the normal curve in a general way in that they rise smoothly from zero to a single maximum and then decline smoothly to zero again. It is for such distributions that the descriptive methods in this chapter are chiefly useful. If the distribution differs completely from the normal curve, for example if it has more than one distinct maximum, then a description of the sort we are about to undertake is not very useful, and the best description of the distribution is the presentation of the frequency tabulation itself.

If the distribution has a general resemblance to the normal curve, then the most obvious property to be described is the *central tendency*, or the value around which the variates are centered. We have already studied two quantities which describe the central tendency (the arithmetic mean and the median), and we will describe others in this chapter.

Any description of central tendency is, however, incomplete because of the obvious fact that two distributions can have the same central tendency and yet be very different in other ways. The most obvious difference is in *dispersion*, or scatter of the variates around the mean. This is a property which we have already described by means of the standard deviation, which tells you whether the variates are widely scattered or whether they are closely clustered around the mean. We will describe other methods of measuring the property of dispersion in this chapter.

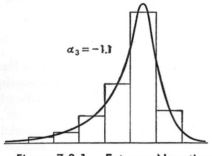

Figure 7-2-1. Extreme Negative Skewness.

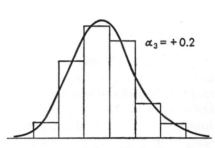

Figure 7-2-2. Moderate Positive Skewness.

If two distributions agree in central tendency and dispersion, they can still differ, but in less obvious ways, and we must next describe these further differences. It is possible, for example, for one of the distributions to be unsymmetrical, that is, for its histogram to descend more steeply on one side than on the other. This property is described as *skewness*, and methods for measuring it will be described in the following articles. Distributions showing varying degrees of skewness are shown in Figures 7-2-1 and 7-2-2.

Now we must raise the question of whether further important differences can occur between distributions which are alike in central tendency, dispersion, and skewness. An inspection of Figures 7-2-3 and 7-2-4 will

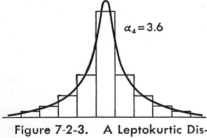

Figure 7-2-3. A Leptokurtic Distribution.

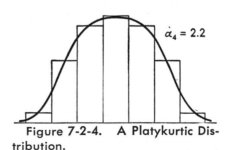

Figure 7-2-4. A Platykurtic Distribution.

show that such a difference is possible. Figure 7-2-3 differs from Figure 7-2-4 in two ways: first, relatively more of its variates are in the central class (which tends to decrease the standard deviation); second, relatively more of its variates are in the *extreme wings* (which tends to increase the standard deviation). If these two effects are balanced, the two distributions will have equal standard deviations. Thus we see that, without altering the standard deviation of a distribution, we can build up the center and the extreme wings at the expense of the "shoulders" of the curve. This property of central peakedness is called *kurtosis*. The primary objective of this chapter is to explain methods for the numerical measurements of central tendency, dispersion, skewness, and kurtosis, for any distribution.

3. MOMENTS

In Article 3, Chapter 4, we introduced the idea of a deviation from the arithmetic mean, or $x - \bar{x}$. It can readily be shown that the arithmetic mean of these deviations is always zero. In the same article, we introduced the concept of the mean of the squares of these deviations, or $\overline{(x - \bar{x})^2}$, from which we obtained the standard deviation. Both of these are special cases of quantities which are called moments. *The nth moment of a distribution around its mean is the mean of the nth power of the deviations of the variates from the mean.* Thus the second moment is $\overline{(x - \bar{x})^2}$, the third moment is $\overline{(x - \bar{x})^3}$, and the fourth moment is $\overline{(x - \bar{x})^4}$. The computation of these moments from the definition is demonstrated in Table 7-3-1.

TABLE 7-3-1. Computation of Moments

x	f	$x - \bar{x}$	$f(x - \bar{x})$	$f(x - \bar{x})^2$	$f(x - \bar{x})^3$	$f(x - \bar{x})^4$
10	1	-7	-7	49	-343	2401
12	2	-5	-10	50	-250	1250
14	5	-3	-15	45	-135	405
16	11	-1	-11	11	-11	11
18	25	$+1$	$+25$	25	$+25$	25
20	6	$+3$	$+18$	54	$+162$	486
Sum	50		0	234	-552	4578
Sum/50			0	4.68	-11.04	91.56

Our purpose in introducing the concept of moments is to investigate their utility as devices for describing distributions. A study of Table 7-3-1 shows that the negative deviations just balance the positive one (as of course they must), but that since the distribution is unsymmetrical this balance is achieved by balancing a few large deviations on one side against many small ones on the other. When these deviations are cubed, the large ones become relatively more important, so that the third moment is negative. Thus we see that the third moment is strongly affected by the asymmetry of the distribution and might be used as a measure of asymmetry. It is not, however, a satisfactory measure of pure skewness, because its size is affected by the size of the units in which x is measured. This is the same problem which confronted us in standardizing the representation of a distribution in Article 3 of Chapter 6, and we can solve it in the same way, by using t units instead of x units. The third moment in t units is called α_3 :

$$\alpha_3 = \overline{t^3} \tag{7-3-1}$$

For purposes of computation, it is convenient to express this in terms of x, which we can do by substituting for t its value $(x - \bar{x})/\sigma$ and simplifying:

$$\alpha_3 = \overline{(x - \bar{x})^3}/\sigma^3 \tag{7-3-2}$$

For the distribution in Table 7-3-1, the value of α_3 is $-11.04/\sqrt{4.68^3}$ or -1.09. It is obvious that a negative value for α_3 indicates that the distribution has a "tail" in the direction of negative values of x, as in Figure 7-2-1, while a positive value indicates a tail extending in the direction of positive values of x, as in Figure 7-2-2. The numerical value of α_3 ranges from about -1 to $+1$ for the most extreme examples of skewness generally found in practical problems. Figure 7-2-2 demonstrates a moderate positive skewness ($\alpha_3 = +0.2$), while Figure 7-2-1 demonstrates a very extreme negative skewness ($\alpha_3 = -1.09$).

The fourth moment (which is computed in the last column of Table 7-3-1) is obviously not affected by skewness, since all the fourth powers will be positive. To see what property the fourth moment measures, we must observe that the higher the power to which we raise each deviation before we take the mean, the more we emphasize the larger deviations in our result. If, therefore, we increase some variates which are already large and decrease some which are already small (that is, if we increase the kurtosis of the curve), the fourth moment will be increased even though we adjust the changes in such a way as to leave the second moment unchanged. The fourth moment, therefore, can be used as a measure of kurtosis. To make it a pure measure, we again remove the effect of the units in which x was measured by using t units instead of x units. The fourth moment, in t units, is called α_4 :

$$\alpha_4 = \overline{t^4} \tag{7-3-3}$$

which we again rewrite in x units for convenience of computation:

$$\alpha_4 = \overline{(x - \bar{x})^4}/\sigma^4 \tag{7-3-4}$$

The value of α_4 for the distribution in Figure 7-2-3 is 3.6, and that for

Figure 7-2-4 is 2.2. It can be shown by advanced mathematics that α_4 for the normal curve is exactly 3, and this should be used as a basis of comparison in interpreting observed values of α_4. If α_4 is greater than 3, as in Figure 7-2-3, the distribution is called *leptokurtic*, and if it is less than 3, as in Figure 7-2-4, it is called *platykurtic*. In practice the value of α_4 usually lies between 2 and 4, representing respectively curves which are extremely flattened and extremely peaked in the center.

PROBLEMS

1. Find α_3 and α_4 for the following distribution:

x	f
2	9
3	6
4	2
5	2
6	1

2. Without computing α_4, state whether you believe Figures 7-2-1 and 7-2-2 to be leptokurtic or platykurtic. Estimate the value of α_4 for each by comparing them, in general appearance, with the normal curve and with the curves in Figures 7-2-3 and 7-2-4.

4.   FORMULAS FOR RAPID COMPUTATION

Equations 7-3-1 to 7-3-4 serve to define α_3 and α_4, but for rapid computation other methods are better. To derive the necessary equations we must extend the method which we used for $\bar{x}$ and σ_x in Article 5 of Chapter 4, which should be reviewed at this point.

As before, we will define x_0 as the class mark of any convenient class, and u as the serial number of any class, starting from the x_0 class and increasing with increasing values of x, as shown in the third column of Table 7-4-1. To compute α_3 and α_4, we must now express them in terms of u and C, which are related to x by equations 4-5-2 and 4-5-4:

$$x = x_0 + Cu \quad \text{and} \quad \bar{x} = x_0 + C\bar{u}$$

If we substitute these for x and $\bar{x}$ in equation 7-3-2 we will have

$$\alpha_3 = \overline{(x - \bar{x})^3}/\sigma_x^3 = C^3\overline{(u - \bar{u})^3}/C^3\sigma_u^3$$

where we have replaced σ_x by $C\sigma_u$, according to equation 4-5-7. Now let us cancel the C's and expand the cubed quantity:

$$\alpha_3 = \overline{(u^3 - 3u^2\bar{u} + 3u\bar{u}^2 - \bar{u}^3)}/\sigma_u^3$$

If we now separate this into four separate means, we note that the last two of these will both involve the cube of $\bar{u}$, and so can be combined, giving us

$$\alpha_3 = (\overline{u^3} - 3\overline{u^2}\bar{u} + 2\bar{u}^3)/\sigma_u^3 \qquad (7\text{-}4\text{-}1)$$

If we apply a similar procedure to equation 7-3-4 we obtain

$$\alpha_4 = \overline{(x - \bar{x})^4}/\sigma_x^4 = \overline{C^4(u - \bar{u})^4}/(C^4\sigma_u^4)$$

$$= \overline{(u^4 - 4u^3\bar{u} + 6u^2\bar{u}^2 - 4u\bar{u}^3 + \bar{u}^4)}/\sigma_u^4$$

or finally,

$$\alpha_4 = (\overline{u^4} - 4\overline{u^3}\bar{u} + 6\overline{u^2}\bar{u}^2 - 3\bar{u}^4)/\sigma_u^4 \tag{7-4-2}$$

The use of these equations for the computation of α_3 and α_4 is shown in Table 7-4-1, which is self-explanatory.

TABLE 7-4-1.   Rapid Procedure for α_3 and α_4

Limits	f	u	fu	fu^2	fu^3	fu^4
100–119	2	−2	−4	8	−16	32
120–139	11	−1	−11	11	−11	11
140–159	16	0	0	0	0	0
160–179	14	+1	+14	14	+14	14
180–199	5	+2	+10	20	+40	80
200–219	2	+3	+6	18	+54	162
Sum	50		+15	71	+81	299
Sum/N			+0.30	1.42	+1.62	5.98

$\bar{u} = +0.30$ $\overline{u^2} = 1.42$ $\overline{u^3} = +1.62$ $\overline{u^4} = 5.98$ $\sigma_u = 1.15$

$\alpha_3 = [1.62 - 3(1.42)(0.30) + 2(0.32)^2]/(1.15)^3 = 0.34$

$\alpha_4 = [5.98 - 4(1.62)(0.30) + 6(1.42)(0.30)^2 - 3(0.30)^4]/(1.15)^4 = 2.70$

PROBLEMS

In the following problems, you can avoid unnecessary duplication of effort if you use the work which you have already done on the problems in Article 4 of Chapter 4.

1. Compute the values of α_3 and α_4 for the two sets of temperatures which you obtained in Problem 1, Article 3, Chapter 2. Do these values, together with the arithmetic means and the standard deviations, adequately describe the differences between these two distributions?

2. Compute α_3 and α_4 for the distribution in Table 4-2-1.

3. Compute α_3 and α_4 for the ages of the dementia praecox patients described in Table 2-5-1. (Use a frequency tabulation with classes 15 to 19, 20 to 24, and so forth.)

4. Write a complete derivation of equation 7-4-2, supplying and explaining the steps which have been omitted.

5. MEASURES OF CENTRAL TENDENCY

In describing the central tendency of a distribution, we present a single value which is representative, or typical, so far as possible, of all the variates. Since there are various purposes for which such a typical value might be used, there are slightly different ways of selecting it. Depending upon the purpose for which it is to be used, any of the following measures might be useful:

I. The Arithmetic Mean

This is a representative value in the following sense. If all the variates had this value, the sum of all the variates would be unchanged. If we know that an office has thirty-eight employees and if we know that the arithmetic mean of the weekly salaries is $41, then we can compute the total weekly payroll by multiplying these two figures together.

II. The Median

The median is the fiftieth percentile, and is computed by the procedure shown in Chapter 2, Article 6. The special property which the median possesses is the fact that exactly as many variates lie above the median as lie below it. For some purposes, this may be a more useful "typical value" than the arithmetic mean. Suppose, for instance, that a student is considering a given profession, and wishes to know the average income which people in that profession earn. If the distribution of income is skewed to the right, that is, if it consists of a large number of small incomes very tightly bunched, plus a very few incomes which are very high, then the mean will be much larger than the median. To take an extreme case, let us suppose that the mean is $6000 and the median is $4000; in this case the student may reason as follows: "$6000 would be sufficient for my needs, if I had a reasonable chance of obtaining it. But in view of the skewness of the distribution, this mean is reached by balancing a high probability of receiving a slightly smaller income against a low probability of receiving a very much higher income. And in the light of my needs these two do not balance; a smaller income would be a serious handicap, while a very large income would exceed my needs and would have less value per dollar to me than a moderate income. For my purposes it is more useful to know the income which I have a fifty per cent chance of reaching." This income is of course the median.

III. The Mode

The mode is the value of the variate for which the frequency curve reaches a maximum; it is therefore the most probable value of the variate. For most purposes the mode can be computed with adequate accuracy by finding the class mark of the class which contains the highest frequency.

Using the symbol Z for the mode, we can abbreviate this definition as follows:

$$Z \cong \text{CM}_{\text{max}} \qquad (7\text{-}5\text{-}1)$$

where CM_{max} refers to the class mark of the class with maximum frequency, and where the symbol $\cong$ means "is approximately equal to." Thus for the distribution in Figure 1-4-1 the mode is 80 feet, and for 1-4-2 it is 14.5 per cent.

A little reflection, however, will show that if we plot the frequencies of a distribution and then draw a smooth curve through the points, the maximum value will lie a little to one side of the highest plotted point, in the direction of whichever point is next highest. An example of this is shown in Figure 7-2-2. It is reasonable to assume that the exact position of the maximum point is determined by the relative sizes of the two adjacent frequencies; and that if, for example, the frequency of the class to the right of the maximum class is twice that of the class to the left, then the maximum will be twice as far from the left edge of the class as it is from the right. This assumption is adopted in the customary definition of the mode:

$$Z = \text{LB}_{\text{max}} + \frac{\text{UF}}{\text{UF} + \text{LF}} \, C \qquad (7\text{-}5\text{-}2)$$

where LB_{max} is the lower (or left hand*) boundary of the class containing the maximum frequency, UF is the upper frequency, that is, the frequency of the class to the right of the maximum class, LF is the lower frequency, or the frequency of the class to the left of the maximum class, and C is the class interval. For the distribution in Table 7-3-1, LB is 17, UF is 6, LF is 11, and C is 2. Thus we find that the mode as given by 7-5-2 is 17.7, as compared to the approximate value of 18 by 7-5-1.

The mode is useful whenever we wish to know which value of the variate is most likely to occur. If, for example, a department store offers a special sale of women's stockings, but does not have room to stock all sizes, then the best sizes to stock would be those near the mode, since these would fit a larger number of customers than any others.

IV. The Geometric Mean

This is defined as the antilog of the mean of the logs of the variates.

$$\text{GM} = \text{antilog} \, (\overline{\log x}) \qquad (7\text{-}5\text{-}3)$$

To find the geometric mean of 3, 4, and 6, for example, we must find the logs of these three numbers (0.4771, 0.6021, and 0.7782), then find the mean of these logs (0.6191) and then find the antilog of this mean (4.160).

The geometric mean is sometimes useful in problems in which a variable increases geometrically with time, as described in Article 6, Chapter 3.

---

*We assume that larger values of x are plotted to the right.

V.   The Harmonic Mean

The reciprocal of a number is equal to one divided by that number. Thus the reciprocal of 6 is 1/6 and the reciprocal of 3/8 is 8/3. The harmonic mean of a set of numbers is the reciprocal of the mean of their reciprocals:

$$\text{HM} = \frac{1}{(1/x)} \qquad (7\text{-}5\text{-}4)$$

Thus to find the harmonic mean of 3, 4, and 6, we find their reciprocals (1/3, 1/4, and 1/6), then find the mean of these (1/4), and then find the reciprocal of this mean, which is 4.

Suppose that a man drives 120 miles at 60 miles per hour, and then makes the return trip at 40 miles per hour, what is his average speed? The question, of course, has no exact meaning until we specify the kind of average, but we can study the relative utility of the various kinds of averages. We might for example require that the average must have the property that *the total time for the trip would have been the same if he had driven at the average speed throughout*. With this requirement in mind, we can readily see that the arithmetic mean (50mph) is not suitable, for if he drives 240 miles at this speed he will require 4.8 hours, while the actual trip required five hours. Instead we must divide the total mileage (240) by the total time actually consumed (5 hours), and we find that the required average speed is 48 miles per hour. An inspection of the actual computations which we have made here shows that we have, in effect, computed the harmonic mean of 40 and 60.

PROBLEMS

1. Compute the arithmetic mean, the median, the geometric mean, and the harmonic mean of the numbers 2, 3, 4 and 12.

2. Find the mode of the distribution in Table 2-3-2, using first equation **7-5-1** and then equation 7-5-2.

6.   MEASURES OF DISPERSION

The following measures of dispersion are widely used in numerical descriptions of distributions:

I.   Standard Deviation

The deviation of any variate from the mean is the difference between that variate and the mean. The square root of the mean of the sum of the squares of these deviations is the standard deviation. In addition to its usefulness as a descriptive device, this quantity is used extensively in the development of the theory of statistics, and so has already been introduced in Chapter 4.

II. Mean Deviation

The absolute value of a number is the size of the number, without regard to whether it is positive or negative. It is denoted by placing vertical bars to the left and the right of the number. For example, $|-3|$ is 3, and $|6|$ is 6. The mean deviation is the mean of the absolute values of the deviations:

$$\text{MD} = \overline{|x - \bar{x}|} \qquad (7\text{-}6\text{-}1)$$

Thus to find the mean deviation of the numbers 3, 4, and 8, we find the deviation of each number from the mean (-2, -1, and $+3$), and find the mean of the corresponding absolute values (2, 1, and 3), which we find to be 2. The mean deviation is usually a little smaller than the standard deviation, since in finding the standard deviation we square all the deviations and thus give more weight to the larger ones.

III. Variance

In finding the standard deviation we begin by squaring all the deviations and finding the mean of the result. If we stop here, we have a quantity which is called the variance and which is frequently used to describe the dispersion of the frequency distribution. Its formal definition is

$$\text{Variance} = \overline{(x - \bar{x})^2} \qquad (7\text{-}6\text{-}2)$$

For example, the variance of the distribution in Table 4-3-1 is 8.33. From its definition it is obvious that the variance is the square of the standard deviation.

IV. Quartile Deviation

In Article 6, Chapter 2, we studied the first quartile and the third quartile, which are defined in such a way that one-fourth of the variates are below the first quartile, and three-quarters are below the third quartile. The interval between these two quartiles is sometimes called the interquartile range. The quartile deviation is defined as half of the interquartile range:

$$Q = \frac{Q_3 - Q_1}{2} \qquad (7\text{-}6\text{-}3)$$

This is very similar to the probable error, as defined in Article 8 of Chapter 6. The quartile deviation has the following property. If a variate is chosen at random, the probability is one-half that it will differ from the mean by less than the quartile deviation.

PROBLEMS

1. Find the mean deviation for the data in Table 4-3-1.
2. Find the mean deviation for the data in Table 4-3-2.

3. What is the variance of the distribution in Table 4-3-1? In Table 4-3-2? In Table 4-5-1?

4. Find the quartile deviation of the distribution shown in Figure 2-6-3. How does this compare with the probable error of the distribution as defined by equation 6-8-1?

7. MEASURES OF SKEWNESS

The following quantities are all widely used as descriptive measurements of skewness.

(a) Alpha sub-three. The quantity α_3 , which we described in the preceding article, is an exact descriptive device which should be used when making a critical comparison between the properties of distributions. For less exact comparisons, any of the following equations may be used:

$$\text{(b)}\quad \text{Sk.} = (Q_3 + Q_1 - 2Q_2)/(Q_3 - Q_1) \qquad\qquad (7\text{-}7\text{-}1)$$

This equation depends upon the fact that if the distribution is skewed, the second quartile will not be midway between the first and third quartiles. The skewness is obtained by subtracting one of these intervals $(Q_2 - Q_1)$ from the other $(Q_3 - Q_2)$ and then dividing by the entire interval $(Q_3 - Q_1)$.

This quantity measures the skewness in only the middle portion of the curve and is not affected by the shape of the wings beyond the first and third quartiles.

$$\text{(c)}\quad \text{Sk.} = (P_{90} + P_{10} - 2P_{50})/(P_{90} - P_{10}) \qquad\qquad (7\text{-}7\text{-}2)$$

This equation takes into account more of the distribution than 7-7-1, but is not affected by the location of the variates below P_{10} or above P_{90}.

$$\text{(d)}\quad \text{Sk.} = 3(\bar{x} - M)/\sigma \qquad\qquad (7\text{-}7\text{-}3)$$
$$\text{(e)}\quad \text{Sk.} = 2(\bar{x} - Z)/\sigma \qquad\qquad (7\text{-}7\text{-}4)$$

These equations use the fact that the median (M) and the mode (Z)* are both displaced from the mean if the distribution is skewed.

Equations b, c, d, and e all give values for the skewness which agree in sign with α_3 , but which cannot be directly compared with it in size. For example, the skewness of Figure 7-2-1 as measured by these equations ranges from -0.3 to -0.7, while the value of α_3 is -1.1.

PROBLEMS

1. Compute the skewness of the ages of dementia praecox* patients in Table 2-5-1, using equation 7-7-1.

---

*The mode should be computed by the exact equation (7-5-2) if it is to be used for this purpose.
*Use the ogive which you constructed for Problem 4, Article 6, Chapter 2.

2. Repeat Problem 1, using equation 7-7-2. Comment on the difference between these two results.

3. Repeat Problem 1 again, using first equation 7-7-3 and then equation 7-7-4.

8.   MEASURES OF KURTOSIS

The following quantities are used to describe the kurtosis of a distribution:

(a)   Alpha sub-four.   The quantity α_4 , which we described in Article 3, should be used whenever an exact comparison of kurtosis between two distributions is to be made.   For less precise comparisons, the following equation can be used.

(b)   Ku. $= Q/(P_{90} - P_{10})$ where $Q = (Q_3 - Q_1)/2$ (7-8-1)

The kurtosis as obtained by this equation has no direct relationship with α_4 , and cannot be compared with it.   The following information will be useful in interpreting the size of this measurement: For Figure 7-2-3 the kurtosis as given by this equation is 0.17; for the normal curve it is 0.26, and for the curve in Figure 7-2-4 it is 0.31.

PROBLEM

1. Compute the kurtosis of the distribution of dementia praecox patients in Table 2-5-1, using equation 7-8-1.   How does this value compare with that of the normal curve?

9.   SUMMARY

Chapter 7 deals entirely with the use of statistical techniques for formulating exact descriptions of distributions.   The descriptions are expressed in terms of numerical measurements of four basic properties, as follows:

(1)   Central tendency, or "most typical value."   The various methods for the measurement of this property are as follows:

(a)   Arithmetic mean; defined by equation 3-10-1.
(b)   Median.   This is the fiftieth percentile, which can be computed by the procedure described in Chapter 2, Article 6.
(c)   Mode, or position of maximum liklihood.   This can be computed approximately by equation 7-5-1, or more exactly by equation 7-5-2.
(d)   The geometric mean.   Defined and computed by equation 7-5-3.
(e)   The harmonic mean.   Defined and computed by equation 7-5-4.

The uses of these various measurements of central tendency are described in Article 5.

2. Dispersion, or amount of scatter of the observations.   This property is measured by any of the following methods:

(a) Standard deviation. Defined by equation 4-3-2 and computed by means of equation 4-4-1, 4-4-3, or 4-5-5.

(b) Mean deviation. Defined and computed by equation 7-6-1. It is similar to standard deviation.

(c) Variance. This is defined by equation 7-6-2. It is simply the square of the standard deviation.

(d) Quartile deviation. Defined by equation 7-6-3. It is usually about two-thirds of the standard deviation.

3. Skewness, or asymmetry. This property can be measured by any of several methods, which are independent of each other except that they all are negative when the "tail" of the distribution extends in the direction of smaller values. The various methods are:

(a) Alpha sub-three. Defined by equation 7-3-1 or 7-3-2, but best computed in general by equation 7-4-1. The meaning of α_3 is indicated by Figures 7-2-1 and 7-2-2.

(b) Measures depending upon asymmetry in the locations of percentiles. Equation 7-7-1 measures the asymmetry of the central portion of the distribution, while equation 7-7-2 measures the asymmetry over a wider range.

(c) Measures depending upon the displacement of the mean relative to the median (equation 7-7-3), or relative to the mode (equation 7-7-4).

4. Kurtosis, or central peakedness as compared with the normal curve. This is measured by either of the following:

(a) Alpha sub-four. Defined by equation 7-3-3 or 7-3-4 but usually computed by the more rapid equation 7-4-2. The meaning of the resulting value of α_4 is indicated by Figures 7-2-3 and 7-2-4, and by the fact that α_4 for the normal curve is exactly three.

(b) Equation 7-8-1 gives a quick measure of kurtosis. Its scale (not the same as that of α_4) is indicated in Article 8.

CHAPTER

• 8 •

SIMPLE CURVE FITTING

1. EXAMPLE OF CURVE FITTING

Curve fitting is the operation of finding the equation of that curve which will best represent the relationship between two statistical variables. The curve may be of any sort, but the simplest and most widely used is the straight line, which is a particular kind of curve in the mathematical sense. In order to focus our discussion of the purpose of curve fitting, let us begin by describing a specific example of a fitted curve.

The stars around us are arranged in highly organized systems called galaxies. Each galaxy contains tens of billions of stars, arranged usually in a huge flat spiral structure. Our galaxy contains all the stars which we can see and many billions more which are too faint to be seen. From our off-center position we see our own galaxy mostly to one side of us, forming the Milky Way. Beyond the edges of our own galaxy we see many other galaxies, more or less like our own, out to the farthest distance that the most powerful telescope can reach. It is possible to measure the distance to some of these galaxies, and by spectroscopic means it is possible to tell whether they are approaching us or receding from us, and with what speed. Some results of these remarkable measurements are given in Table 8-1-1.

It is seen from this table that the galaxies are receding from us, or we from them, with extraordinarily high velocities (the velocity of a bullet, for example, is in the neighborhood of only *one* mile per second), and that the velocities of recession are related to the distances in a very systematic way. This relationship becomes even more conspicuous if we plot the data, as we can see from Figure 8-1-1. In this figure we see that the points all *fall nearly along a straight line*. The straight line in the figure has been drawn in by inspection, that is, by juggling a ruler around on the drawing until it appeared to represent most of the points as well as possible. The equation of the line is:

$$\text{Velocity} = 18.9 \times \text{Distance} \qquad (8\text{-}1\text{-}1)$$

TABLE 8-1-1. Distances and Velocities of Galaxies

Galaxy Group	Distance in Billions of Billions of Miles	Velocity in Miles per Second
Virgo	40	750
Pegasus	130	2400
Perseus	210	3200
Coma	270	4700
Ursa Major No. 1	500	9300
Leo	610	12400
Gemini No. 1	670	14300
Boötes	1340	24200
Ursa Major No. 2	1380	26100

More precise methods of finding a line to represent the data will be discussed in this chapter, but first let us consider the uses to which such a line can be put.

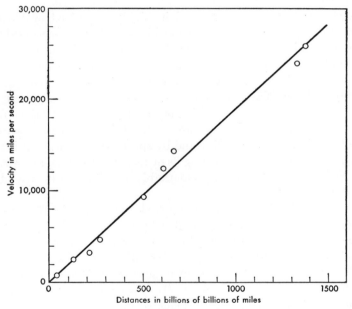

Figure 8-1-1. Velocities of the Galaxies.

2. PURPOSES OF CURVE FITTING

Curve fitting is an operation which is used widely by scientists, educators, psychologists, sociologists, test administrators, and others. The purpose for which the procedure is used may be any of several, depending somewhat upon the field which is under investigation. The primary purposes will be described here, and illustrated where appropriate by means of the example in Article 1.

I. Estimating

The direct methods for finding distances to galaxies fail when astronomers try to apply them to the most distant galaxies which can be observed. It is however possible to find the velocities of some of them even at these very great distances. By inserting these velocities into equation 8-1-1, we can compute the distance to each of these galaxies. For example, if a galaxy is too far away for its distance to be measurable, but is known to have a velocity of 38,000 miles per second, as determined from spectroscopic measures, we can insert 38,000 for "velocity" into equation 8-1-1 and compute its approximate distance:

$$38,000 = 18.9 \times \text{Distance}$$

or   Distance = 2010 billion billion miles

The distance deduced in this way is obviously less reliable than a distance which has been measured directly. We will discuss later the factors which affect the accuracy of such estimates and the way in which their precision can be estimated.

II. Concise Description

A single equation may express the essential facts from many pages of data. If two sets of similar data are to be compared, the comparison can be greatly facilitated if we begin by expressing both in the form of equations. The essential differences and the essential similarities will then be readily apparent.

III. Analysis of Causes

In any attempt to explain *why* changes in x produce or cause changes in y, or are accompanied by them, the first step is to *describe* as precisely as possible the relationship which we are trying to explain. The formulation of an equation expressing this relationship is one of the clearest ways to describe it.

In the case of the galaxies, the equation shows us that the velocities of recession are *directly proportional* to the distances from us, and this is the first step in understanding the physical situation which this implies, namely, that our entire universe of galaxies must be *expanding uniformly*, so that an observer on any galaxy must see all other galaxies receding from him and that the farther away a galaxy is, the faster its distance from the observer will be increasing.

IV. Measurement of Physical Quantities

The constants in the equation relating x and y are in some cases physical quantities which the investigator wishes to determine. For example, the well-known law for the pressure and volume of a gas at constant temperature ($PV = C$, where C is a constant) is not quite exact because it ignores the size of the molecules of the gas. A more exact law is:

$$P(V - a) = C \qquad (8\text{-}2\text{-}1)$$

where a is a small quantity related to the size of the molecules. If a number of very exact observations of pressure and volume of a gas are made, and equation 8-2-1 is fitted to the observations by adjusting a and C, the value of a so determined can be used to estimate the size of the molecules of the gas.

V. Prediction

For most users, the outstandingly important use of curve fitting is that of estimating a value of y when x can be measured but y cannot. A very important special kind of estimating arises when we establish an equation relating early measures to later measures on the same object, and then use the equations for predicting *future* behavior of other similar objects. This use is of course logically identical with the first item in this list, but it will be described separately because of its importance in statistical studies.

Let us suppose that for several years a school has kept records of the scores made on entrance examinations by candidates for admission. Suppose furthermore that the examining officials have kept track of the examinees who were admitted to the school and have compiled their subsequent grades in their courses. Then, if we let x equal the score made on the entrance examination and y the subsequent grade average made by the student, we can fit a curve to these two variables and use it to predict the probable *future* grade average of any candidate *now* applying for admission, if we have his entrance examination score. Such predictions can obviously be of great value in screening applicants for admission to schools or in screening candidates for employment. The procedure is applicable to any situation in which we know some of the controlling factors and wish to know their probable future effect; for example, it can be used to predict the size of the nation's fall wheat crop if we know, during the summer, the total rainfall, average temperature, and other similar factors.

Obviously such predictions will be subject to error, since the causation factors are usually far too numerous to be included in the equation, and we must generally limit ourselves to the one or two causes which influence the result the most. Fortunately the theory of statistics can be used to determine the *precision* of a prediction from the same data used for making the prediction itself. The precision of predictions will be discussed in later chapters.

3. EQUATION OF A STRAIGHT LINE

The simplest and most frequently used "curve" in curve fitting is the straight line. Before proceeding to the fitting of straight lines, we must review the fundamental equation of a straight line and the meaning of the quantities contained in it.*

The equation of any straight line (unless it is parallel to the y axis) can be written in the form

$$y = mx + b \qquad\qquad (8\text{-}3\text{-}1)$$

where x and y are the coordinates of any point on the line, and m and b are numbers which characterize the line and distinguish it from any other straight line. For example, if we give m the value 2 and give b the value 3, the equation becomes $y = 2x + 3$, which is the equation of the specific straight line shown in Figure 8-3-1. Similarly, $y = 5x + 7$ is a straight line, with $m = 5$ and $b = 7$, and $y = -3/4\,x - 9$ is a straight line with $m = -3/4$ and $b = -9$. Furthermore, $5x + 2y - 7 = x + y - 1$ is also

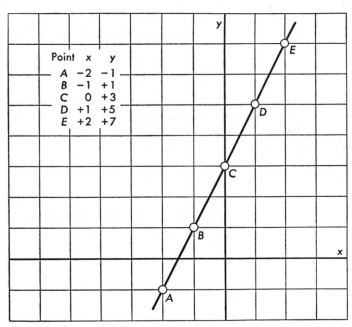

Point	x	y
A	−2	−1
B	−1	+1
C	0	+3
D	+1	+5
E	+2	+7

Figure 8-3-1.   The Line $y = 2x + 3$.

---

*If you are already familiar with the standard "slope intercept" form for the equation of a straight line, you should omit Articles 3, 4, and 5.

a straight line, since we can collect terms and reduce it to $y = -4x + 6$, which has the standard form.

Plot the following lines:

1. $y = 3x - 5$
2. $y = -2x + 1$
3. $2x + 3y - 2 = 5x - 7y - 8$

4.   MEANING OF m AND b

We can readily discover the meaning of b by examining the table of values in Figure 8-3-1: *b is the value which y takes on when $x = 0$.* Or, graphically, *b is the height at which the line crosses the y axis.* Since b is 3 in our illustrative equation, the line must cross the y axis 3 units above the origin. In the equation $y = 2x - 5$, b is -5 and the line must therefore cross the y axis at a height of -5, or five units *below* the origin.

The meaning of m is a little more complex. Suppose that we let the coordinates x_1 and y_1 stand for any fixed point on the line. Then since (x_1, y_1) is on the line, it satisfies the equation of the line; that is, $y_1 = mx_1 + b$. If (x_2, y_2) is another point on the line, then $y_2 = mx_2 + b$. If we subtract one of these equations from the other and solve for m, we have

$$m = \frac{y_2 - y_1}{x_2 - x_1} \qquad (8\text{-}4\text{-}1)$$

This equation makes it possible for us to find m if we know the coordinates of any two points on the line. For example, if we know that a line goes through points D and E in Figure 8-3-1, we can find m by calling E point 2 and D point 1, and applying equation 8-4-1:

$$m = \frac{7 - 5}{2 - 1} = 2$$

If we had made the choice in the opposite way, by choosing to call E point 1 and D point 2, the equation would have been a little different, but the final result would have been the same:

$$m = \frac{5 - 7}{1 - 2} = \frac{-2}{-1} = 2$$

The term "slope" is frequently used for m, and the term has the same meaning in mathematics that it has in road building, namely, the ratio of "rise" to "run." If the slope is positive, the line runs from lower left to upper right; if negative, from upper left to lower right. If m is very small, the line is nearly horizontal, if it is very large, the line is nearly vertical.

PROBLEMS

Compute the value of m for the line through each of the following pairs of points:

1. (3, 5) and (6, 17)
2. (−2, 4) and (3, −6)
3. (−1, −2) and (−3, 0)
4. (−3, 5) and (2, 5)

5. EQUATION OF A GRAPHED LINE

The relations in the preceding paragraph can be used to discover the equation of a line for which a graph has been made. The procedure is as follows.

1. Extend the line if necessary to cut the y axis, and read the value of y where it crosses. This value, with its plus or minus sign, is b.

2. Select any two points on the line and label them "1" and "2." (It is easy to make mistakes about signs here, and it is better to label the two points on the graph than it is to try to remember which one is being called "1" and which "2.") Read the coordinates x_1 and y_1 from point 1, and x_2 and y_2 from point 2, *with* their minus signs if they are negative, and insert these values in equation 8-4-1 to obtain m.

3. Insert these values of m and b in equation 8-3-1. For example, let us find the equation of line A in Figure 8-5-1. We first observe the point

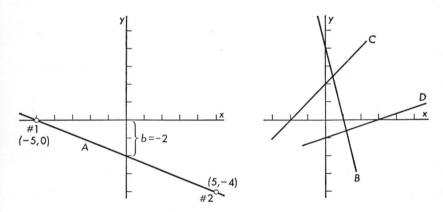

Figure 8-5-1.   Finding the Equation from a Graph.

at which the line crosses the y axis. The value of y at this point is −2, which is therefore the value of b. Next we select two points on the line and read their coordinates. Any two points will serve, but if the numbers are large, it is obviously faster if we select points differing in x by 10 or 20 or some other simple number. For the points chosen in line A, x_2 is 5,

y_2 is -4, x_1 is -5, and y_1 is 0. We insert these in formula 8-4-1, and obtain the value of m for the line:

$$m = \frac{-4 - 0}{5 - (-5)} = -\frac{4}{10}$$

Inserting these values of m and b in 8-3-1, we have the equation of line A:

$$y = -\frac{4}{10}x - 2$$

PROBLEMS

1. Write the equation of line B in Figure 8-5-1.
2. Write the equation of line C in Figure 8-5-1.
3. Write the equation of line D in Figure 8-5-1.

6. CRITERION OF BEST FIT

In general when a set of observed values of x and y are plotted, they will not all lie on any straight line. In many cases the deviations arise from the fact that y measures something which is dependent not only upon x but also upon other variables. In other cases, y is exactly related to x, but the investigator has not been able to measure y with adequate precision, so that an unknown error of measurement is contained in each y. In either case we can picture each value of y as being made up of two parts, one of which is completely *dependent* upon x and the other of which is completely *independent* of x. The completely dependent part is the part which we can expect to predict exactly from a knowledge of x. Let us call it the *predictable* part, or y_p. The remaining part, which is independent of x, we will call y_r, or the random part of y. Then we have assumed that for any y in our tables:

$$y = y_p + y_r$$

or, if we solve this for y_r:

$$y_r = y - y_p \tag{8-6-1}$$

This random part of y is often called a *deviation*, since it is the amount by which the observed value of y differs or deviates from the predicted value. It is, in other words, the amount by which the best prediction would fail.

Now it is customary and reasonable, unless there is evidence to the contrary, to assume that the random contributions (that is, the values of y_r) would, if collected into a frequency tabulation, form a normal curve. Let us call the standard deviation of this distribution σ_r. We may regard this as a fixed number which would become known to us if we had information about the contributions to y from other variables, but which is unknown to us in practice. The relationship between y, y_p, and y_r is shown in the left half of Figure 8-6-1, and the nature of the assumed distribution of the values of y_r is indicated in the right half of the figure.

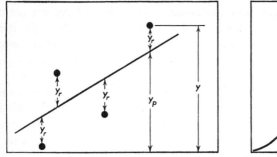 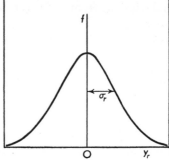

Figure 8-6-1.   The Deviations from a Straight Line.

Since we assume that the values of y_r are distributed normally, the probability of occurrence of a y_r of a given size is given by the equation of the normal curve (6-5-1), which we can write:

$$P(y_r) = Ce^{-(y_r{}^2/2\sigma_r{}^2)}$$

where C is a constant which need not concern us here. The probability that *all* of a given set of deviations will occur is the *product* of the probabilities that each will occur, according to equation 5-6-1. If we call the several deviations $(y_r)_1$, $(y_r)_2$, and so forth, then the probability that all of the given set will occur is:

$$P[(y_r)_1 \ and \ (y_r)_2 \ and \ \cdots] = Ce^{-[(y_r)_1{}^2/2\sigma_r{}^2]} Ce^{-[(y_r)_2{}^2/2\sigma_r{}^2]} \cdots$$

If we let N be the number of deviations in the set and if we combine the exponents according to equation 3-3-1, we can write this:

$$P[(y_r)_1 \ and \ (y_r)_2 \ and \ \cdots] = C^N e^{-[(y_r)_1{}^2 + (y_r)_2{}^2 + \cdots]/2\sigma_r}$$

Using the summation notation for the bracketed part of the exponent, this becomes:

$$P[\text{that all the } y_r\text{'s will occur}] = C^N e^{-\Sigma y_r{}^2/(2\sigma_r{}^2)}$$

The quantity $\sum y_r^2$ is the *sum of the squares of the deviations*. Since this sum is preceded by a minus sign in the equation, we can see by referring to equation 3-3-6 that, as the sum becomes larger and larger, the probability of obtaining the given set of deviations becomes smaller and smaller. In other words, the larger the sum of the squares of a given set of residuals, the smaller the probability that the set of residuals will occur. The set of residuals 0, 1, 0, 0, and 5 is less likely to occur than the set 2, 3, 2, 2, and 1, because the sum of the squares of the first set is 26 while that for the second set is only 22.

For the present purpose we use this principle with a reversed orientation. We have shown that for a *given line*, the most likely to occur of *several sets of observations* is that set which makes the sum of the squares of the deviations from the given line a minimum. Now if we have *one* set of observations and *several* competing candidates for the line of best fit, it is reasonable to choose the one *in the light of which the observations are most likely*, that is, the one for which the sum of the squares of the deviations is a minimum.

This is a very important principle in statistics, sometimes referred to as the *principle of least squares*. A generalized statement of the principle is this: Of several competing hypotheses which are in other respects equal in merit, the one which makes the sum of the squares of the deviations a minimum is the most likely to be correct.

This principle is used in many fields. In order to familiarize the reader with it, let us pause for a moment to study a simple example of its application. A scientist measures a fixed quantity, and obtains a series of values x_1, x_2, $\cdots$ x_N, which differ slightly from each other because of small uncontrollable errors of his instruments. In reporting his conclusions, he must choose one of these values as the one most likely to be correct, or perhaps he will choose a value computed from them, such as the arithmetic mean, or the median, or some other kind of average. Suppose that in order to make a wise choice he postpones a decision and temporarily calls this unknown best value "X." Then the deviations from X will be $x_1 - X$, $x_2 - X$, and so forth, and the sum of the squares of these deviations will be:

$$\Sigma d^2 = (x_1 - X)^2 + (x_2 - X)^2 + \cdots = \Sigma(x - X)^2$$

where we have used the summation notation for convenience. We can express this in a still simpler form if we divide by N to convert both sides to arithmetic means:

$$\Sigma d^2/N = \overline{d^2} = \Sigma(x - X)^2/N = \overline{(x - X)^2}$$

or, if we multiply this out and apply equations 3-10-2, 3-10-4, and 3-10-5,

$$\overline{d^2} = \overline{x^2 - 2xX + X^2} = \overline{x^2} - 2\bar{x}X + X^2$$

To see how this can be made a minimum, let us add $\bar{x}^2$ to the right-hand side and then subtract it again. This gives us

$$\overline{d^2} = (X^2 - 2\bar{x}X + \bar{x}^2) + \overline{x^2} - \bar{x}^2$$

or

$$\overline{d^2} = (X - \bar{x})^2 + \overline{x^2} - \bar{x}^2$$

This is the quantity which we wish to make a minimum by a suitable choice of X. The quantities $\overline{x^2}$ and $\bar{x}^2$ do not contain X and so cannot be altered by our choice. The term $(X - \bar{x})^2$ must always be positive, since it is the square of a number. We can make this term smaller and smaller by choosing X closer and closer to $\bar{x}$, and the smallest possible value (zero) occurs when X equals $\bar{x}$. In other words, if we choose X equal to $\bar{x}$, we will make the sum of the squares of the deviations as small as they can possibly be made. The best choice of a "most likely value of x" is therefore the arithmetic mean, rather than the median or any other possible type of average.

7. GRAPHICAL PROCEDURE

With the principle of least squares in mind, it is possible for a careful worker to draw by inspection a line of adequate accuracy for most purposes. This is best accomplished by plotting the points as rather conspicuous large dots, so that the whole configuration can be taken in at a glance, and then laying a transparent ruler along the dots and shifting it around until the points which lie above the line are well balanced by the points which lie below. In this operation, it must be kept in mind that one large deviation is more to be avoided than two smaller ones, each half as large, since the *square* of the large one is much larger than the sum of the squares of the two small ones. One should carefully avoid the temptation to secure a perfect fit with almost all the points at the expense of a very large deviation for one or two points.

As an example of these principles, let us fit a line to the data given in the first two columns of Table 8-7-1. The points are plotted in Figure 8-7-1, and a straight line has been drawn by inspection, in such a way as to

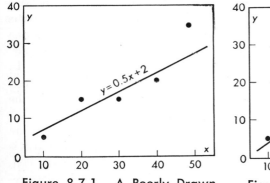

Figure 8-7-1. A Poorly Drawn Line.

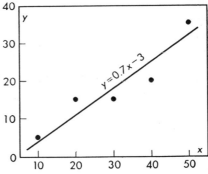

Figure 8-7-2. A Better Line.

illustrate the error described in the paragraph above. The deviations are the vertical distances between the points and the line; and it is readily seen that four of these deviations have been made small at the expense of the last one, which is as a result excessively large. A better least squares line, fitted to the same data, is shown in Figure 8-7-2. Here the line has been readjusted so that there is no outstandingly large deviation, and we should expect this to prove to be a better line.

To test these two straight lines by the criterion of least squares, we first obtain the equation of the first line by the methods of Article 5, and

TABLE 8-7-1.   Least Squares Test of Line

Data		Test of $y_p = 0.5x + 2$			Test of $y_p = 0.7x - 3$		
x	y	y_p	$(y - y_p)$	$(y - y_p)^2$	y_p	$(y - y_p)$	$(y - y_p)^2$
10	5	7	−2	4	4	1	1
20	15	12	3	9	11	4	16
30	15	17	−2	4	18	−3	9
40	20	22	−2	4	25	−5	25
50	35	27	8	64	32	3	9
				85			60

find it to be $y_p = 0.5x + 2$. Next, we compute the values of y_p corresponding to each value of x (column 3 of Table 8-7-1), and we then find the deviations of the original y's from these computed y's (column 4). Finally, we square these deviations (column 5) and add the results. We see that the sum of the squares of the deviations from the first line is 85. To apply the test to the second line we obtain its equation in a similar manner ($y_p = 0.7x - 3$) and carry out the same computation as before (columns 6, 7, and 8). We see that the sum of the squares of the deviations from the second line is only 60. Thus the second line is better than the first line. If a third line can be drawn so that the sum of the squares of the deviations is even less than 60, it will be better than either of the two tested, in the sense that it will have a higher probability of being the correct one. This method of testing a line by evaluating the sum of the squares of its deviations is rarely needed in practice, and the primary purpose of this article is to illustrate the criterion of least squares. In practice the best possible line is usually found, not by trial and error, but by a single mathematical procedure which will be described in the following article.

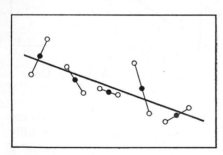

Figure 8-7-3.   The Use of Master Points.

If the points on the diagram are numerous and scattered, so that it is difficult to "see" a line in the configuration, it may be helpful to replace each pair of points by a "master point" halfway between the two and thus reduce the number of points and also reduce the scatter. If the scatter is still excessive, pairs of master points can be combined. This process should be used with reserve and carried only far enough to make it possible to draw a fairly unambiguous line. An example of replacing scattered points by master points is shown in Figure 8-7-3.

PROBLEMS

1. Plot the mathematics grades (second column of Table 1-4-4) against the entrance exam scores (first column). Combine the points by pairs to form master points, then combine these by pairs. Draw a straight line by inspection and write its equation.

2. The scores made by five children on a part of an intelligence test are:

Child's Age (x)	Points Scored (y)
2	12
3	15
3	13
5	16
7	20

Plot these points, draw a straight line fitting them as well as possible, and write its equation.

3. Two students fitted the following two lines to the data in the preceding problem:

$$\text{(a) } y = 1.5x + 9.4$$
$$\text{(b) } y = 1.7x + 8.6$$

Test these two lines by the criterion of least squares and state which is better. Retain your answers for future use.

8. LEAST SQUARES LINE

In the preceding article we have considered the means by which an investigator could, by visual inspection, fit a line which will satisfy the least squares criterion approximately. In this article we will show how we can, by a mathematical procedure, obtain in one step a line which makes the sum of the squares of the deviations an absolute minimum and which is therefore the best possible fit out of all the infinite number of possible lines which might be fitted to the data.

Since we are assuming that the line of best fit is to be a straight line, we can write

$$y_p = mx + b \qquad (8\text{-}8\text{-}1)$$

If we insert this in 8-6-1, we obtain for the deviations,

$$y_r = y - y_p = y - (mx + b)$$

The sum of the squares of the deviations can therefore be written

$$\Sigma(y - y_p)^2 = \Sigma[y - (mx + b)]^2$$

Let us divide both sides of this by N and rewrite it in terms of arithmetic means. Then if we expand the right hand side and simplify, we have

$$\overline{(y - y_p)^2} = \overline{y^2} + m^2\overline{x^2} + b^2 - 2m\overline{xy} - 2b\bar{y} + 2mb\bar{x} \qquad (8\text{-}8\text{-}2)$$

This is the term which we wish to make as small as possible. In order to accomplish this, we are free to try various straight lines, that is, various values of m and b, until we have reduced the entire right-hand side to its smallest possible value.

To see how we should choose m and b to accomplish this, let us consider for a moment a simpler experimental problem of the same type. Suppose that we wish to choose m in such a way as to make $m^2 - 6m + 14$ a minimum. We could begin by rewriting it in the form $(m^2 - 6m + 9) + 5$, or

$$m^2 - 6m + 14 = (m - 3)^2 + 5 \qquad (8\text{-}8\text{-}3)$$

Now, obviously, since it is the square of a number, $(m - 3)^2$ cannot be negative, and the smallest value it can possibly attain is zero. To make it zero, we must make $m = 3$. This is therefore the answer to our experimental problem.

In order to apply this procedure to equation 8-8-2, we must group the terms containing m and express the entire quantity as the *square of a quantity containing m*, plus other quantities which *do not contain m*, just as we did in equation 8-8-3. The result of this grouping is:

$$\overline{(y - y_p)^2}$$
$$= \overline{x^2}\left[\left(m - \frac{\overline{xy} - b\bar{x}}{\overline{x^2}}\right)^2 + \frac{\overline{y^2} + b^2 - 2b\bar{y}}{\overline{x^2}} - \left(\frac{\overline{xy} - b\bar{x}}{\overline{x^2}}\right)^2\right] \qquad (8\text{-}8\text{-}4)$$

Our objective is to adjust m in such a way as to make the above expression as small as possible. Only the first parenthesis in the brackets contains m, and, following the same logic as that used in the experimental problem, we choose m in such a way as to make this parenthesis zero. Placing the parenthesis equal to zero and solving for m, we have

$$m = \frac{\overline{xy} - b\bar{x}}{\overline{x^2}} \qquad (8\text{-}8\text{-}5)$$

This is the value of m which will make the sum of the squares of the deviations as small as it can be made by adjusting m, but it is not yet a useful result because it contains b, which is itself a quantity which we must adjust in an effort to reduce the sum of the squares of the deviations. To find the best value for b, we must repeat the above procedure, but this time we must group the terms in such a way that they consist of *the square of a term containing b*, plus other terms not containing b. Grouping the terms in 8-8-2 in this way, we have

$$\overline{(y - y_p)^2} = [b - (\bar{y} - m\bar{x})]^2 + m^2\overline{x^2} - 2m\overline{xy} - (\bar{y} - m\bar{x})^2 + \overline{y^2}$$

Only the first brackets contain b, and again we put this quantity equal to zero. This gives us

$$b - (\bar{y} - m\bar{x}) = 0 \qquad (8\text{-}8\text{-}6)$$

If we solve this for b and substitute the result in equation 8-8-5, we can then solve the resulting equation for the desired value of m. The result is

$$m = \frac{\overline{xy} - \bar{x}\,\bar{y}}{\overline{x^2} - \bar{x}^2}$$

The denominator is equal to σ_x^2 by equation 4-4-1, and it is customary to write the equation for m in the form

$$m = \frac{\overline{xy} - \bar{x}\,\bar{y}}{\sigma_x^2} \qquad (8\text{-}8\text{-}7)$$

If all the values of x and y are very large, it is convenient to use another form of this equation, in terms of the deviations from their means:

$$m = \frac{\overline{(x - \bar{x})(y - \bar{y})}}{\sigma_x^2} \qquad (8\text{-}8\text{-}8)$$

You can readily verify the fact that this is identical to 8-8-7 by multiplying out the numerator in the right-hand side, applying equations 3-10-2, 3-10-4, and 3-10-5, and collecting terms.

As soon as we have obtained m from either of these equations, we can obtain b most quickly by using equation 8-8-6 in the form

$$b = \bar{y} - m\bar{x} \qquad (8\text{-}8\text{-}9)$$

These values of m and b can now be inserted in the equation $y_p = mx + b$. The resulting equation is then the one which will make the sum of the squares of the deviations an absolute minimum and which has therefore the highest possible probability of expressing exactly the relation between x and the predictable part of y, as distinguished from the random part.

An alternative form for the equation of the line of best fit is obtained if we substitute b from 8-8-9 directly into $y_p = mx + b$, in which case we obtain

$$y_p = \bar{y} + m(x - \bar{x}) \qquad (8\text{-}8\text{-}10)$$

To demonstrate the procedure of using these equations, let us again use the data in the first two columns of Table 8-7-1. The work can be

TABLE 8-8-1.   Least Squares Procedure

	x	y	xy	x^2
	10	5	50	100
	20	15	300	400
	30	15	450	900
	40	20	800	1600
	50	35	1750	2500
Sum	150	90	3350	5500
Mean	30	18	670	1100
	$(\bar{x})$	$(\bar{y})$	$(\overline{xy})$	$(\overline{x^2})$

organized as shown in Table 8-8-1. From the way in which they are computed in these operations, we see that 30 is $\bar{x}$, 18 is $\bar{y}$, 670 is $\overline{xy}$, and 1100 is $\overline{x^2}$. Using equation 4-4-1, we find that $\sigma_x^2 = 200$. Inserting these values in equation 8-8-7, we have:

$$m = \frac{670 - 30 \times 18}{200} = 0.65$$

Inserting this value in 8-8-9, we obtain:

$$b = 18 - (0.65)(30) = -1.5$$

The equation of the least squares line is then obtained by placing these values in 8-8-1:

$$y_p = 0.65x - 1.5 \tag{8-8-11}$$

which is the required line. The sum of the squares of the deviations from this line should be less than those from any other possible line. If we apply the least squares test as demonstrated in Table 8-7-1, we obtain 57.5 for the sum of the squares of the deviations, and we know from the theory outlined above that no other straight line can produce a smaller sum of the squares of the deviations, and thus no other straight line has a larger probability of being correct.

PROBLEMS

1. Write a mathematical proof of equation 8-8-8, using equation 8-8-7 as a starting point.

2. Fit a least squares line to the data in Problem 2 of the preceding section. Test this line by the criterion of least squares and compare your results with those obtained in Problem 3 in that section.

3. Fit a least squares line to the relationship between age (x) and height (y) in Table 3-9-1.

4. Write a complete derivation of equation 8-8-7, supplying and explaining all the missing steps.

5. Apply the least squares test to equation 8-8-11. Compare your result with the results in Table 8-7-1 and explain its significance.

9. SIMPLE CURVILINEAR CURVE FITTING

In any curve fitting operation, there is an unavoidable tendency to simplify the relationship, since the scatter of the individual points frequently obscures the finer details of the relationship and reveals only the general trend. For this reason a straight line fit is appropriate for a very large percentage of statistical problems. If, however, the points show an unmistakable curvature, then an attempt should be made to express the relationship in the form

$$Y = mX + b$$

where Y stands for any mathematical expression depending upon y alone and X is one depending upon x alone. In some cases the form of the expressions X and Y is given by independent knowledge of restrictions which the variates are known to fulfil, but generally they are chosen by the investigator by trial and error. In the latter case the investigator should begin by trying the simplest possible expressions for X and Y, and should proceed to more complex forms only if the simple ones fail. Some suggested forms for X are x^2, $\sqrt{x}$, x^3, $\log x$, $1/x$, and so forth.

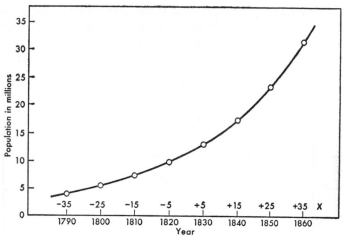

Figure 8-9-1. Population of the United States.

For an example of a situation in which the form of the curve is suggested by the nature of the data, let us consider Table 8-9-1, which gives the population of the continental United States from 1790 to 1840. To avoid the use of large numbers in the equations we have let x stand for the year, measured from 1825. If we now plot y against x (Figure 8-9-1), we see that the points lie along a curve which becomes steeper as x increases and that no straight line can be made to fit the data very well. But we

TABLE 8-9-1. Population of United States*

Year	x	Pop. (y)	Log Pop.
1790	-35	3,929,214	6.5943
1800	-25	5,308,483	6.7249
1810	-15	7,239,881	6.8597
1820	-5	9,638,453	6.9840
1830	$+5$	12,866,020	7.1096
1840	$+15$	17,069,453	7.2322
1850	$+25$	23,191,876	7.3653
1860	$+35$	31,443,321	7.4975

*Reprinted from *Encyclopaedia Britannica*, 1941, Volume 22, page 732, by permission.

saw in Article 6 of Chapter 3 that it is reasonable to expect populations to increase in accordance with a different law, namely, that the logarithm of the population should increase uniformly with time. Using this law, we would expect the relationship between x and y to be given by an equation of the form

$$\log y = mx + b \qquad (8\text{-}9\text{-}1)$$

This equation leads us to expect that if we plot x against $\log y$ we should obtain approximately a straight line. To test this hypothesis, we tabulate the logs of each value of y (column 3 of Table 8-9-1) and plot them against x (Figure 8-9-2). Since the points now fall almost along a straight line,

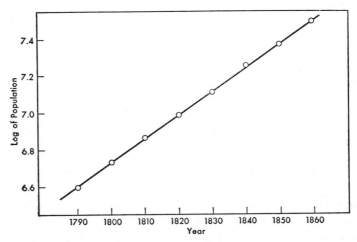

Figure 8-9-2. Logarithm of Population.

we regard the hypothesis as acceptable and proceed to fit an exact least squares line to the numbers in the second and fourth columns of Table 8-9-1, using the methods which we have already studied. The result is

$$Y = 7.0459 + 0.01282X$$

where Y is $\log y$ and X is simply x. In terms of the original variables, this is

$$\log y = 7.0459 + 0.01282x$$

which is the required curve. Using this equation, we can now compute a few predicted values of y, plot them, and draw a smooth curve for comparison with the original data. Such a curve has been drawn in Figure 8-9-1.

PROBLEMS

1. Fit a curve of the form 8-9-1 to the data in Table 8-9-1, and verify the results given in the accompanying discussion.

2. In the following table, x is the distance in miles of each of eight communities from a large city and y is the per capita amount which residents of each community spend in the city each month:

x	y
10	$94
28	35
33	31
57	20
61	16
64	18
87	9
92	12

Assuming that the relationship between these variables is of the form $y = m(1/x) + b$, fit the best possible curve to this data.

10. SUMMARY

Curve fitting is the operation of finding *what* the relationship is between two variables, while correlation theory is a study of the *strength* of that relationship. The investigator who works on one of these two topics is usually interested in the other as well, and there is considerable economy of operation in undertaking them simultaneously. The following summary of operations should be used, therefore, only if you wish to fit a curve to a set of data but do not wish to measure the correlation. *If you wish to measure the correlation as well, then you should use instead the summary of operations at the end of the following chapter.*

There are two procedures which can be used to obtain the line of best fit. The first is approximate; the second is exact.

I. APPROXIMATE PROCEDURE

1. Graph the data.

2. If the points on the graph are numerous and scattered, replace each pair of them by a more conspicuous point halfway between them. Repeat if necessary. In any case, be certain that the final points are large and conspicuous, and that they form a visual pattern which stands out from the rest of your diagram.

3. If the pattern of points forms an unmistakable curve which cannot be reconciled with any straight line, then the methods of part III of this summary should be used. Before reaching this conclusion, however, you should make certain that the deviation from a straight line is established by a number of points, and not by an isolated one or two. Remember that you are trying to separate the systematic or predictable part of the variation from the random part, and if you draw a curve which bends to reach a single point, you may have mistakenly included a random variation in your estimate of what is predictable. Your subsequent predictions will

then erroneously ascribe this particular random deviation to all other cases having a similar value of x. In most practical cases of curve fitting a straight line is adequate, and the cases genuinely requiring curvilinear equations are rare.

4. If you decide that the points are representable by a straight line, draw a best fitting line by inspection. Remember that it is generally bad to balance one large deviation against several small ones, unless you estimate their squares and adjust the line so that the sum of the squares of the deviations is minimized. If the points are numerous and well distributed, a simple visual bisection of the pattern of points is usually sufficient.

5. Extend the line to cut the y axis, and read off the value of y at this point. (Remember that y is negative if the line crosses below the origin.) Call this value b.

6. Select any two points on the line (not two of the original plotted points) and label them "1" and "2." Then compute m from equation 8-4-1:

$$m = \frac{y_2 - y_1}{x_2 - x_1}$$

7. Insert m and b in the equation $y_p = mx + b$. This is the equation of the line of best fit, and may be used for predicting values of y to be expected for any value of x.

II. EXACT PROCEDURE

1. List the data as in Table 8-8-1, and compute xy and x^2 for each entry. Add all columns, and then divide each of the resulting sums by the number of observations. Label the results $\bar{x}$, $\bar{y}$, $\overline{xy}$, and $\overline{x^2}$ as shown at the bottom of the columns in Table 8-8-1.

2. Compute σ_x^2 from $\sigma_x^2 = \overline{x^2} - \bar{x}^2$.

3. Compute m from equation 8-8-7:

$$m = \frac{\overline{xy} - \bar{x}\,\bar{y}}{\sigma_x^2}$$

4. Compute b from equation 8-8-9:

$$b = \bar{y} - m\bar{x}$$

5. Insert these in $y = mx + b$. This is the equation of the line of best fit. A complete demonstration is found in Table 8-8-1 and the discussion following it.

III. SIMPLE CURVILINEAR CURVE FITTING

1. Plot the points. If the resulting graph displays a well-established curvature, which cannot be explained on the hypothesis of random deviations from a straight line, then the following procedure is applicable.

2. Select the type of curve to be fitted. This may be given by the conditions of the problem, or it may be selected as a result of trial and error on the part of the investigator. For the methods here described to be applicable, the equation must be of the form $Y = mX + b$, where Y depends upon y alone and X upon x alone. Some typical trial values for X are x^2, x^3, $\sqrt{x}$, log x, $1/x$, and so forth.

3. Compute X and Y for each entry in the table of data.

4. Fit a straight line to the variables X and Y, using either Method I or Method II.

5. In the resulting straight line equation, replace X and Y by their values in terms of x and y. This is the desired equation. The procedure is illustrated in Article 9.

CHAPTER

· 9 ·

SIMPLE CORRELATION

I. INTRODUCTION

In the preceding chapter, we studied the methods by which a line of best fit may be found, and the methods by which it can be used for estimating or predicting the value of one variable when the corresponding value of the other is known. In order to make the best possible use of such a prediction, it is necessary that we know something about its *reliability* or its *limits of trustworthiness*. Without such information, the prediction would be of little use as a basis for a practical decision. For this purpose we need a measure of the *degree* or *strength* of the dependence of one variable upon another. If the strength of the relationship is very limited, that is, if the two variables are nearly independent, then any prediction of one from the other would be of little value, while if they are closely related, the prediction can be made with a high accuracy.

In a general way, the strength of the relationship is at once apparent from a visual inspection of a graph of the two variables. In Figure 9-1-1, for example, the number of chirps per minute for 115 crickets has been plotted against the temperature in degrees Fahrenheit. We see that all the points fall almost exactly upon a straight line, and we draw the rather surprising conclusion that there is a very close relationship between the frequency of cricket chirps and the temperature. It would be possible to estimate the temperature with high precision by counting the chirps of crickets, or, conversely, to predict the frequency of cricket chirps very accurately if we know the temperature.

In Figure 9-1-2, we see the results of graphing the estimated brain weight of members of the United States Senate against their legislative ability, as estimated by a complicated scoring system from their legislative records. The points scatter so widely that it is almost impossible to guess where the line of best fit should be. It is evident that there is practically no relationship between brain weight and legislative ability, and that if we estimated legislative ability from brain weight, our results would be so uncertain as to be of extremely little use. It would clearly be very unwise to choose senators on the basis of measurements of their brain weights.

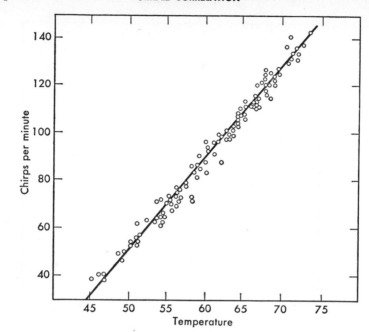

Figure 9-1-1.   Temperature and Cricket Chirps. (Based upon data by Bert. E. Holmes. Reprinted by permission of Prentice-Hall, Inc., from "Applied General Statistics" by Croxton and Cowden. Copyright 1939 by Prentice-Hall, Inc. See also "Vocal Thermometers," "Scientific Monthly," September, 1927.)

In the above examples, we can see by an inspection of the graphs that the degree of relationship, or *correlation*, between chirps and temperature is much greater than the correlation between legislative ability and brain weight.   Why then do we need a more exact measurement of "degree of relationship," or "correlation"?   To answer this question let us examine the following situations.

I. A school screens applicants for admission on the basis of an entrance examination.   A graph of examination scores plotted against later performance in school shows a large scatter, but an obvious relationship. The entrance officials are examining a new test, which, they think, might make more accurate predictions possible and permit a selection of better candidates.   A graph of the results of the new test, however, also shows a considerable scatter, and it is impossible to tell, from a visual inspection of the graphs, which is better.   Some kind of exact numerical measurement of the correlation is needed in order to choose the better test.

II. A scientist has shown that the rate of tree growth is, on the average, somewhat more rapid during years when there are many spots on the surface of the sun, and slow in years when there are few spots.   He has,

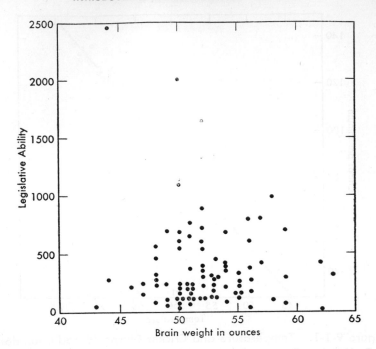

Figure 9-1-2.   Ability and Brain Weight. (Based upon data by Arthur MacDonald. Reprinted by permission of Prentice-Hall, Inc., from "Applied General Statistics" by Croxton and Cowden. Copyright 1939 by Prentice-Hall, Inc.)

in other words, discovered a correlation between sunspot abundance and rate of three growth. In publishing his results he can save time and words if it is possible to express the *amount* of the correlation by giving a single number which will be immediately and precisely understood by other scientists.

III. It is evident from the scientist's results that the rate of growth of trees is not wholly controlled by spot abundance; that is, that spot abundance does not constitute 100 per cent of the cause of changes in rate of growth. But what percentage does it constitute? Has he explained only 10 per cent of the total cause or causes, leaving 90 per cent unexplained, or has he succeeded in pinning down as much as 30 per cent of the causation of variation in tree growth?

From the above examples, it is seen that we have two objectives. First, we wish to describe a standard numerical measure of the degree of correlation; and secondly, we wish to relate this, so far as possible, to the somewhat elusive concept of "percentage causation," or "percentage of related variation."

PROBLEMS

1. Using the data in Table 3-9-1, plot height against age, and then plot I.Q. against age. In which case do you think that there is the greater correlation? Retain your answers for comparison with later results.

2. Collect a set of data in which you think that some correlation might conceivably exist and make a graph of your results. Your data will be most useful for further exercises if you collect *three* pieces of information about each individual. The possibilities for collecting such data are almost unlimited, but if you find a choice difficult, the following suggestions are offered:

   (a) Height, weight, and age of college students.
   (b) Grades, hours of study, and IQ's of college students.
   (c) Grades, hours of study, and number of dates per week.
   (d) Length, width, and number of veins in a set of leaves selected at random from a plant.
   (e) Alcohol consumption per year, cigarettes smoked per year, and any index of general health such as number of days of illness last year.
   (f) Number of aces in a bridge hand; number of cards in the longest suit; number of tricks won by the hand.
   (g) Grades; number of hours of employment per week; pay per hour.
   (h) Shoe size; length of span of right hand; length of span of left hand.

2. COEFFICIENT OF DETERMINATION

Our objective is to find a measure for the degree to which x and y are related or dependent, and the degree to which they are unrelated or independent. For this purpose, let us begin by dividing each value of y into two parts, one of which is completely dependent upon x, and the other of which is completely independent of x. We can then expect to measure relatedness by some kind of comparison between the sizes of these two parts. We have already discussed such a separation of the components of y in Article 6 of Chapter 8, where we introduced the notation y_p, or "y predicted," for the part of y which is related to x, and which is exactly predictable if we know the corresponding value of x.

In some cases this mathematical separation of y into components corresponds to an obvious physical separation into related and unrelated parts. For example, if x is the measured radius and y the measured circumference of each of a set of circles, and if we have measured them to the nearest tenth of a millimeter, then the separation into components is obvious: y_p is the true circumference and is exactly related to x by the equation $y_p = 2\pi x$, and $y - y_p$ is a small error of measurement, positive or negative, which is completely independent of x. We will see, however, that the process of separating the components can be carried out whether the investigator sees such a physical separation or not. The mathematical analysis shows him how large the two components are, and he can then, with this information, construct a hypothesis to explain their relative sizes.

For the sake of the student who is not accustomed to following a discussion involving a number of abstract symbols, let us examine a specific problem as we proceed. Five students compared notes on the length of time each spent in study for an examination and discovered the following data:

Student	x Hours of Study	y Score on Exam
Jackson	5	26
Petoskey	4	17
Goldberg	3	17
Bellini	2	11
Schwartz	1	14

If we fit a straight line to these data by the method of least squares (Article 8, Chapter 8), we obtain:

$$y_p = 3x + 8$$

This is the best possible equation for predicting the score which other students will make on the examination if we know only how long they have studied for it. If we test the equation on the five men above to see how well it would have predicted their scores, we find the following:

Student	x	y	y_p	$y - y_p$
Jackson	5	26	23	3
Petoskey	4	17	20	−3
Goldberg	3	17	17	0
Bellini	2	11	14	−3
Schwartz	1	14	11	3

Thus we see that our hypothesis about the separability of y leads us to the conclusion that of the 26 points Jackson scored, 23 were predictable from a knowledge of the length of time which he studied for the examination, and 3 were unrelated to time of study and therefore not predictable from it.

At first glance it might appear that the fraction 23/26 might be used as a measure of the success of the equation $y_p = 3x + 8$ in predicting Jackson's grade. A little reflection, however, will show that it would be foolish to compare the related part, y_p, directly with the original value of y. The numerical size of y depends upon such extraneous factors as the zero point chosen by the investigator in tabulating his results. One investigator might convert the letter grades A, B, C, D, and F into numbers by assigning the values 1, 2, 3, 4, and 5 to them; another might use the numbers 0, 1, 2, 3, and 4; still another might record only the number of mistakes which the examinee made, in which case the best grades would be those with the smallest values of y. It is clearly not very revealing to ask "What fraction of y does the equation succeed in predicting?" and we should ask instead "What fraction of the *deviation of y from its mean* does the equation succeed in predicting?"

If we rewrite our illustrative problem in terms of deviations from the mean, we will have the results shown in Table 9-2-1.

TABLE 9-2-1.   Components of the Deviations

Student	y	y_p	$y - \bar{y}$ (Tot. dev.)	$y_p - \bar{y}$ (Expl. dev.)	$y - y_p$ (Unexpl. dev.)
Jackson	26	23	9	6	3
Petoskey	17	20	0	3	−3
Goldberg	17	17	0	0	0
Bellini	11	14	−6	−3	−3
Schwartz	14	11	−3	−6	3

The average of all the y's is 17, and Jackson's score deviates from this average by 9, which we call the *total deviation*. His predicted score is 23, which deviates from the mean by 6, and we will call this the *explained deviation*. This is the part of the total deviation which is predicted exactly by the equation, and is therefore totally dependent upon x. The remaining

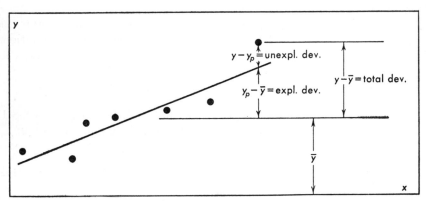

Figure 9-2-1.   Components of the Total Deviations.

part of the total deviation, $y - y_p$, or 3 in the case of Jackson, is the residual amount which cannot be predicted from a knowledge of x, and is totally independent of x. We will call this part the *unexplained deviation*. The relations between these quantities are shown in Figure 9-2-1.

We are seeking some way of averaging each of these three sets of deviations so that we can define the "percentage dependence" and the "percentage independence" in some such way as follows:

$$\text{Percentage dependence} \quad = \frac{\text{Average explained deviation}}{\text{Average total deviation}}$$
$$\text{Percentage independence} = \frac{\text{Average unexplained deviation}}{\text{Average total deviation}}$$
$$\left.\right\} \quad (9\text{-}2\text{-}2)$$

To make these definitions complete, it remains only to specify what kind of averages we should use. At first glance it might appear that we are free to choose any kind of average which might be convenient, but a little further reflection will show that we are not quite free. If we are to interpret the results as percentages of dependence and independence, respectively, *then an obvious property which they must possess is that they must total* 100 *per cent*, and we must choose a method of averaging which will bring this about. If, for example, y is 80 per cent dependent upon x, then it must necessarily be 20 per cent independent of x. If this restriction were not present we might use the average of the absolute values of the deviations, or the root mean squares of the deviations, or their logarithmic means, or the means of their cubes, or any other kind of average which might appear useful. We could use any of these in equations 9-2-1 to give us a kind of measure of relatedness, but we can interpret the results as *percentage dependence* and *percentage independence only if the sum of the two percentages equals* 1. We will now prove that this will be true if we use one specific kind of average, namely the average of the squares of the deviations, or the *variance*.

To prove this important fact, we must express in comparable terms the averages of the squares of each of the three kinds of deviations in equations 9-2-1. Let us begin with the average of the squares of the explained deviations. We shall call this average the *explained variance*.

$$\text{Expl. Var.} = \overline{(y_p - \bar{y})^2} = \overline{[(mx + b) - \bar{y}]^2}$$

where we have substituted for y_p its value, $mx + b$, from equation 8-8-1. Now let us substitute for b its value, $\bar{y} - m\bar{x}$, given by equation 8-8-9:

$$\text{Expl. Var.} = \overline{(mx + \bar{y} - m\bar{x} - \bar{y})^2} = \overline{m(x - \bar{x})^2} = m\overline{(x - \bar{x})^2}$$

We recognize $\overline{(x - \bar{x})^2}$ as σ_x^2 from equation 4-3-2, and the above equation becomes:

$$\text{Expl. Var.} = m\sigma_x^2 \qquad (9\text{-}2\text{-}2)$$

If we proceed similarly with the unexplained deviations, $y - y_p$, we will obtain the *unexplained variance*:

$$\text{Unexpl. Var.} = \overline{(y - y_p)^2} = \overline{[y - (mx + b)]^2} \qquad (9\text{-}2\text{-}3)$$
$$= \overline{[y - mx - \bar{y} + m\bar{x}]^2}$$
$$= \overline{[(y - \bar{y}) - m(x - \bar{x})]^2}$$

If we square out the right-hand side and express the results as three separate means, we will have

$$\text{Unexpl. Var.} = \overline{(y - \bar{y})^2} - 2m\overline{(y - \bar{y})(x - \bar{x})} + m^2\overline{(x - \bar{x})^2}$$

The terms $\overline{(y - \bar{y})^2}$ and $\overline{(x - \bar{x})^2}$ are the squares of σ_y and σ_x, respectively, from equation 4-3-2. The term $\overline{(y - \bar{y})(x - \bar{x})}$ is the numerator in the formula for m (equation 8-8-8), and is therefore equal to $m\sigma_x^2$. Making these substitutions, we have:

$$\text{Unexpl. Var.} = \sigma_y^2 - 2m(m\sigma_x^2) + m^2\sigma_x^2 = \sigma_y^2 - m^2\sigma_x^2 \qquad (9\text{-}2\text{-}4)$$

Equations 9-2-2 and 9-2-4 give us expressions for the explained variance and the unexplained variance, and we need in addition only the *total variance*, or the average of the squares of the total deviations. This we recognize immediately from equation 4-3-2 as the square of the standard deviation of y:

$$\text{Total Var.} = \overline{(y - \bar{y})^2} = \sigma_y^2 \qquad (9\text{-}2\text{-}5)$$

Using these variances for the ratios in equations 9-2-1, we obtain:

$$\frac{\text{Explained variance}}{\text{Total variance}} = \frac{m^2\sigma_x^2}{\sigma_y^2} \qquad (9\text{-}2\text{-}6)$$

$$\frac{\text{Unexplained variance}}{\text{Total variance}} = \frac{\sigma_y^2 - m^2\sigma_x^2}{\sigma_y^2} \qquad (9\text{-}2\text{-}7)$$

If we add these two, we have

$$\frac{\text{Expl. Var.}}{\text{Tot. Var.}} + \frac{\text{Unexpl. Var.}}{\text{Tot. Var.}} = \frac{m^2\sigma_x^2 + \sigma_y^2 - m^2\sigma_x^2}{\sigma_y^2} = 1 \qquad (9\text{-}2\text{-}8)$$

Thus we have shown that if we use ratios of variances in equation 9-2-1, we can interpret the results as percentages of dependence and independence. We therefore adopt, as a measure of the percentage of the variation in y which is related to variation in x, the *explained variance divided by the total variance*. This quantity is called the *coefficient of determination*, or D. The *unexplained variance divided by the total variance* is called the *coefficient of alienation*, or A, and is obviously equal to $1 - D$. It is the percentage of variation in y which is independent of variation in x. A summary of these relations is as follows:

$$D = \frac{\overline{(y_p - \bar{y})^2}}{\overline{(y - \bar{y})^2}} = \frac{\text{Expl. Var.}}{\text{Tot. Var.}} \qquad (9\text{-}2\text{-}9)$$

$$A = 1 - D = \frac{\overline{(y - y_p)^2}}{\overline{(y - \bar{y})^2}} = \frac{\text{Unexpl. Var.}}{\text{Tot. Var.}} \qquad (9\text{-}2\text{-}10)$$

PROBLEMS

Fill in the following spaces:

Problem	Expl. Var.	Unexpl. Var.	Tot. Var.	D	A
1	22	28			
2	10		90		
3		5		0.90	
4			20	0.75	
5		20			0.40
6	14				0.30

3. COEFFICIENT OF CORRELATION

Most statisticians do not compute the coefficient of determination directly, but compute instead a quantity called the *coefficient of correlation*, (r), which is *the square root of D*. Sometimes this coefficient of correlation is then squared to obtain D, but more often the results are reported by giving the value of r alone, and it is left to the reader to compute D.

For reasons of mathematical convenience, r is given a plus or minus sign to agree with the sign of m. In other words, r is assigned a positive value if y increases when x increases, and a negative value if y decreases as x increases. A summary of these relations, obtained by combining the definition of r with the information in equations 9-2-9 and 9-2-6, is as follows:

$$r = \text{Coef. of Corr.} = \pm\sqrt{D} = \pm\sqrt{\frac{\text{Expl. var.}}{\text{Tot. var.}}} = m\frac{\sigma_x}{\sigma_y} \quad (9\text{-}3\text{-}1)$$

Equations 9-2-9 and 9-3-1 define D and r, but are not very useful for computing them. More rapid computational formulas will be developed in later Articles.

PROBLEMS

1 to 6. Compute r for each of the problems at the end of Article 2.

4. COMPARISON BETWEEN r AND D

The student will perhaps feel that it is wasteful and unnecessary to master two separate statistical terms which measure, in different ways, exactly the same thing, namely, closeness of relationship. In order to see why both are in use by statisticians, and why both are useful, let us examine briefly the merits of both in a specific problem.

Suppose that in a given situation y is dependent partly upon x, and partly also upon another variable z which has also been measured by the investigator, and suppose also that x is totally independent of z. We now have several possible coefficients of determination between various pairings of x, y, and z; let us distinguish them by subscripts. Let us suppose that

D_{zy} is 0.3 and D_{zy} is 0.5. Since z and x are independent, D_{zz} is zero. Now, in view of the meaning of the coefficient of determination, we can assert that 30 per cent of the total variance in y is predictable from changes in x, and that 50 per cent is predictable from changes in z. Since x is independent of z, the 30 per cent does not overlap or duplicate any of the 50 per cent, and we can deduce that 80 per cent of the total variance in y is predictable from variation in x and z, leaving only 20 per cent of it unexplained. In other words, 20 per cent of the total variation in y is related to neither x nor z and is presumably caused by other factors not measured by the investigator.

This additive property is not possessed by r. In this example r_{zy} is the square root of D_{zy}, or 0.55, and r_{yz} is the square root of D_{yz}, or 0.71. The sum of these two does not measure the total correlation in any way.

We can state this additive property in another way. If y is known to be completely determined by several variables, x, z, u, and v, which are all independent of each other, then:

$$D_{yx} + D_{yz} + D_{yu} + D_{yv} = 1 \qquad (9\text{-}4\text{-}1)$$

There is another reason for considering r a somewhat clumsy mathematical device. The *nature* of the relationship between x and y is described by the line of best fit, and the *strength* of the relationship is described by D. But r is a composite quantity which describes the strength of the relationship by its absolute value, and part, but not all, of the nature of the relationship by its plus or minus sign.

It is suggested that you regard r as an intermediate mathematical step and D as the final objective. In short, r should be studied because it is widely used in statistical reports and because it is a useful mathematical tool for a variety of purposes; but it is recommended that when you read a report containing a value of r, you should mentally square it to obtain D for the purpose of interpreting the results.

It is sometimes useful to think of D somewhat loosely as the "percentage causation," although it is important to notice that we know nothing about the *nature* of the causation from the size of D or r. Variations in x may be causing variations in y, or vice versa, or both may be caused by variations in a third variable which was not measured by the investigator, or x and y may have varied together by chance. The interpretation of r and D will be discussed at a later point.

PROBLEMS

1. In a given agricultural area, it was found that the coefficient of correlation (r) between the amount of spring rainfall and the size of the annual hay crop is 0.80. What fraction of the variance in annual hay crop is caused by or related to spring rainfall?

2. What is the largest possible coefficient of correlation between size of hay crop and any variable which is completely independent of spring rainfall, such as the amount of fertilizer applied by the farmer?

3. Would a larger value of r than this be possible between hay crop and average temperature? Explain.

5. NUMERICAL COMPARISON OF VARIANCES

The additive property of the variances, proved in the preceding article and described in equation 9-2-8, is a very important one. It is well worth while to follow our numerical example through a further step in order to demonstrate this property, and to show that it is not possessed by other kinds of averages of the components of the deviations.

In order to compute the variances we must square all the deviations in Table 9-2-1. The complete computations are shown in Table 9-5-1. The

TABLE 9-5-1. Comparison of Variances

Student	x	y	y_p	$y - \bar{y}$	$(y - \bar{y})^2$	$y_p - \bar{y}$	$(y_p - \bar{y})^2$	$y - y_p$	$(y - y_p)^2$
Jackson	5	26	23	9	81	6	36	3	9
Petoskey	4	17	20	0	0	3	9	−3	9
Goldberg	3	17	17	0	0	0	0	0	0
Bellini	2	11	14	−6	36	−3	9	−3	9
Schwartz	1	14	11	−3	9	−6	36	3	9
Sum	15	85			126		90		36
Mean	3	17			25.2		18		7.2
					(Tot. Var.)		(Expl. Var.)		(Unexpl. Var.)

variance of the observed y's is 25.2. This is the *total variance*, and we wish to account for as much of it as possible in our predicting equation. The variance of the predicted values is 18.0; this is the variance which we have succeeded in accounting for by the equation $y = 3x + 8$; it is, in other words, the *explained variance*. The variance of the remaining deviations after the explained portions have been removed is 7.2; this is the *unexplained variance*. We see that the sum of the explained variance and the unexplained variance is the total variance, verifying the important principle proved in Article 2. Notice that this property is not possessed by any other kind of average of the deviations. If, for example, we form the mean of the absolute values of the deviations, we have:

$$\text{Mean total deviation} \quad = 3.6$$
$$\text{Mean explained deviation} \quad = 3.6$$
$$\text{Mean unexplained deviation} = 2.4$$

Thus this method of averaging will not give us additive averages.

We can now compute the coefficients of determination, alienation, and correlation from these variances. The equation succeeds in explaining the fraction 18/25.2, or 71 per cent, of the total variance, thus the coefficient of determination is 0.71. The remaining fraction, 7.2/25.2, or 29 per cent of the total variance is left unexplained; therefore the coefficient of alienation is 0.29. The coefficient of correlation, r, is the square root of 0.71, which is 0.85. We interpret these results as follows: The score which a student makes on the examination is 71 per cent controlled by or related to the length of time which he studies for it, and 29 per cent controlled by other factors, such as his native ability or his knowledge prior to studying.

It is important to notice that coefficients of correlation and of determination do not contain any information about the *nature* of the causation. In the illustrative problem, we know only that it is possible to predict 71 per cent of the variance in y from the corresponding values of x. We do not know whether changes in x cause changes in y, or whether it is the changes in y which cause the changes in x, or whether both are partially caused by other variables. Any hypothesis about the *cause* of the relationship between x and y must be made from whatever additional knowledge the statistician may have about the specific situation; it cannot be deduced from the size of D or r. This is a fertile source of error in interpreting statistical analysis, and it should be emphasized that the statistician must be familiar with the data and its sources as well as the statistical methods of treatment. There is no substitute for common sense in interpreting coefficients of correlation.

It is also important to note that the value of D measures only the relationship which we have been able to incorporate into our straight-line equation. The true degree of relationship may be greater than this, but if the relationship is curvilinear, for example, it cannot be encompassed in any straight line equation and so will be partly lost.

6. BASIC COMPUTATIONAL FORMULA FOR r

The definition of r given in Article 3 is completely general and can be used later to define a coefficient of "multiple correlation" in situations where several related variables are used simultaneously for prediction, and also for a "coefficient of non-linear correlation" in situations in which a curve is fitted to the data instead of a straight line. Like many fundamental definitions, it is not very useful for computing the thing it defines, and our next task will be to set up various formulas for rapid computation of r.

To obtain a basic computational formula, let us recall that m is equal to $(\overline{xy} - \bar{x}\bar{y})/\sigma_x^2$ from equation 8-8-7, and let us substitute this into equation 9-3-1:

$$r = m\frac{\sigma_x}{\sigma_y} = \frac{\overline{xy} - \bar{x}\bar{y}}{\sigma_x^2}\frac{\sigma_x}{\sigma_y} = \frac{\overline{xy} - \bar{x}\bar{y}}{\sigma_x\sigma_y} \qquad (9\text{-}6\text{-}1)$$

or, if we obtain m from equation 8-8-8 instead;

$$r = \frac{\overline{(x - \bar{x})(y - \bar{y})}}{\sigma_x \sigma_y} \qquad (9\text{-}6\text{-}2)$$

In words, equation 9-6-1 tells us that the coefficient of correlation between x and y is equal to the average value of xy, minus the average value of x times the average value of y, all divided by the product of the standard deviations of x and y. To see how this equation is used, let us apply it to the illustrative problem in Article 2.

We begin by computing $\bar{x}$, $\bar{y}$, $\overline{xy}$, $\overline{x^2}$, and $\overline{y^2}$, by means of the computa-

TABLE 9-6-1. Computation of r

	x	y	xy	x^2	y^2
	5	26	130	25	676
	4	17	68	16	289
	3	17	51	9	289
	2	11	22	4	121
	1	14	14	1	196
Sum	15	85	285	55	1571
Mean	3	17	57	11	314.2

tions shown in Table 9-6-1. We then compute σ_x and σ_y from equation 4-4-1, and insert these in 9-6-2:

$$r = \frac{57 - 3 \times 17}{\sqrt{(11 - 3^2)}\,\sqrt{(314.2 - 17^2)}} = 0.85$$

If x and y are simple numbers, we can sometimes use equation 9-6-2 instead. In this case we begin by computing $\overline{(x - \bar{x})(y - \bar{y})}$, $\overline{(x - \bar{x})^2}$,

TABLE 9-6-2. Alternative Procedure for r

	x	y	$x - \bar{x}$	$y - \bar{y}$	$(x - \bar{x})^2$	$(y - \bar{y})^2$	$(x - \bar{x})(y - \bar{y})$
	5	26	2	9	4	81	18
	4	17	1	0	1	0	0
	3	17	0	0	0	0	0
	2	11	−1	−6	1	36	6
	1	14	−2	−3	4	9	6
Sum	15	85			10	126	30
Mean	3	17			2	25.2	6

and $\overline{(y - \bar{y})^2}$ as shown in Table 9-6-2. We next obtain σ_x and σ_y from 4-3-2, and have for r,

$$r = \frac{6}{\sqrt{2}\sqrt{25.2}} = 0.85$$

In general, equation 9-6-1 produces faster results than equation 9-6-2.

PROBLEMS

1. Write a mathematical proof that equations 9-6-1 and 9-6-2 are equivalent.

2. *Compute the coefficient of correlation between the ages and the intelligence test points for the five children described in Problem 2, Chapter 8, Article 7. Compute D and A.

3. *Compute r, D, and A for the relationship between age and height of the five children described in Table 3-9-1. (Use equation 9-6-2.)

7. REGRESSION EQUATIONS

A statistician sometimes computes a value of r for its own sake and does not wish to use the prediction equations. Sometimes he is interested only in a prediction equation and does not care about knowing the value of r. More frequently, however, he wishes to measure the degree of correlation and also to set up an equation for estimating or predicting one of the variables. In this latter case, some simplification can be achieved by combining the two procedures.

Suppose that we have begun by computing the value of r from equation 9-6-1 or 9-6-2. The prediction equation, from equation 8-8-10, is:

$$y_p = \bar{y} + m(x - \bar{x})$$

Equation 9-3-1 tells us that $r = m\sigma_x/\sigma_y$. If we solve this for m and substitute the result in the above equation, we have:

$$y_p = \bar{y} + \frac{\sigma_y}{\sigma_x} r(x - \bar{x}) \tag{9-7-1}$$

If we wish to predict or estimate x from a known value of y, the roles of the two variables are reversed, and the prediction equation ** is:

$$x_p = \bar{x} + \frac{\sigma_x}{\sigma_y} r(y - \bar{y}) \tag{9-7-2}$$

These prediction equations are frequently called the "regression" equa-

---

*Retain your computations for future use.

**It is interesting to note that these equations become extremely simple if we express x and y in t units. Equation 9-7-1 becomes $(t_y)_p = rt_x$; 9-7-2 becomes $(t_x)_p = rt_y$; and 9-6-2 becomes $r = \overline{t_x t_y}$.

tions, and the constants in them are called coefficients of regression. The following terminology is often used:

$$\text{Coefficient of regression of } y \text{ on } x = b_{yx} = \frac{\sigma_y}{\sigma_x} r \qquad (9\text{-}7\text{-}3)$$

$$\text{Coefficient of regression of } x \text{ on } y = b_{xy} = \frac{\sigma_x}{\sigma_y} r \qquad (9\text{-}7\text{-}4)$$

The regression equations are frequently written in terms of b_{yx} and b_{xy} :

$$y_p = \bar{y} + b_{yx}(x - \bar{x}) \qquad (9\text{-}7\text{-}5)$$

and $\qquad\qquad x_p = \bar{x} + b_{xy}(y - \bar{y}) \qquad (9\text{-}7\text{-}6)$

When plotted, the line 9-7-3 (or 9-7-5) is called the line of regression of y on x, and the line 9-7-4 (or 9-7-6) is called the line of regression of x on y.

PROBLEMS*

1. Write the regression equation for predicting the height which a child will reach at a given age, using the data in Table 3-9-1.

2. Using this result, estimate the height which a child of 13 should have.

3. Write the regression equation for estimating the age of a child when its height is known.

4. If a child is 47 inches tall, what is his probable age?

5. Write the regression equation for estimating the points which a child of a given age will score, using the data in Problem 2, Chapter 8, Article 7.

8.   STANDARD ERROR OF ESTIMATE

When a prediction has been made by means of the regression equations, the result is of little value unless something is known about its precision. If an oil company wishes to send a crew into a jungle region known to have a serious health hazard, it might be useful to set up an equation for predicting the rate of infection, based upon data concerning temperatures, humidity, insect population, and infection rates in similar jungles and to know that this equation predicts an annual infection rate of nine cases of the disease in question per thousand of inhabitants. But perhaps the doctors, while able to handle a rate of 9 per thousand, would be utterly unable to cope with a rate of 50 per thousand, and would be unable to prevent the latter rate from snowballing into a disastrous epidemic. It now becomes very important to know the probability that the predicted rate might turn out to be this far in error. In this case, as in many others, it is fully as important to know the range of reliability of the prediction as it is to know the prediction itself.

If we assume that the errors of prediction, $y - y_p$, will be distributed normally, we can solve all such problems by means of the normal curve

---

*Retain your computations for future use.

tables. The standard deviation of these errors is called the *standard error of estimate*, and denoted by S_y :

$$S_y = \sqrt{\overline{(y - y_p)^2}} \qquad (9\text{-}8\text{-}1)$$

Its use can be most readily explained by means of a demonstration. Suppose that in the above example the doctors compute the standard error of estimate and find that it is equal to 7. We know then, from our knowledge of the normal curve, that the probability that the actual value will turn out to be within 7 of the predicted value is 0.68; in other words, the probability is 0.68 that the actual infection rate will be between 2 and 16 per 1000. If we wish to know the probability that the true rate of infection will be as high as or higher than some other fixed number, say 20 per thousand, we proceed as follows. An occurrence of 20 would be a deviation of 11 from the expected value of 9, and if we divide this deviation by 7 we will convert it into t units. Thus we find that $t = 11/7 = 1.57$, and we find in Appendix V that for $t = 1.57$, the area is 0.4418. We conclude that the probability is 0.44 that the rate will be between 9 and 20. To obtain the probability that the rate will be above 20 we must subtract 0.4418 from 0.5000. This probability is 0.0582, or roughly 6 per cent. To apply this method to our original question, where the rate to be examined is 50 per 1000, we find t as before:

$$t = (50 - 9)/7 = 5.9$$

We look up $t = 5.9$ in Appendix V, and find that the residual area is less than 0.000 000 003, so that the probability that the rate will exceed 50 is negligible.

PROBLEMS

1. In Article 2 we derived the equation $y_p = 3x + 8$ for predicting the examination score (y) from the hours of study (x), based upon the data for five students. Compute the predicted score for a student who works six hours.

2. What is the standard error of estimate of this prediction? (Use the data in Table 9-5-1).

3. What is the probability that his actual score will be between 26 and 27.7? Above 27.7? Above 30? Below 15?

9. FORMULA FOR STANDARD ERROR OF ESTIMATE

The definition of S_y given in the preceding article is, like many defining equations, not suitable for rapid computations. To find a faster way to compute S_y, let us begin by squaring equation 9-8-1:

$$S_y^2 = \overline{(y - y_p)^2}$$

From equation 9-2-3 we see that this is simply the unexplained variance, and from equation 9-2-4 we see that it can be written as follows:

$$S_y^2 = \sigma_y^2 - m^2 \sigma_x^2$$

From 9-3-1 we see that $m = r(\sigma_y/\sigma_x)$. Making this substitution, we have:

$$S_y^2 = \sigma_y^2 - \left(r\frac{\sigma_y}{\sigma_x}\right)^2 \sigma_x^2 = \sigma_y^2(1 - r^2)$$

or, taking the square root:

$$S_y = \sigma_y \sqrt{1 - r^2} \qquad (9\text{-}9\text{-}1)$$

This is the basic computational formula for S_y. To illustrate its use, let us apply it to the problem of grade prediction discussed in Articles 2 and 5 of this chapter. We have:

$$S_y = \sqrt{25.2}\sqrt{1 - 0.85^2} = 2.7$$

This tells us that if we use the equation $y_p = 3x + 8$ to predict the scores which other students will make on the examination, and tabulate the errors of prediction, we can expect the distribution of these errors to have a standard deviation of 2.7. Therefore, for any one prediction, the probability is 0.68 that the true score will be within 2.7 of the predicted score.

We can use this result in another way. Equation 6-8-1 tells us that the probable error is 0.6745 times the standard deviation, and this gives us a probable error of 1.8 for the predicted score. To see how this is used, let us predict the score of a student named Don Poller who studied two and one-half hours for the examination. His predicted score is 15.5, and the probable error of the prediction is 1.8; that is, the chances are 50 per cent that his true score will be within 1.8 units of 15.5. This can be expressed in the customary way:

$$y_p = 15.5 \pm 1.8$$

Equation 9-9-1 tells us that r must be fairly high if the regression equations are to be useful. If we did not have the regression equations, the best guess as to the value of a y chosen at random would be $\bar{y}$, in which case the standard deviation of the errors of estimation would be simply σ_y. When we use the regression equation, the errors of estimation have a standard deviation of S_y, which is equal to σ_y multiplied by the fraction $\sqrt{1 - r^2}$. If, for instance, r is 0.4, then S_y is $\sqrt{1 - 0.4^2}$ times σ_y, or 92 per cent of σ_y, and the size of the errors of prediction are reduced by only 8 per cent when we use the regression equations, as compared to the errors we would have made if we had assumed that every y was simply equal to $\bar{y}$. If r is 0.6, then the errors of estimate are reduced by 20 per cent, and if r is 0.8, they are reduced by 40 per cent. The size of r is a deceptive guide to the usefulness of the relationship for predicting or estimating, and the standard error of estimate should always be computed.

If, on the other hand, we are interested in predicting the average value for a large number of individuals, then a smaller value of r can be used with good results. This situation will be discussed further in Chapter 10.

Let us summarize the procedure for finding the coefficient of correlation, the prediction equation, and the standard error of estimate.

First step: Compute r from equation 9-6-1, or, if the values of x and y are large numbers and their range is small, from equation 9-6-2.

Second step: Using this value of r, write the prediction equation for y from equation 9-7-1.

Third step: Again using this value of r, compute the standard error of estimate from equation 9-9-1.

PROBLEMS

1. Compute S for the estimate of height which you made in Problem 2, Article 7.
2. What is the probability that the child's true height will be within 4 inches of the predicted height?
3. Compute S for the estimate of age which you made in Problem 4 of Article 7.
4. What is the probability that the child will actually be over 10 years of age?

10.   PROCEDURE FOR LARGE VARIATES

In many cases the investigator deals with values of x and y which are very large, and equation 9-6-1 is then too laborious to use. In such cases the work can be simplified by using the alternative equation for r,

$$r = \frac{\overline{(x - x_0)(y - y_0)} - \overline{(x - x_0)}\;\overline{(y - y_0)}}{\sigma_x \sigma_y} \qquad (9\text{-}10\text{-}1)$$

where x_0 and y_0 stand for any convenient fixed numbers chosen by the investigator. The proof of this equation is left to the student as an exercise. The use of the equation is illustrated in Table 9-10-1, in which 12,300

TABLE 9-10-1.   Change of Zero Point

x	y	$x - x_0$	$y - y_0$	$(x - x_0)^2$	$(y - y_0)^2$	$(x - x_0)(y - y_0)$
12303	2570	3	0	9	0	0
12318	2591	18	21	324	441	378
12314	2588	14	18	196	324	252
12305	2571	5	1	25	1	5
12310	2582	10	12	100	144	120
Sum		50	52	654	910	755
Mean		10	10.4	130.8	182.0	151.0

$$\sigma_x = \sqrt{130.8 - 10^2} = 5.55$$

$$\sigma_y = \sqrt{182 - 10.4^2} = 8.59$$

$$r = \frac{(151 - 10 \times 10.4)}{5.55 \times 8.59} = 0.986$$

has been chosen for x_0 and 2570 for y_0. The values of σ_x and σ_y are computed from equation 4-4-3; otherwise the details of the computation are self-explanatory.

An alternative procedure is to use equation 9-6-2, which will automatically reduce the size of the numbers with which we must deal. The procedure is illustrated in Table 9-10-2, with the same data as before.

TABLE 9-10-2.   Use of Deviations from Mean

x	y	$x - \bar{x}$	$y - \bar{y}$	$(x - \bar{x})^2$	$(y - \bar{y})^2$	$(x - \bar{x})(y - \bar{y})$
12303	2570	-7	-10.4	49	108.16	$+72.8$
12318	2591	8	10.6	64	112.36	$+84.8$
12314	2588	4	7.6	16	57.76	$+30.4$
12305	2571	-5	-9.4	25	88.36	$+47.0$
12310	2582	0	1.6	0	2.56	0
Sum		0	0	154	369.20	$+235.0$
Sum/N		0	0	30.8	73.84	47.0

Computations

$$\bar{x} = 12310$$

$$\bar{y} = 2580.4$$

$$r = \frac{47}{\sqrt{30.8}\sqrt{73.84}}$$

$$= 0.986$$

To use this method, we must begin by computing $\bar{x}$ and $\bar{y}$, which in this case are 12310.0 and 2580.4. We then subtract these means from each value of x and y in the table, and proceed as shown in Table 9-10-2. In general, this is slower than the procedure demonstrated in Table 9-10-1.

PROBLEMS

1. Write a mathematical proof of equation 9-10-1. (Hint: Show that it is equivalent to equation 9-6-2.)

2. The following table shows the barometric pressure in inches on five occasions, and the rainfall in inches during the subsequent 24 hours:

Pressure	Rainfall
30.1	0.00
28.2	0.74
29.9	0.31
29.1	0.00
28.1	0.52

Compute the coefficient of correlation between these two variables. (Hint: Use equation 9-10-1 with $x_0 = 29$ and $y_0 = 0.3$. Note that some of the quantities involved will be negative.)

3. Find the coefficient of determination and the coefficient of alienation for the above problem.

4. Write the regression equation for predicting the rainfall which will follow a given barometer reading.

5. If the barometer reading is 28.0 inches, what rainfall should be expected during the following 24 hours?

6. What is the probability that the actual rainfall will exceed 1 inch?

7. Find the coefficient of correlation between the voltages and amperages given in Table 1-2-1. (Use equation 9-10-1 with a suitable choice of x_0 and y_0.)

11. PROCEDURE FOR GROUPED DATA*

If the number of pairs of values of x and y is very large, a great saving of time may be effected by forming a frequency tabulation of the data and using suitably modified procedures. The frequency tabulation is formed in the same way as in the case of a single variable, except that we now require a class for each *pair* of values of x and y. The tabulation is best performed by means of a two-dimensional array of cells, in which each column contains a class in x, and each row a class in y. The details of the procedure are best made clear by an example. Table 9-11-1 shows the

TABLE 9-11-1. Scores of Twenty-Eight Students on Two Examinations

x	y	x	y	x	y	x	y
41	32	40	32	71	66	36	31
62	54	27	21	46	32	46	42
43	39	64	59	56	48	44	41
42	34	56	55	57	50	56	51
57	53	37	21	68	64	61	55
71	66	22	15	32	18	51	34
60	52	38	28	59	57	44	40

scores made by twenty-eight students in 15 minutes and in 12 minutes on the same test. To form a frequency tabulation of these data, we must first choose a set of limits for x and another for y. For convenience of tabulation, we choose 10 for the interval in both cases, and construct a tally sheet as shown in Table 9-11-2.

---

*Articles 11 and 12 are rather lengthy explanations of practical procedures for finding r, which do not contribute to the development of the *theory* of statistics. If you prefer to postpone these two articles until you have a need for the techniques, you can now proceed directly to Article 13 without loss of continuity.

TABLE 9-11-2.   Tally Sheet for Student Scores

Limits in y / y \\ Limits in x / x		20–29 24.5	30–39 34.5	40–49 44.5	50–59 54.5	60–69 64.5	70–79 74.5
10–19	14.5							
20–29	24.5	|	||				
30–39	34.5		|	⫴⫴	|		
40–49	44.5			|||	|		
50–59	54.5				⫴⫴	||||	
60–69	64.5					|	||

We now assign a value of u to each class in x, letting $u = 0$ for the class of largest frequency, and assigning the numbers -1, -2, etc., to the successive classes of smaller x, and $+1$, $+2$, etc., to those of larger x, exactly as we did in Chapter 4 in finding the mean and standard deviation. The present situation is different, however, in that we now have another variable, y, which must also be treated in the same way. We assign the letter v to the corresponding numbers for the y classes as shown in Table 9-11-3. In order to obtain the greatest possible advantage from

TABLE 9-11-3.   Assignment of u and v

x / y	24.5	34.5	44.5	54.5	64.5	74.5	v
14.5	1	1					-2
24.5	1	2					-1
34.5		1	5	1			0
44.5			3	1			1
54.5				5	4		2
64.5					1	2	3
u	-2	-1	0	1	2	3	

the simplicity of the new variables u and v, we must now express the coefficient of correlation in terms of the new variables instead of the old ones. The relationship between u and x, from 4-5-2, is $x = x_0 + C_x u$, where we have added a subscript to the class interval in x in order to distinguish it from the class interval in y. The value of $\bar{x}$ is $x_0 + C_x \bar{u}$, from equation 4-5-4, and $x - \bar{x}$ is therefore equal to $C_x(u - \bar{u})$. Similarly, $y - \bar{y}$ is equal to $C_y(v - \bar{v})$, where C_y is the class interval in y. If we substitute these in the standard equation for r (9-6-2), we have

$$r = \frac{\overline{C_x(u - \bar{u})C_y(v - \bar{v})}}{C_x \sigma_u C_y \sigma_v}$$

where we have used the fact that $\sigma_x = C_x \sigma_u$ from equation 4-5-7. If we multiply out the parentheses, simplify, and cancel the C's, this becomes

$$r = \frac{\overline{uv} - \overline{u\bar{v}} - \overline{\bar{u}v} + \bar{u}\bar{v}}{\sigma_u \sigma_v}$$

With the aid of equation 3-10-4 we see that the last three terms in the numerator are alike and can be combined, giving us

$$r = \frac{\overline{uv} - \bar{u}\bar{v}}{\sigma_u \sigma_v} \tag{9-11-1}$$

This tells us that the equation for the coefficient of correlation has exactly the same form when we use the new units, u and v, as it had when we used the old ones, x and y. We can therefore complete the problem of finding r without making any further use of x_0, y_0, C_x, or C_y.

The student can work out his own procedure for computing $\overline{uv}$, $\bar{u}$, $\bar{v}$, σ_u, and σ_v in any given problem. There are several standard procedures for carrying out the computations rapidly, of which two will be described here.

FIRST METHOD

This method should be used if most of the cells in the frequency tabulation are empty, as in the problem being used here for illustration. If there are more than about fifteen occupied cells, then the second method is usually faster.

The first method is illustrated in Table 9-11-4. The specific steps are as follows.

1. Make up a computing form like that shown in Figure 9-11-4, and enter the frequencies in the appropriate cells.

2. Add the frequencies across each row and enter the result under column f at the right. Similarly, add the frequencies in each column and enter the result opposite f at the bottom.

3. Assign a value of u to each class in x, and a value of v to each class in y. It is usually best to let u and v equal zero for the classes with the

largest frequencies. The negative values of u must be assigned to the smaller values of x, and similarly for v.

TABLE 9-11-4. First Method for Grouped Data

x \ y	24.5	34.5	44.5	54.5	64.5	74.5	v	f	vf	v^2f
14.5	1_4	1_2					-2	2	-4	8
24.5	1_2	2_1					-1	3	-3	3
34.5		1_0	5_0	1_0			0	7	0	0
44.5			3_0	1_1			1	4	4	4
54.5				5_2	4_4		2	9	18	36
64.5					1_6	2_9	3	3	9	27
u	-2	-1	0	1	2	3	Σ	28	24	78
f	2	4	8	7	5	2	28	Mean	$0.857 = \bar{v}$	$2.79 = \overline{v^2}$
uf	-4	-4	0	7	10	6	15	$0.536 = \bar{u}$		
u^2f	8	4	0	7	20	18	57	$2.04 = \overline{u^2}$		

$$\sigma_v = \sqrt{2.79 - (0.857)^2} = 1.43 \qquad \sigma_u = \sqrt{2.04 - (0.536)^2} = 1.32$$

$$\Sigma uv = 61 \qquad \overline{uv} = 2.18$$

$$r = \frac{2.18 - (0.536)(0.857)}{(1.32)(1.43)} = +0.91$$

4. Multiply each value in the f column by v and enter the result in the vf column.

5. Multiply each of these values again by v and enter the result in the v^2f column.

6. Sum the f, vf, and v^2f columns and enter the result opposite Σ.

7. Divide the last two sums by N to obtain $\bar{v}$ and $\overline{v^2}$. In the example, we divide 24 by 28 to obtain 0.857, which is $\bar{v}$, and we divide 78 by 28 to obtain 2.79, which is $\overline{v^2}$.

8. Compute σ_v from the equation $\sigma_v = \sqrt{\overline{v^2} - \bar{v}^2}$. In the example, σ_v is 1.43.

9. Similarly, compute the values of uf and u^2f and enter them in the rows at the bottom of the table; sum these rows and divide by N to obtain $\bar{u}$ and $\overline{u^2}$; and then compute σ_u. In our example, $\bar{u}$ is 0.536, $\overline{u^2}$ is 2.04, and σ_u is 1.32.

10. Compute the value of uv for each cell and write it in the corner of the cell. Note that these will be negative when u and v are of opposite sign. In our example, for the upper left-hand cell u is -2 and v is -2, so that uv is 4, which we write in the corner of the cell.

11. Multiply the frequency of each cell by the value of uv for that cell and add the results for all cells. In our example, the products are, reading from left to right across each row, 1×4, 1×2, 1×2, 2×1, 1×0, 5×0, 1×0, 3×0, 1×1, 5×2, 4×4, 1×6, and 2×9. The sum of all these products is 61.

12. Divide this sum by N to obtain $\overline{uv}$. In our example, $\overline{uv}$ is 61/28 or 2.18.

13. Substitute $\overline{uv}$, $\bar{u}$, $\bar{v}$, σ_u, and σ_v in equation 9-11-1. The computation is shown at the bottom of the table. The final result is

$$r = +0.91$$

SECOND METHOD

This method should be used if the number of cells containing entries is very large. To illustrate this method, we will use a set of data for which most of the cells contain entries. Table 9-11-5, containing a tabulation of the score made by students on an entrance examination and their subsequent grade averages, is of this sort. The procedure for computing r by this method is shown in full in the table, and the specific steps are described below.

1. Make up a computing form like the one in Table 9-11-5, allowing enough cells for the number of classes you have chosen. Enter the frequency in each cell.

2. Assign values of u and v, and compute the entries in the f, vf, and v^2f columns in the same way as for the First Method.

3. Multiply each frequency in the first row of the table by the corresponding value of u, and add the results for the row. Write the sum in the Σuf column. Repeat this operation for each of the remaining rows. Example: The frequencies in the first row are 2, 5, 1, and 1. The corresponding values of u are -2, -1, 1, and 3. The products of these in pairs are -4, -5, 1, and 3. The sum of these products is -5, which we write in the Σuf column.

4. Multiply each of these entries in the Σuf column by the corresponding value of v for that row, and write the result in the $v \Sigma uf$ column. Example: The first Σuf is -5, and the corresponding v is -2. We write their product, 10, in the $v \Sigma uf$ column.

5. Add the f, vf, v^2f, Σuf, and $v\Sigma uf$ columns, and write the sums at the bottoms of the columns.

6. Compute the entries in the f, uf, and u^2f rows at the bottom of the table.

TABLE 9-11-5.   Second Method for Grouped Data

x \ y	158	161	164	167	170	173	v	f	vf	v^2f	Σuf	$v\Sigma uf$
65	2	5		1		1	-2	9	-18	36	-5	10
70	5	41	34	5			-1	85	-85	85	-46	46
75	4	46	81	46	5	1	0	183	0	0	5	0
80		22	84	49	18	1	1	174	174	174	66	66
85	1		23	23	7	2	2	56	112	224	41	82
90		3	4	8	4		3	19	57	171	13	39
95			1	1		1	4	3	12	48	4	16
u	-2	-1	0	1	2	3	Σ	529	252	738	78	259
f	12	117	227	133	34	6	529					
uf	-24	-117	0	133	68	18	78					
u^2f	48	117	0	133	136	54	488					
Σvf	-7	-20	112	116	44	7	252					
$u\Sigma vf$	14	20	0	116	88	21	259					

Checks

$$\bar{v} = 252/529 = 0.476 \qquad \overline{v^2} = 738/529 = 1.395$$

$$\bar{u} = 78/529 = 0.147 \qquad \overline{u^2} = 488/529 = 0.922$$

$$\overline{uv} = 259/529 = 0.490$$

$$\sigma_u = \sqrt{0.922 - (0.147)^2} = 0.949$$

$$\sigma_v = \sqrt{1.395 - (0.476)^2} = 1.081$$

$$r = \frac{0.490 - (0.147)(0.476)}{(0.949)(1.081)} = 0.409$$

7. Multiply each frequency in the first column by its corresponding v, and add the results. Write the sum at the bottom of the column opposite Σvf. Repeat for each of the other columns. Example: For the first column we have -2 times 2, plus -1 times 5, plus 0 times 4, plus 2 times 1. The total of these is -7, which we enter in the Σvf row.

8. Multiply each value of Σvf by the corresponding value of u. Example: In the first column, Σvf is -7 and u is -2; their product is 14, which we enter in the $u\Sigma vf$ row.

9. Add each of the rows f, uf, u^2f, Σvf, and $u \Sigma vf$, and write the sum at the right end of each row. A valuable check on the computations is provided by the fact that N, Σu, Σv, and Σuv are each found in two ways in this method.

10. Divide all these sums and all the sums of the vertical columns by N. These ratios give us the values of $\bar{u}$, $\bar{v}$, $\overline{u^2}$, $\overline{v^2}$, and $\overline{uv}$, as shown at the bottom of the table.

11. Compute σ_u from equation 4-5-6:

$$\sigma_u = \sqrt{\overline{u^2} - \bar{u}^2}$$

Similarly, compute σ_v. In the example we obtain 0.949 and 1.081 for these two quantities.

12. Substitute $\overline{uv}$, $\bar{u}$, $\bar{v}$, σ_u, and σ_v in equation 9-11-1:

$$r = \frac{\overline{uv} - \bar{u}\bar{v}}{\sigma_u \sigma_v}$$

The computation is shown at the bottom of the table. The final result is

$$r = +0.409$$

PROBLEMS*

The following problems should be solved with the data for twenty-five students given in Table 1-4-4. It is suggested that you use the following class limits, in order to obtain an exact check with the answers given in the back of the book: column 1, 15 to 17, 18 to 21, etc; columns 2 and 3, 40 to 49, 50 to 59, etc; column 4, 140 to 159, 160 to 179, etc.

1. Compute the coefficient of correlation between the entrance test score and the subsequent mathematics grade.

2. Compute the coefficient of correlation between the entrance test score and the subsequent language grade.

3. Compute the coefficient of correlation between the experimental test score and the subsequent mathematics grade.

4. Compute the coefficient of correlation between the experimental test score and the subsequent language grade.

5. With the above results, answer all parts of Question X, Chapter 1, Article 4.

6. Compute the coefficient of correlation between the two test scores.

7. Compute the coefficient of correlation for any of the data which you gathered for Problem 2 of Article 1.

---

*Retain your results of these computations for future use.

12. REGRESSION EQUATIONS FOR GROUPED DATA

When either of the above procedures has been used to obtain r, and the investigator wishes to obtain the regression equations and the standard error of estimate as well, the operational procedure is continued from this point by the methods described in Articles 7 and 8. For the purpose of presenting a unified illustration, we will carry the example in Article 11 through the remaining necessary steps, numbering them serially to continue the sequence of steps in the preceding paragraph.

13. Compute $\bar{x}$ and $\bar{y}$ from equations 4-5-4:

$$\bar{x} = x_0 + C_x \bar{u} = 164 + 3(0.147) = 164.44$$

$$\bar{y} = y_0 + C_y \bar{v} = 75 + 5(0.476) = 77.38$$

14. Compute σ_x and σ_y from 4-5-7:

$$\sigma_x = C_x \sigma_u = 3(0.949) = 2.85$$

$$\sigma_y = C_y \sigma_v = 5(1.081) = 5.40$$

15. Write the regression equation (9-7-1):

$$y_p = 77.38 + \frac{5.40}{2.85}(0.409)(x - 164.44)$$

or, simplifying,

$$y_p = 0.77x - 50.1$$

16. Compute S_y from 9-9-1:

$$S_y = \sigma_y \sqrt{1 - r^2} = 5.40\sqrt{1 - (0.409)^2} = 4.93$$

PROBLEMS

1. Compute r for the following data, using the Second Method of Article 11:

Husband's Age

	15 to 24	25 to 34	35 to 44	45 to 54	55 to 64	65 to 74	75 to 84	85 to 94
Wife's Age								
15 to 24	15	12	2					
25 to 34		38	26	8	2		2	
35 to 44		2	31	30	5	1		
45 to 54	1		9	40	24	14	2	
55 to 64			1	8	19	17	2	1
65 to 74				2	1	21	6	
75 to 84							8	1
85 to 94								2

2. Write the regression equation for estimating the wife's age when the husband's age is known.

3. Find the standard error of estimate.

4. Write the regression equation for estimating the husband's age if the wife's age is known.

5. Estimate the wife's age if it is known only that the husband's age is 53.

6. Compute the probability that in Problem 5 the wife is under 30.

13.   GRAPHICAL METHOD

Many statisticians prefer to work with graphical procedures when speed is desirable and high accuracy is not necessary. Others prefer to begin with a graphical procedure even when an exact computation is planned as well, in order to verify the assumption that a straight-line equation is suitable for the data, and to have a check upon the subsequent computations. From the point of view of the student, the method is well worth studying in any case, since it provides additional insight into the nature of the regression equations and the coefficient of correlation.

As a practical procedure, the method is particularly time-saving when only the regression equations and the coefficient of correlation are desired and is less so when the standard error of estimate is also wanted.

In order to be able to compare the graphical results with those obtained by the exact procedures, let us take as an example the problem in Table 9-11-5, which we have already worked by the other method. The new procedure is shown in Table 9-13-1. We begin by computing the average value of x for each row and the average value of y for each column. Let us denote the row averages of x by $\bar{x}_r$ and the column averages of y by $\bar{y}_c$. These are computed in any of the customary ways. For example, we can use the formula $\bar{x} = \Sigma fx/N$, and obtain, for the $\bar{x}_r$ of the first row,

$$\bar{x}_r = \frac{1}{9} (2 \times 158 + 5 \times 161 + 1 \times 167 + 1 \times 173) = 162.3$$

The results of this computation are shown in the right-hand column of Table 9-13-1.

Now suppose that an incoming student scores 173 on his entrance examination and we wish to predict the grade average which he will earn if he remains in school. We see from our table that the 6 students who made this score had a subsequent grade average of 80.8, and, if we had no other data, this would be the best possible estimate for the future grade average of the new student. The chief weakness of this prediction is that it is based upon the records of only six students, and any conclusion based upon so few cases is very vulnerable to accidents of random selection.

This weakness can be avoided if we base the prediction also upon the adjacent columns. To do this, we plot the values of $\bar{y}_c$ against the corresponding values of x and draw a smooth curve which fits all points as well

TABLE 9-13-1.   Computations for Graphical Procedure

Entrance Exam Score

y \ x	158	161	164	167	170	173	f	$\bar{x}_r$
65	2	5		1		1	9	162.3
70	5	41	34	5			85	162.4
75	4	46	81	46	5	1	183	164.1
80		22	84	49	18	1	174	165.1
85	1		23	23	7	2	56	166.2
90		3	4	8	4		19	166.1
95			1	1		1	3	168.0
f	12	117	227	133	34	6		
$\bar{y}_c$	72.1	74.1	77.5	79.4	81.5	80.8		

(Subsequent Grade Average — left axis label for y)

as possible. We then read off the value of $\bar{y}_c$ from this curve for the given value of x, and thus obtain a "smoothed" prediction which is not so much affected by accidental groups of unusual grades. If the points, when plotted, do not exhibit enough curvature for the investigator to be certain that it exists, then a straight line should be drawn instead of a curve, and, in what follows, we will assume that a straight line has been drawn.

In Figure 9-13-1, the values of $\bar{y}_c$ are plotted against the corresponding values of x, and the resulting points have been indicated by large dots. (The other curve, whose points are indicated by crosses, does not concern us here and will be discussed later.) A line has been fitted to the dots by visual inspection. In fitting this line, the author has attempted to give more weight to the middle four points, since these depend upon more cases.

If we use this line to predict the grade average of the new student whose entrance score was 173, we find that y at this point is 83.0, which is therefore the best prediction we can make. If another entering student makes a score of 168, his predicted grade average will be 79.8. In short, this line is the line relating any value of x to the corresponding predicted value of y and is therefore identical in principle with *the line of regression of y on x,* described in Article 7. In practice the graphical line will probably not coincide exactly with the computed line, but any difference between them

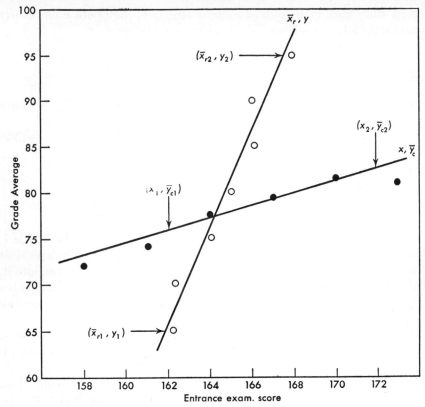

Figure 9-13-1. The Regression Lines.

will be small if the line has been properly drawn. In any case the slope of the graphical line provides a good approximation to the slope of the theoretical line. The equation of the theoretical line is, from 9-7-5,

$$y_p = \bar{y} + b_{yx}(x - \bar{x})$$

and this equation must then be the equation of the graphical line, or nearly so. We can therefore write,

$$\bar{y}_c = \bar{y} + b_{yx}(x - \bar{x}) \tag{9-13-1}$$

Our objective is to obtain from the graph a measurement of the quantity b_{yx}. For this purpose, let us mark any two points on the line and label their coordinates x_1 and $(\bar{y}_c)_1$, and x_2 and $(\bar{y}_c)_2$, respectively. These two points may be anywhere on the line, but it is somewhat more convenient to select points which are not too close together and which differ by a simple number in their x coordinates. The two points selected in the illustrative problem are marked by arrows, and their coordinates are as follows: $x_1 = 162$; $(\bar{y}_c)_1 = 75.8$; $x_2 = 172$; $(\bar{y}_c)_2 = 82.5$.

Now since both of these points are on the line, they both must satisfy equation 9-13-1. In other words, it must be true that

$$(\bar{y}_c)_1 = \bar{y} + b_{yx}(x_1 - \bar{x})$$

and
$$(\bar{y}_c)_2 = \bar{y} + b_{yx}(x_2 - \bar{x})$$

If we subtract the first of these from the second and solve for b_{yx}, we have

$$b_{yx} = \frac{(\bar{y}_c)_2 - (\bar{y}_c)_1}{x_2 - x_1} \qquad (9\text{-}13\text{-}2)$$

or, for the two points selected in our example,

$$b_{yx} = \frac{82.5 - 75.8}{172 - 162} = 0.67$$

This number is the *coefficient of regression of y on x*, described in Article 7. It is a quantity which describes the line of regression, and it is independent of the choice of the two points whose coordinates are used to compute it. If the reader is not experienced in computing, he should note that either the numerator or the denominator, or both, may turn out to be negative and that errors in sign are easy to make in this computation.

Now let us consider the inverse problem. If we know the value of y, how can we best estimate the corresponding value of x? For example, if a given student did not take the entrance examination, but made a subsequent grade average of 83.0, what is the best estimate of the score which he would have made on the entrance examination if he had taken it? The role of the two variables is now reversed, and we need an *average* value of x for all the students who subsequently earned a grade of y; in other words, we need a line obtained by plotting $\bar{x}_r$ against y. Such a graph is shown in Figure 9-13-1, where the points are indicated by crosses to distinguish them from the points of the previously discussed line. A straight line (dotted) has been drawn in by visual inspection and labelled $\bar{x}_r$, y. The desired estimate is now made by finding the point on this line where y equals 83.0, and reading the corresponding value of x. This value is 165.3, which is consequently the best possible estimate of the score which the student would have made on the entrance examination.

Since the dotted line shows the relation between each value of y and the best estimate of the corresponding value of x, it is identical in principle with the line of regression of x on y discussed in Article 7. Any two points on the dotted line must then satisfy equation 9-7-6. If we select two such points and call their coordinates $(\bar{x}_r)_1$, y_1, $(\bar{x}_r)_2$, and y_2, we can therefore write

$$(\bar{x}_r)_1 = \bar{x} - b_{xy}(y_1 - \bar{y})$$

and
$$(\bar{x}_r)_2 = \bar{x} - b_{xy}(y_2 - \bar{y})$$

and, proceeding as before,

$$b_{xy} = \frac{(\bar{x}_r)_2 - (\bar{x}_r)_1}{y_2 - y_1} \qquad (9\text{-}13\text{-}3)$$

Two such points have been selected in Figure 9-13-1 and marked with arrows. Their coordinates are as follows: $(\bar{x}_r)_1 = 161.9$, $y_1 = 65.0$, $(\bar{x}_r)_2 = 167.6$, and $y_2 = 95.0$. When these values are inserted in equation 9-13-3, we have

$$b_{xy} = \frac{167.6 - 161.9}{95.0 - 65.0} = 0.19$$

This quantity is the *coefficient of regression of x on y*, described in Article 7.

The two lines in the diagram can be used for estimating or predicting, either directly in the graphical form or in the form of the regression equations. There remains the objective of finding the coefficient of correlation between x and y. An inspection of equations 9-7-3 and 9-7-4 shows that this objective can be readily achieved by multiplying the two regression coefficients together and finding the square root of the results:

$$\sqrt{b_{yx} b_{xy}} = \sqrt{r \frac{\sigma_y}{\sigma_x} r \frac{\sigma_x}{\sigma_y}} = \sqrt{r^2} = r \qquad (9\text{-}13\text{-}4)$$

In our example,

$$r = \sqrt{(0.67)(0.19)} = 0.36$$

This is to be compared with the value of 0.409 obtained by the exact method described in Article 11. The agreement is only fair, and illustrates the limitations of the graphical procedure. In general, the method will work well if the points fall nearly upon a straight line and are of nearly equal weight and will work less well if there is a large scatter of the plotted points or if they are of markedly unequal weight.

The graphical procedure has the advantage that the degree of correlation becomes apparent in a general way as soon as the two sets of points are plotted. If the correlation is high, the two lines will nearly coincide, while if it is low, one line will be nearly vertical and the other nearly horizontal. To secure best results from the graphical procedure, the following points should be kept in mind:

1. In view of the principle of least squares, one large deviation is more to be avoided than two deviations each half as large. It is wrong to secure a perfect fit with almost all the points at the expense of a large misfit for the remaining one or two points.

2. Not all the points have the same weight, since some of them depend upon many cases and others upon only a few. Try to secure the best fit with the points which represent most data.

3. If the points exhibit an excessive and confusing scatter, it is sometimes advantageous to replace two points by one master point halfway

between them (or nearer one than the other if the two are of unequal weights), and thus to reduce the number of points to be visualized. Only points arising from *adjacent* columns or rows should be combined. This process of combination should be used with caution and should be carried only far enough to make it possible to visualize a good line of best fit.

4. Since the process depends upon a sort of visual balancing of a number of points on your diagram, it is well to make these points conspicuous. They should be sufficiently large and black so that they stand out above any writing or labeling on the diagram, and so that the entire pattern can be taken in at a single glance.

PROBLEMS

1. Using the graphical procedure, find the equations of the regression lines for the data in Problem 1 of Article 12. Compute from the slopes of these lines the coefficient of correlation. Compare your graphical results with the exact results which you obtained in Article 11.

14. CORRELATION BY RANKS

In many cases an investigator finds himself dealing with data of a non-quantitative sort, in which the items are arranged in order of size or quality, although the exact size or quality of each is unknown or even unmeasurable. A voter may be fully confident, for example, that he likes Candidate A better than Candidate B, and Candidate C better than either. Or, again, it may be clear from the record that F is a better fighter than G, who in turn is a better fighter than H. To try to measure the exact *amount* of the voter's liking for C, or to estimate the *quantity* of F's fighting ability, would be difficult or absurd. The methods of correlation can however be readily adapted to such cases in spite of the non-numerical nature of the data, and, in fact, a considerable simplification of procedure is possible.

To illustrate the procedure, let us use the following data. Ten men compete in elimination tournaments in both golf and tennis, so that they can be listed in order of ability in each sport:

Player	Rank in Tennis (m)	Rank in Golf (n)
Jones	4	$2\frac{1}{2}$
Brubaker	1	$2\frac{1}{2}$
Connor	10	7
Harrison	7	9
Linteau	9	10
Grady	2	1
Orsini	3	4
Deutsch	8	5
Rodriguez	6	7
Swenson	5	7

Brubaker won the tennis championship and so has rank "one" in tennis; Grady came in second and so has rank 2, and so forth. In golf, Jones and Brubaker were tied for second place. If one had beaten the other, they would have had ranks 2 and 3, so, since they were tied, we assign each of them the average of these two ranks, or $2\frac{1}{2}$. In the same way, Connor, Rodriguez, and Swenson were involved in a three-way tie and would otherwise have had ranks 6, 7, and 8, so we assign each of them the average of these three numbers, or 7. Data of this sort are called *ranked* data.

In order to apply our equations to this problem, let us make the assumption that ability in tennis is divided in ten *equal* steps, that is, that Brubaker is just as much better than Grady as Grady is better than Orisini, and so on through the set of ten men. In other words, if x measures tennis ability, and m is a player's rank in tennis, we assume that $x = x_0 + mC_x$, where C_x is the difference in ability between successive ranks, and x_0 is a suitable starting point of measurement. This equation is purely formal, to be used only for the derivation of the formula for the coefficient of correlation for ranked data, and it is not necessary to assign a value to x_0 or to C_x. In the same way, if y is a measure of a player's ability in golf, and n is his rank, we assume that $y = y_0 + nC_y$. If we now average these values of x and y and form the deviations from the mean we will have

$$x - \bar{x} = C_x(m - \bar{m})$$

and

$$y - \bar{y} = C_y(n - \bar{n})$$

Let us now insert these values in 9-6-2:

$$r = \frac{\overline{C_x(m - \bar{m})C_y(n - \bar{n})}}{\sigma_x \sigma_y}$$

or, by the same procedure which we used in deriving 9-11-1,

$$r = \frac{\overline{mn} - \bar{m}\bar{n}}{\sigma_m \sigma_n} \tag{9-14-1}$$

This formula can be simplified if we introduce the *difference* between tennis rank and golf rank for each player. We observe that

$$\overline{(m - n)^2} = \overline{(m^2 - 2mn + n^2)} = \overline{m^2} - 2\overline{mn} + \overline{n^2} \tag{9-14-2}$$

or, solving for $\overline{mn}$,

$$\overline{mn} = \tfrac{1}{2}\overline{m^2} + \tfrac{1}{2}\overline{n^2} - \tfrac{1}{2}\overline{(m - n)^2}$$

If we substitute this in 9-14-1, we will have:

$$r = \frac{\tfrac{1}{2}\overline{m^2} + \tfrac{1}{2}\overline{n^2} - \tfrac{1}{2}\overline{(m - n)^2} - \bar{m}\bar{n}}{\sqrt{\overline{m^2} - \bar{m}^2}\sqrt{\overline{n^2} - \bar{n}^2}} \tag{9-14-3}$$

where we have also made the usual substitution (4-4-1) for σ_m and σ_n. We can simplify this by using equations 3-11-1 and 3-11-2:

$$\bar{m} = \bar{n} = \frac{N+1}{2}$$

$$\overline{m^2} = \overline{n^2} = \frac{(N+1)(2N+1)}{6}$$

where N is the number of items in the ranked data. (In our example, $N = 10$.) Making these substitutions in 9-14-3 and simplifying the resulting expression, we have:

$$r = 1 - \frac{6\overline{(m-n)^2}}{N^2 - 1} \tag{9-14-4}$$

This is customarily written with $\overline{(m-n)^2}$ replaced by $\dfrac{\Sigma(m-n)^2}{N}$:

$$r = 1 - \frac{6\Sigma(m-n)^2}{N(N^2 - 1)} \tag{9-14-5}$$

which is the standard formula for correlation by ranks.

For our example the necessary computations are shown in Table 9-14-1,

TABLE 9-14-1.   Correlation by Ranks

m	n	$\lvert m-n \rvert$	$(m-n)^2$
4	$2\frac{1}{2}$	$1\frac{1}{2}$	$2\frac{1}{4}$
1	$2\frac{1}{2}$	$1\frac{1}{2}$	$2\frac{1}{4}$
10	7	3	9
7	9	2	4
9	10	1	1
2	1	1	1
3	4	1	1
8	5	3	9
6	7	1	1
5	7	2	4
			$34\frac{1}{2}$

from which we find that $\Sigma(m-n)^2$ is $34\frac{1}{2}$. Inserting this in equation 9-14-5:

$$r = 1 - \frac{6(34.5)}{10(10^2 - 1)} = 0.791$$

This formula is so easy to use and so rapid in computation that it is sometimes used to secure an approximate value of r even for cases in which the values of x and y are accurately known. We will illustrate this by applying it to the data in Article 5 of this chapter. We assign a rank to each student in hours of study and examination grade, as shown in Table 9-14-2. We then find for r,

$$r = 1 - \frac{6(2.5)}{5(5^2 - 1)} = 0.875$$

This is to be compared to the value 0.845 obtained by more exact means in Article 5. The agreement is very close, because the actual steps in x

TABLE 9-14-2. Comparison with Exact Method

Name	x	y	m	n	$\lvert m - n \rvert$	$(m - n)^2$
Jackson	5	26	1	1	0	0
Petoskey	4	17	2	$2\frac{1}{2}$	$\frac{1}{2}$	$\frac{1}{4}$
Goldberg	3	17	3	$2\frac{1}{2}$	$\frac{1}{2}$	$\frac{1}{4}$
Bellini	2	11	4	5	1	1
Schwartz	1	14	5	4	1	1
						$2\frac{1}{2}$

are equal to each other, and those in y are nearly equal to each other, so that the assumptions made in deriving 9-14-5 are nearly fulfilled. In general we cannot expect such close agreement. If a precise value of r is needed, the methods of ranks should of course not be used.

PROBLEMS

1. The manager of an office believes that Mr. Bjorkman is his most valuable assistant, followed by Dimitroff, Siebert, Smart, Kendall, Barrett, and Turner, in that order. Bjorkman has been in the office for 14 years, Dimitroff 7 years, Kendall and Turner 5 years, Siebert 3 years, and Barrett and Smart 2 years. Using the method of correlation by ranks, find the coefficient of correlation between value and length of service.

2. Five friends, Allison, Daily, Johnson, Manchetti, and Wojicki, held a tournament in tennis and another tournament in chess, with the following results:

Chess					Tennis			
Game	Won	Tie	Lost		Game	Won	Tie	Lost
1	D		A		1	J		D
2	W		J		2	M		A
3		W, D			3	A		W
4		J, A			4	J		W
5	M		J		5		M, J	
6	D		J		6	M		W
7	D		M		7	W		D
8		A, M			8	A		D
9	W		M		9	J		A
10	W		A		10	M		D

Find the coefficient of correlation between ability in chess and ability in tennis. (Hint: Notice that Manchetti has higher rank than Allison in chess, even though they tied, because Manchetti defeated Johnson and Johnson tied Allison.)

15. COEFFICIENT OF CORRELATION FOR AN UNKNOWN UNIVERSE

In the material presented so far in this chapter, we have considered the coefficient of correlation to be a number describing the relationship between the set of x's and y's in our tables of data. As such it is an exact measure, and no question can arise as to how well it fits the data or as to its range of uncertainty. We are usually interested, however, not only in describing the data in hand, but in drawing conclusions about the universe from which the data came, and in this case we must consider the question of how well a value of r computed from a sample can be expected to describe the universe from which the sample was drawn. To discuss this question in detail would take us out of the field of elementary statistics, and we will content ourselves with two statements which we will present here without proof.

(1) The coefficient of correlation for the universe can be expected to be a little smaller than that of the sample. The reason for this can be seen if we recall that the coefficient of correlation measures the closeness of fit between the points on a scatter diagram and the line of best fit. Now if there are only a few points, we can adjust the line to fit some of their accidental deviations, and thus secure a misleadingly good fit. To carry the argument to its extreme, if we reduce the number of points to two we can always secure a perfect fit with a straight line, and thus the coefficient of correlation would always turn out to be exactly 1. To obtain the best possible estimate of the value which we would find for r if we could study the entire universe, we must use a formula which removes this effect of overestimating the correlation when the sample is small. The appropriate formula is

$$r_u = \sqrt{r^2 - \frac{1 - r^2}{N - 2}} \qquad (9\text{-}15\text{-}1)$$

where r_u is the best estimate of the coefficient of correlation of the universe, and N is the number of observations contained in the sample. If, for example, r is 0.5 and N is 10, then the best estimate of the coefficient of correlation in the universe from which the sample was taken is 0.4. Again, if r is 0.5 and N is 5, then r_u is zero. Thus we see that if we find a coefficient of correlation of 0.5 from a sample containing only five items, we cannot be certain that there is any correlation whatever in the universe; while if we obtain the same result from a sample of ten, we can assert that a correlation probably exists in the universe, but its most likely value is only 0.4, as compared to 0.5 for the sample.

Differences in the second decimal of the coefficient of correlation have little practical meaning, and if r_u differs from r by less than about 0.05 the correction is scarcely worth applying unless high precision is needed. With this arbitrary limit in mind, equation 9-15-1 tells us that no correction is necessary if r is 0.2 or greater and N is 50 or greater, or if r is 0.5 or greater and N is 20 or greater, or if r is 0.7 or greater and N is 10 or greater. Since most practical problems in correlation fall beyond these limits, it is generally reasonably safe to assume that the coefficient of correlation obtained from the sample is also representative of the universe, and formula 9-15-1 is necessary only if either r or N is very small, or if high precision is desired.

(2) If a number of samples are drawn from the same universe, the values of r obtained from them would differ a little from one sample to another. It can be shown theoretically that such a set of r's would form a population whose standard deviation is

$$\sigma_r = \frac{1 - r^2}{\sqrt{N - 1}} \qquad (9\text{-}15\text{-}2)$$

where the r on the right refers to the universe. If, for example, r is 0.5 and N is 101, then σ_r is 0.075. This tells a great deal about the reliability, or range of uncertainty, of r. We know, for instance, that the probability is 0.68 that our value of r is within 0.075 of the value of r which we would have obtained by averaging the r's from a number of samples of 101 each, which we can assume is very near to the r of the universe. This information can also be expressed in terms of the probable error of r, which is 0.6745 times 0.075, or 0.051. This tells us that the probability is 0.5 that our value of r is within 0.051 of the value of r for the universe, or, in standard notation,

$$r_u = 0.50 \pm 0.05$$

where we have ignored the small correction given by equation 9-15-1. The probability that r_u will lie between any given limits can then be found by means of the normal curve tables.

If N is small, or if r is large, then the sample r's will no longer form an approximately normal distribution, and the normal curve tables can no longer be used with equation 9-15-2 to compute confidence limits. Roughly speaking, if N is less than 50 or if r is larger than 0.6, then the skewness of the distribution of r's is so great as to make the normal curve tables unsuitable.

Equations 9-15-1 and 9-15-2 indicate that it is rarely worth while to compute a correlation coefficient with fewer than twenty-five variates, and it is advisable to have fifty or more to determine r with moderate accuracy, or several hundred to determine it with high accuracy.

PROBLEMS

1. Compute the best estimate of the coefficient of correlation for the universe, and its probable error, for the following cases:

(a) $r = 0.7$, $N = 10$; (b) $r = 0.7$, $N = 50$; (c) $r = 0.7$, $N = 500$;
(d) $r = 0.2$, $N = 25$; (e) $r = 0.2$, $N = 1000$; (f) $r = 0.9$, $N = 5$.

In which cases do you think that a real correlation undoubtedly exists in the universe?

2. Using your answer to Problem 3, Article 6, compute the coefficient of correlation which you would expect to find in a very large group of similar children.

3. Compute the probable error of your answer to the preceding problem.

4. Using your answer to Problem 1, Article 11, compute the coefficient of correlation which you would expect to find in the universe. Compute also the probable error of your answer.

5. Repeat Problem 4 above, this time using your answer to Problem 1, Article 12.

6. Compute the standard deviation of a value of r obtained from a sample of five items from Table 10-5-1, using the fact that the value of r for this table is 0.83. Test your result by choosing ten random samples of five each, computing the value of r for each sample, and then computing the standard deviation of the resulting ten values of r. If you can divide the work with other students, repeat this test with samples of other sizes.

16. SUMMARY

The procedures described in this chapter have three objectives: (a) To measure the correlation between two variables, (b) to find an equation for predicting the value of one variable when the other is known, and (c) to find the range of uncertainty of such a prediction. These three objectives are fulfilled as follows.

(a) The correlation is measured by the *coefficient of correlation*, r, which ranges from zero when the variables are independent to one when they are totally dependent and which is positive or negative depending upon whether y increases or decreases with increasing x.

(b) The task of predicting one variable from known values of the other is accomplished by means of a pair of *regression* or *prediction* equations, and the subscript "p" is used to indicate which variable is being predicted from the other.

(c) The uncertainty of prediction is measured by the *standard error of estimate*, S_y, which is the standard deviation of the errors which the equation makes in predicting the values of y in the original data, and which is therefore assumed to be the standard deviation of the errors which will occur in using the equation to predict values of y corresponding to new values of x.

CHOICE OF PROCEDURES

Three main procedures will be described, with subdivisions to be noted later. The exact procedure is the procedure which should be used in almost all practical problems, while the other two procedures are specialized methods for occasional use. The graphical procedure is to be used if: (a) approximate results are sufficient for the needs of the problem and (b) the investigator wishes to compute only r and the regression equation and does not wish to find S_y . Some investigators carry out the graphical procedure as well as the exact procedure, in order to have a check upon their results. The procedure for ranked data is used for data which is non-quantitative, but which can be arranged in an order of quality or size. The procedure is also used occasionally as a quick approximate method for finding r for quantitative data.

EXACT PROCEDURE

I. Plot the data, or, if it is extensive, plot part of it. This step is not rigidly necessary, but is recommended as a check upon the validity of the assumption that the relationship between the two variables can be described by a linear equation. If there is conspicuous curvature of the trend of the plotted points, then the methods of this chapter are not applicable, and Part III of the summary at the end of Chapter 8 should be used instead.

II. Compute r by whichever of the following procedures is applicable:

A. If a slide rule is to be used, and there are fewer than about twenty-five variates, then use one of the following procedures:

(1) If the variates are small numbers, use equation 9-6-1:

$$r = \frac{\overline{xy} - \bar{x}\,\bar{y}}{\sigma_x \sigma_y}$$

The procedure is demonstrated in Table 9-6-1.

(2) If the variates are large numbers with a moderate spread, subtract a fixed number x_0 from each value of x and a fixed number y_0 from each value of y, to reduce them to manageable size. Compute r from equation 9-10-1,

$$r = \frac{\overline{(x - x_0)(y - y_0)} - \overline{(x - x_0)}\ \overline{(y - y_0)}}{\sigma_x \sigma_y}$$

in which it is most convenient to compute σ_x and σ_y from equation 4-4-3. The procedure is demonstrated in Table 9-10-1. (An alternative procedure, which is occasionally faster if the means are whole numbers, is demonstrated in Table 9-10-2).

B. If a computing machine is to be used, and there are fewer than about one hundred variates, then use either method 1 or 2 in section A. Note that it is not necessary to record the individual values of xy, x^2 , and y^2 , because these can be accumulated in the machine as they are computed.

C. If the data are too numerous for the above methods (more than about twenty-five if a slide rule is to be used; more than about one hundred if a computing machine is to be used), then form a double frequency tabulation as shown in Table 9-11-2.   Proceed as follows:

1. If most of the cells are empty, as they are for example in Table 9-11-3, then carry out the procedure which is shown in Table 9-11-4 and which is described as the First Method in Article 11.

2. If most of the cells are filled, as they are for example in Table 9-11-5, then carry out the procedure which is shown in that table and which is described as the Second Method in Article 11.

III. The regression equation is obtained by inserting the proper values into equation 9-7-1,

$$y_p = \bar{y} + \frac{\sigma_y}{\sigma_x} r(x - \bar{x})$$

or, if x is to be estimated or predicted from y, into equation 9-7-2,

$$x_p = \bar{x} + \frac{\sigma_x}{\sigma_y} r(y - \bar{y})$$

IV. The standard error of estimate is now computed from equation 9-9-1,

$$S_y = \sigma_y \sqrt{1 - r^2}$$

This is the standard deviation of the errors to be expected in any predictions which we obtain from the regression equation.

GRAPHICAL PROCEDURE

I. Form a double frequency tabulation as shown in Table 9-11-2.

II. Compute x-average for each row and label it $\bar{x}_r$; compute y-average for each column and label it $\bar{y}_c$, as shown in Table 9-13-1.

III. Plot each value of x against the corresponding value of $\bar{y}_c$ and draw a line of best fit by visual inspection, as shown in Figure 9-13-1.   Using a different symbol, plot each value of y against the corresponding value of $\bar{x}_r$ and draw a line of best fit.   Before drawing these lines, review the suggestions at the end of Article 13.

IV. Select two points on each line and read their coordinates.   Then compute b_{yx} and b_{xy} from equations 9-13-2 and 9-13-3,

$$b_{yx} = \frac{(\bar{y}_c)_2 - (\bar{y}_c)_1}{x_2 - x_1}$$

$$b_{xy} = \frac{(\bar{x}_r)_2 - (\bar{x}_r)_1}{y_2 - y_1}$$

V. Compute r from equation 9-13-4,

$$r = \sqrt{b_{yx} b_{xy}}$$

The value of r so obtained can be checked roughly from the relative position of the two lines of regression on the graph.   If the lines nearly coincide, then r is very large, while if the lines are nearly at right angles to each other, then r is very small.

VI. To predict y for a given value of x, either of two procedures can be followed:

A. Find the value of x on the graph and read the value of $\bar{y}_c$ from the proper line. The value of $\bar{y}_c$ so obtained is the best predicted value of y. If an estimated or predicted value of x is needed for a known value of y, use the line relating y to $\bar{x}_r$.

B. If you prefer to work with a regression equation read the approximate value of $\bar{x}$ and $\bar{y}$ from the *intersection* of the two lines, and insert these and b_{yx} into equation 9-7-5,

$$y_p = \bar{y} + b_{yx}(x - \bar{x})$$

A similar equation for estimating or predicting x from known values of y can be obtained from the corresponding equation 9-7-6,

$$x_p = \bar{x} + b_{xy}(y - \bar{y})$$

This procedure is illustrated in Article 13.

PROCEDURE FOR RANKED DATA

I. Assign a rank, or order number, to each variable. Let m be the rank in x and n the rank in y. In other words, let $m = 1$ for the entry with the smallest x, $m = 2$ for the entry with the next smallest x, and so forth. If several entries are tied, assign to each of them the average of the ranks they would have had if they had just missed being tied. (For example, if two entries are tied for third place, they would otherwise have had ranks 3 and 4, therefore assign both the rank of $3\frac{1}{2}$.)

II. Compute the coefficient of correlation from equation 9-14-5:

$$r = 1 - \frac{6\Sigma(m - n)^2}{N(N^2 - 1)}$$

An example is shown in Table 9-14-1.

INTERPRETATION

I. For a quantitative interpretation, r is less valuable than the coefficient of determination, D, which is equal to the square of r. The quantity D can be loosely described as the "percentage of relatedness," and the corresponding quantity $1 - D$ can be thought of as the "percentage of independence." More exactly, D is the fraction of the total variance which is predicted or explained by the relationship described by the regression equation, and $1 - D$ is the fraction of the total variance which the regression equation fails to predict or explain.

II. It is important to remember that a large coefficient of correlation does not mean that changes in x "cause" changes in y. It is equally likely

that y is the causative factor and x the resultant, or that both are result-
ants of other causative factors and have no direct effect upon each other.
It is also possible, particularly if r is small, that there is no causal relationship of any sort between x and y, but that accidents of selection of
data have produced the apparent relationship.

The use of coefficients of correlation in interpreting data is beset with
many pitfalls of logic, and the careless investigator can easily be trapped
into drawing unwarranted conclusions. The safest insurance is a thorough
knowledge of the field which you are investigating, and a habit of carrying
out a "common sense" analysis along with the statistical analysis. Some
specific suggestions in this direction will be discussed in Chapter 13.

III. When a prediction has been made, the standard error of estimate
can be used in any of several ways to express the uncertainty of the prediction:

(a) S_y is the standard deviation of the expected errors of prediction,
and the probability is therefore 0.68 that the true value of y will differ
from the predicted value by less than S_y.

(b) We can compute the probable error of the estimated value of y by
multiplying S_y by 0.6745. This can then be used with a plus or minus
sign with the standard scientific meaning. Thus:

$$y_p = 1807 \pm 43$$

means that the probable error of the estimated value is 43, and that the
probability that the true value lies between $1807 + 43$ and $1807 - 43$ is
one-half.

(c) The probability that the true value will lie within any given range
of values can be found as follows. Subtract each boundary of the range
from y_p; divide the results by S_y; find the resulting values in the t column
of the standard curve tables; read the two corresponding values in the
"area" column; and finally, subtract the smaller from the larger of these
two areas, or, if the two values of t differ in sign, add the two areas. This
procedure is illustrated in Article 8.

IV. The value of r obtained by the procedures outlined above is a
quantity which describes exactly the correlation existing in the data used
for the computations. It is not necessarily the best possible guess as to
the amount of correlation existing in the universe from which the data
were taken, and if we wish to make the best possible estimate of the correlation in the universe, a small correction is necessary. The larger the
sample, the more nearly the value of r will describe the universe, and the
following limits are suggested:

If r is 0.2 or greater and N is 50 or greater; or
if r is 0.5 or greater and N is 20 or greater; or
if r is 0.7 or greater and N is 10 or greater; then

no correction is necessary unless high accuracy (closer than 0.05) is desired in the estimate for the universe. If the values of r and N fall below these limits, then the value of r for the universe should be computed from equation 9-15-1,

$$r_u = \sqrt{r^2 - \frac{1 - r^2}{N - 2}}$$

V. The standard deviation of an estimated r for the universe is given by equation 9-15-2,

$$\sigma_r = \frac{1 - r^2}{\sqrt{N - 1}}$$

This can be used to compute confidence limits in the usual way if N is large, but if N is small the distribution of r's ceases to be approximately normal, and the normal curve tables are no longer appropriate for the computation of confidence limits.

CHAPTER
. 10 .
SAMPLING AND RELIABILITY

1. THE UNIVERSE AND THE SAMPLE

Sometimes a statistical problem is of such a nature that all the relevant data are available to the investigator. For example, if a statistician were studying the age distribution of the members of the present United States Senate, he could obtain the birth date of every man now in the Senate, and he could compute an arithmetic mean and a standard deviation which would be completely accurate for the group. No question could arise of whether the arithmetic mean and the standard deviation "represent" the group.

This situation is however an unusual one. In general it is not feasible to obtain data concerning all of the group about which you wish to draw conclusions, and in many cases it is entirely impossible to do so. If, for example, an investigator wishes to study the distribution of heights of American men, it would not be feasible to collect data concerning all the millions of American men now living. Furthermore, it would not be necessary. Instead a group of several hundred men would be chosen in as representative a way as possible, and the mean and standard deviation of this selected group, or *sample*, would be computed. The investigator would then make the assumption that the mean and standard deviation of the heights of all the men in America are the same as those of the sample, or are nearly enough so for his purposes.

Or let us suppose that an agricultural research worker wishes to study the advantages and disadvantages of raising a given variety of tomatoes in southeastern Ohio. He would undertake to find the average yield per acre and the standard deviation of this average yield, and he would collect all available records of crop sizes for this purpose. But it is very unlikely that he would be able to discover the yield per acre from every farmer who had ever raised this variety of tomatoes. He must, then, compute the mean and standard deviation from the data available, and assume that these are representative not only of his working data, but also of the data which were not available to him. Furthermore, even if he were able to collect data about all the tomatoes which had ever been raised in Ohio, this would not fulfil the purpose of his study. If his ultimate purpose is to make recommendations to farmers, then he must assume that his results are representative also of all tomatoes of this variety *which will be raised in the future* in southeastern Ohio. One part of his "universe" is therefore completely inaccessible to him.

Again, let us suppose that a company manufactures ammeters for automobile instrument panels and has an output of 7000 per day. The resistances of the ammeters would be nearly alike, but there are small variations from one to another, and it is desirable to study the distribution of these resistances. In this case the statistician is not limited by the availability of data—he could measure the resistance of all 7000 each day if he wished—but he would nevertheless select a sample containing a much smaller number solely for the purpose of saving time. The statistician here makes the assumption of "representativeness" of his own volition.

A slightly different situation arises if we suppose that the same company also manufactures fuses for electric circuits and requires a description of the distribution of the amperages at which the fuses "blow" or break. Such information is necessary in the marketing of the fuses, but each time a specific fuse is tested it is of course destroyed in the process and is not available for marketing. The statistician in this case has no choice; he is forced to test a sample and assume that his results are valid for the universe.

We have seen that in all such cases the statistician uses the term "sample" to describe the small group of items which are used in the study, and the term "universe" for the entire group of comparable items about which he wishes to draw conclusions. Sometimes it is difficult to decide just what the limits of the universe are, particularly if the statistician is working with data collected by other investigators for their own purposes. What is the universe, for example, corresponding to a table of heights and weights of the male members of the Senior class at Ohio University in 1950? Does the universe consist of all American men? All American male college students? Or all Ohio men? The answer to such questions is very difficult, and an unwise answer can invalidate many of the statistician's conclusions.

Another aspect of the problem arises when the statistician knows what his universe must be and wishes to select a sample which will represent it. Suppose that he wishes to know the average income of Ohio University male students. Can he use the members of a given fraternity for a sample? Obviously not, because there is a tendency for fraternities to select students with higher than average incomes. Can he obtain a representative sample by questioning students at random on the campus? Perhaps so, but it is conceivable that at the time of his census a number of students are working and that the students who are walking the campus are the non-employed ones, who represent a non-typical sample so far as income goes. The problem of securing a truly random sample is a very difficult one, filled with unexpected problems, and failure to secure a representative sample is one of the major sources of error in practical statistical investigations. A detailed discussion of this aspect of the problem will be postponed until Chapter 13, and in the present chapter it will be assumed that the universe is homogeneous and unambiguously defined and that the sample is free from systematic errors of selection.

In all cases we study the special properties of the sample and assume that the universe has the same or similar properties. This assumption introduces two specific questions:

A. Are there any systematic and predictable differences between the properties of the sample and properties of the universe? If we find that the standard deviation of a sample of twenty-five items is 2.7, does it follow that 2.7 is the best possible guess as to the standard deviation of the universe? If not, what corrections should we apply to obtain the most likely value or "best guess"?

B. When we have estimated the most likely value of any descriptive quantity for the universe, within what limits can we trust it to agree with the facts? If the mean breaking amperage of a sample of twenty fuses is 24.75 amperes and the standard deviation is 0.38 ampere, can we be reasonably sure that the mean of the entire output is between 24.50 and 25.00? Between 24.70 and 24.80? What is the specific probability that the true value will fall within each of these two ranges?

In a general way, the range of reliability is obvious from a common sense inspection of the problem. In B for instance, if a different set of twenty fuses had been chosen, it is highly unlikely that it would also have a mean breaking amperage of 24.75 and a standard deviation of 0.38. It would not be astonishing, for instance, if a second sample had a mean of 24.85, with a standard deviation of 0.45. If it were possible to sample the entire day's output, it would probably differ from both of these results. On the other hand, it would probably not differ from them by very much. If we have only the first sample, the most that we can say is that the mean of the day's output is probably very close to 24.75, or that it is equal to 24.75 plus or minus a possible small error, and we cannot make a more exact statement until we know something about the distribution of the possible values of this small error. One way to investigate this distribution experimentally is to select several other samples and observe the range between their means. If, for instance, we find that when five samples are selected and studied, the five means all agree within 0.50 ampere, then we could reasonably conclude that the mean of the universe will probably not differ from the sample means by more than this.

But there is a much better way to determine this range of uncertainty. It depends not upon experiment but upon theoretical laws, which will be derived in the following paragraphs. First, however, we must set up a specific method for describing this range of uncertainty in a quantitative manner.

2. STANDARD DEVIATION AS MEASURE OF RANGE OF UNCERTAINTY

The discerning reader will have noted that in the course of the preceding chapters the meaning of the standard deviation has undergone a change of emphasis. In Chapter 3 the standard deviation was introduced as a descriptive device, used for the purpose of condensing and summarizing the essential data contained in a frequency table, and it was defined as the square root of the average of the squares of the deviations from the arithmetic mean. In later chapters it was used to indicate the half-width of the region containing 68 per cent of the probability of occurrence of a variate chosen at random, in the same way that the probable error is used to indicate the half-width of the region containing 50 per cent of the probability of occurrence. In the illustrative problem in Article 9 of Chapter 9, for example, we computed the predicted score for a student, Don Poller, and found it to be 15.5, with a standard deviation of 2.7, or a probable error of 1.8. It is true that this standard deviation describes the distribution of errors of prediction for all students comparable to Mr. Poller, but we are not interested in all students, or indeed in any but Don Poller when we state this probable error. The standard deviation of 2.7 tells us that the probability is 0.68 that Mr. Poller will score between 12.8 and 18.2, and the probable error of 1.8 tells us that the probability is 0.50 that he will score between 13.7 and 17.3. The standard deviation has now become a device for stating our beliefs about the probability of occurrence of a given event, and we can use it in this sense whenever we have sufficient evidence about the probabilities to do so. The probable error is used in this sense somewhat more than the standard deviation, particularly by workers in the exact sciences. For instance, the mean distance from the earth to the sun is reported in astronomical publications as 93,005,000 miles ± 9000 miles. This means that, from an analysis of the results of all modern measurements of this distance, by any method, the investigators have concluded that the probability is 0.50 that the true distance to the sun lies somewhere between 92,996,000 miles and 93,014,000 miles. This meaning of the standard deviation and the probable error will be useful to us in this chapter for stating the range of reliability of any conclusions which we draw about a universe from a study of a sample.

3. TABLE FOR SAMPLING EXPERIMENTS

In the following paragraphs we will develop a set of formulas for finding the standard deviation of the sum of two variates, of the difference of two variates, and of the arithmetic mean of any number of variates. These formulas are very remarkable; in fact many students feel that they are a little uncanny in their ability to predict the standard deviations of distributions which do not yet exist! In order to provide you with an opportunity to work with these formulas, several sampling tables are included here, and it is strongly urged that you carry out for yourself the experiments described.

Table 10-3-1 contains 300 numbers which form a normal distribution, with an arithmetic mean of 70.5 and a standard deviation of 4.87. The 300 numbers are tabulated in a random order. Samples may be chosen from this table in either of two ways. First, you may make a set of 300 slips of paper and write one of the numbers on each slip, and then, to draw a sample, you can mix the slips thoroughly and take the required number of slips from the top of the pile. Secondly, you can use the table as it is printed and choose the required set of numbers according to any

TABLE 10-3-1.　Experimental Sampling Table

$$\bar{x} = 70.5 \qquad \sigma_x = 4.87$$

66	77	78	71	75	75	76	64	79	69	79	75	68	71	78
70	67	73	62	70	77	69	77	73	68	63	71	73	68	68
68	70	74	76	69	71	65	64	63	69	78	70	78	66	62
70	62	75	81	74	68	72	67	71	73	75	71	66	76	70
61	68	72	63	69	77	70	70	60	65	71	72	73	68	82
67	73	76	66	76	69	70	71	72	61	72	75	63	68	70
79	71	73	62	75	69	69	70	75	69	65	69	73	75	71
64	59	67	66	79	69	69	74	68	72	76	73	64	70	63
72	74	72	70	67	74	74	74	75	77	65	69	70	66	70
73	74	68	69	74	69	67	73	74	75	69	67	68	70	63
71	78	66	71	70	64	71	68	67	67	76	70	74	71	66
73	73	66	67	67	71	71	77	67	71	71	65	83	65	69
70	65	68	74	80	80	77	78	68	65	79	64	66	76	70
75	66	71	64	73	78	72	66	69	75	65	59	76	72	67
65	69	75	72	72	62	80	66	81	79	76	73	74	74	81
74	63	72	66	72	69	71	66	61	65	70	72	67	67	77
63	80	69	71	67	67	70	74	74	76	68	68	66	65	74
72	58	72	61	70	73	71	68	68	78	73	69	72	72	71
73	64	67	82	60	76	70	72	64	62	75	72	76	60	75
74	73	67	72	73	77	64	69	72	68	77	71	68	65	73

previously selected pattern; for example, you may select the first number in the first column, the second number in the second column, the third number in the third column, and so forth; or you may select the fifth, tenth, fifteenth, twentieth, and so forth from the numbers in the table. The pattern of selection should of course be chosen in advance, in order to avoid the possibility that one might be subconsciously selecting larger than average numbers or otherwise non-random numbers. As you perform the experiments, record all your results, since some of the experiments will demonstrate or verify several of the standard formulas simultaneously.

4.   STANDARD DEVIATION OF A DIFFERENCE

To find this experimentally, select about twenty pairs of numbers at random and subtract the first from the second of each pair. This will give you a new distribution of twenty numbers, some of which will be positive and some negative. Compute the standard deviation of this new distribution, and see how it compares with the standard deviation of the original distribution. Do you, at this point, expect it to be larger, or smaller, or about the same?

In order to discuss a specific result of this experiment, let us carry it out for the following sample. Subtract each number in the second column from the corresponding number in the first column. Thus the first difference in our sample is 66 minus 77, or -11, and the following numbers are 3, -2, 8, -7, -6, 8, 5, -2, -1, -7, 0, 5, 9, -4, 11, -17, 14, 9, and 1. The arithmetic mean of these twenty differences is 0.8. The expected or most likely value for this mean is zero, and the fact that we did not obtain zero in the experiment is a demonstration of the fact that conclusions drawn from a sample cannot be expected to apply exactly to the universe.

Our chief interest in this experiment, however, lies in the *standard deviation* of these twenty differences. The twenty numbers are scarcely worth grouping into a frequency tabulation, and we use formula 4-4-1, which gives us:

$$\sigma_{x-y} = \sqrt{61.8 - 0.64} = 7.82$$

Thus we conclude from this sample that the standard deviation of the difference between two random numbers in the table is 7.8 and that the mean of such a difference is 0.8. This is an experimental determination, to be compared with a theoretical value to be computed later. In the language of probability it asserts that if a pair of numbers is chosen from this table at random, the probability is 0.68 that the difference will be within 7.8 units of 0.8, that is, that it will be between -7.0 and 8.6

It will be noted that the standard deviation of the difference between two variates is somewhat larger than the standard deviation of the original table of variates; it is in fact about one and a half times as large. Our primary purpose is to find a way to predict this standard deviation from a theoretical formula, so that we will have a rapid and accurate measure of the uncertainty of a difference between two quantities, when their separate uncertainties are known. This can be achieved as follows.

If we denote the first of the variates by x, and the second by y, then the difference between the two is $x - y$, and the standard deviation of this difference can be denoted by σ_{x-y}. If we apply our basic computational formula 4-4-1 to this, we have

$$\sigma_{x-y} = \sqrt{\overline{(x-y)^2} - \overline{(x-y)}^2}$$

or

$$\sigma_{x-y} = \sqrt{\overline{(x^2 - 2xy + y^2)} - (\bar{x} - \bar{y})^2}$$

or, removing parentheses and regrouping,

$$\sigma_{x-y} = \sqrt{(\overline{x^2} - \bar{x}^2) + (\overline{y^2} - \bar{y}^2) - 2(\overline{xy} - \bar{x}\bar{y})}$$

We recognize $\overline{x^2} - \bar{x}^2$ as the square of σ_x, and $\overline{y^2} - \bar{y}^2$ as the square of σ_y. The factor $\overline{xy} - \bar{x}\bar{y}$ is a measure of the correlation between x and y, and we recognize it as the numerator of the standard expression for r in equation 9-6-1. If we solve 9-6-1 for $\overline{xy} - \bar{x}\bar{y}$, we see that it is equal to $r_{xy}\sigma_x\sigma_y$, where we have added a subscript to r to avoid confusion. Making these substitutions, we have

$$\sigma_{x-y} = \sqrt{\sigma_x^2 + \sigma_y^2 - 2r_{xy}\sigma_x\sigma_y} \qquad (10\text{-}4\text{-}1)$$

In the experimental example there is no correlation between the first member and the second member of a pair; in other words, the value of the first does not have any systematic influence on the value of the second, and r_{xy} is therefore zero. This situation occurs so frequently that it is convenient to have a separate formula for it:

$$\sigma_{x-y} = \sqrt{\sigma_x^2 + \sigma_y^2} \quad \text{(No correlation between } x \text{ and } y) \qquad (10\text{-}4\text{-}2)$$

In words, this formula says that the standard deviation of a difference between two independent variates is the square root of the sum of the squares of their separate standard deviations. In our experimental example, the standard deviation of the first variate is simply 4.87, as is also that of the second, and the standard deviation of the difference between the two is therefore

$$\sigma_{x-y} = \sqrt{4.87^2 + 4.87^2} = 6.89$$

Thus the result predicted by the formula for our experimental standard deviation is 6.9, while the actual result of the experiment is 7.8. The theoretical value is the standard deviation of the universe of all possible differences between numbers in the table, while the experimental result is the standard deviation of a sample of twenty such differences. If we took larger and larger samples upon which to base our experimental standard deviation of a difference, we would, on the average, come closer and closer to 6.89. The students who will perform this experiment with a number of different samples* will discover that the observed standard deviations will cluster around 6.89, and that a result based upon a large

---

*Such a set of experiments is valuable, but laborious. If an entire class is studying this material simultaneously, it is suggested that the work be divided, each member choosing his sample in a different way.

sample is likely to be closer to 6.89 than one based upon a small sample.

Before we proceed to the standard deviations of other quantities, let us study some illustrations of equations 10-4-1 and 10-4-2:

(1) In a golf tournament between two rival clubs, the members of one club are matched at random with members of the other club. If the average score of club A is 97, with a standard deviation of 16, and that of club B is 93, with a standard deviation of 12, what will be the average margin of victory of club B over club A, and what will be the standard deviation of the margin of victory? What fraction of the matches should the poorer club expect to win?

Answer: The expected average margin of victory will obviously be 97 − 93, or 4, and the standard deviation of this average will be, from formula 10-4-1, $\sqrt{16^2 + 12^2}$ or 20. Thus, for 68 per cent of the games, we should expect the margin of victory for Team B to be between 24 and minus 16, where of course a negative margin of victory indicates defeat for Team B. To answer the remainder of the question, we must use the normal curve to find what fraction of the differences will be negative. In other words we wish to know what fraction of a distribution will be less than zero if the mean of the distribution is 4 and the standard deviation is 20. If we convert zero to t units, remembering that the arithmetic mean is 4 and the standard deviation is 20, we find that t is minus 0.2. We look up this value of t in the normal curve tables and find that the corresponding value of area is 0.0793. Thus we expect 0.079 of the total games to end in victories between zero and 4, and of course we expect 0.50 to end in victories greater than 4. This leaves 0.421 for the percentage which should end in victories less than zero, in other words, in defeats for Team B. Team A can therefore be expected to win about 42 per cent of the games.

(2) In a glass factory, it is necessary to take the hot glass from one room to another in which the temperature may be different. A sudden cooling of 10 degrees or more may crack the glass. The mean daily temperature in the first room is the same as that in the second, but the standard deviation of the temperature in the first room is 8 degrees and that in the second room is 6 degrees. What proportion of the products should the manufacturers expect to lose by cracking?

Answer: It would be a serious blunder to apply here the method used for the preceding problem. It is extremely unlikely that the temperatures in the two rooms are independent, because both are likely to be influenced by the same factors, such as outside temperature or the effectiveness of the heating system. The problem can be answered only if we know the coefficient of correlation between the temperature in the first room and that in the second. If, for example, this coefficient is 0.80, then we would have, from equation 10-4-1:

$$\sigma_{x-y} = \sqrt{6^2 - 2 \times 6 \times 8 \times 0.80 + 8^2} = 4.8$$

To find what fraction of the differences should be greater than 10, we convert 10 to t units as before, and find that t is 10/4.8, or 2.08. The area corresponding to this value of t is 0.481. Of the 0.50 which we expect to be greater than the mean, this leaves 0.019 which will deviate from the mean by more than 10. In other words, about 2 per cent of the products can be expected to be lost by cracking.

PROBLEMS

1. In Table 1-4-1, σ_M is 13.5, σ_L is 14.7, r_{ML} is 0.32, $\overline{M}$ is 71.3, and $\overline{L}$ is 70.5. Compute the standard deviation of the difference between a student's mathematics grade and his language grade. If an entry in Table 1-4-1 is picked at random, what is the probability that this difference will be larger than 10? Test your answer by making several random selections from the table.

2. For the data in Problem 1, Article 12, Chapter 9, compute the average difference between the ages of husband and wife, and the probable error of the difference. What is the probability that a husband chosen at random will be at least ten years older than his wife?

5. STANDARD DEVIATION OF DIFFERENCES BETWEEN CORRELATED VARIATES

To illustrate the application of the formulas for correlated data, we must use a table of pairs of numbers in which there is a relationship between the first and the second. Table 10-5-1 contains such a set of pairs. We can

TABLE 10-5-1.   Sampling Table of Correlated Data

x	y	x	y	x	y	x	y	x	y
54	32	49	32	55	31	51	30	53	32
50	29	43	27	50	31	51	30	51	31
46	29	52	31	50	30	53	31	52	30
57	34	55	32	45	29	55	34	49	29
53	33	49	30	48	31	52	30	47	27
46	28	53	33	49	30	45	28	49	31
54	33	52	29	50	30	58	32	47	32
52	30	48	28	59	35	51	31	48	30
54	33	48	29	47	28	56	32	42	26
56	33	44	28	51	31	50	31	46	29

$$\bar{x} = 50.5 \qquad \sigma_x = 3.83$$
$$r_{xy} = 0.837$$
$$\bar{y} = 30.5 \qquad \sigma_y = 1.94$$

experiment with this table in either of two ways. If we form a set of differences between each x and *its corresponding* y, we must use the formula for correlated data:

$$\sigma_{x-y} = \sqrt{3.83^2 + 1.94^2 - 2(3.83)(1.94)(0.837)} = 2.45$$

If, on the other hand, we form a set of differences between each x and *some other y chosen at random*, then there is no correlation and we must use the formula for uncorrelated data:

$$\sigma_{x-y} = \sqrt{3.83^2 + 1.94^2} = 4.29$$

In both cases the average value of our differences will be (except for sampling errors) the difference between the average value of x and the average value of y, that is, $50.5 - 30.5$ or 20.0.

Let us test this conclusion by forming a set of differences between the first twenty pairs of numbers, reading down the columns. The first difference is $54 - 32$, or 22, the next is 21, and so forth. The mean value of $x - y$ is 20.10, and the standard deviation is 2.28, which is in satisfactory agreement with the predicted value of 2.45.

To test the prediction that the standard deviation will be about 4.29 if we choose the y's at random with relation to the x's, let us subtract each y from the x *preceding it* in the table. Since the pairs of numbers were thoroughly mixed before tabulating, this will give us a random pairing of x's and y's. We have then the series of numbers beginning with $54 - 29 = 25$, $50 - 29 = 21$, $46 - 34 = 12$, and so forth. The mean of the twenty differences is 20.15 and the standard deviation is 4.49, thus confirming the predicted value of 4.29 and demonstrating the fact that a random selection will give us a different standard deviation from a systematic selection. The reader is urged to make various selections himself to verify these formulas and to investigate the limits of their accuracy of prediction.

PROBLEMS

Table 9-11-1 shows the scores made by twenty-eight students on a given examination in twelve minutes (y) and in fifteen minutes (x). The values of $\bar{x}$, $\bar{y}$, σ_x, σ_y, and r_{xy} can be obtained from the data at the bottom of Table 9-11-4.

1. Find the mean of the additional scores made by the students in the last three minutes, that is, of the differences $x - y$.

2. Find the standard deviation of these differences.

3. Compute the probable error of these differences.

4. Test this probable error by selecting a few pairs at random from the table and computing the differences between x and y. Approximately half of these differences should differ from the average value of $x - y$ by less than your probable error, and the other half should differ from the average value by more than the probable error.

6. STANDARD DEVIATION OF A SUM

Let us again begin our discussion with an experiment. Select twenty pairs of numbers from Table 10-3-1 as before, but this time add the members of each pair instead of subtracting them. Now compute the standard deviation of the distribution consisting of these twenty sums and compare it with your earlier results. Do you expect it to be larger than, or smaller than, or about the same as the standard deviation of Table 10-3-1 itself? How do you expect it to compare with the standard deviation of a difference which we obtained in Article 5?

Again we will describe such an experiment based upon a specific sample and leave it to the reader to perform similar experiments based upon other samples. Let us add each of the numbers in column one to the corresponding numbers in column two. This gives us a set of twenty numbers beginning with 143, 137, 138, and so forth. The mean of these numbers is 139.2, and the standard deviation is 7.15. The reader may be surprised to note that this standard deviation is about the same as that for the *difference* between any two numbers in the table.

If we repeat the derivation in Article 4, replacing $x - y$ by $x + y$, we obtain

$$\sigma_{x+y} = \sqrt{\sigma_x^2 + \sigma_y^2 + 2r_{xy}\sigma_x\sigma_y} \qquad (10\text{-}6\text{-}1)$$

or, if there is no correlation,

$$\sigma_{x+y} = \sqrt{\sigma_x^2 + \sigma_y^2} \quad \text{(No correlation between } x \text{ and } y) \qquad (10\text{-}6\text{-}2)$$

which is identical with the standard deviation of the difference. The expected result of this experiment is therefore also 6.89.

To complete the experimental verification of these formulas, let us choose twenty x's at random from the table of correlated data (10-5-1) and add them to their corresponding y's. If we choose the first twenty pairs as before, we have the sums 86, 79, 75, and so forth, with a mean and standard deviation of 81.4 and 5.85. Since these pairs are correlated, we use formula 10-6-1, obtaining for the theoretical standard deviation:

$$\sigma_{x+y} = \sqrt{3.83^2 + 1.94^2 + 2(3.83)(1.94)(0.837)} = 5.56$$

as compared to 5.85 for the experimental result. Now let us pair the y's with the x's at random, by adding each y to the x preceding it in the table, thus destroying the correlation. We then have the twenty numbers 83, 79, 80, and so forth, with a mean and standard deviation of 81.35 and 4.36. To find the theoretical values, we use formula 10-6-2, which gives us as before $\sigma_{x+y} = 4.29$.

PROBLEMS

1. A coffee packaging machine automatically weighs and packages coffee in 1-pound bags. There is a little random variation in weight from bag to bag, and the standard deviation of the actual weights is 0.02 pound. There is a small demand for coffee in 2-pound bags, and the owner plans to readjust the machine so that it operates twice each time such a bag is presented. How large should he expect the standard deviation of the weights of the 2-pound bags to be, assuming that there is no correlation between successive operations of the machine?

2. Upon further investigation of the coffee packaging machine, it is found that part of the variation in weight is due to the retention of a small amount of coffee in the machine, so that a slightly underweight bag is frequently followed by a slightly overweight one. There is, in other words, a correlation between the amount of coffee dispensed in any operation with the amount dispensed in the previous operation, and the correlation coefficient is −0.40. How should the answer to Problem 1 be modified?

3. In Table 9-11-1, what is the standard deviation of the sum of the two scores? Compute the probable error of such a sum and test it by selecting several sums at random to see if approximately half of them are within one probable error of the expected value.

4. Derive equation 10-6-1 in detail.

7. STANDARD DEVIATION OF ARITHMETIC MEAN

Let us now perform an experiment to discover the nature of the distribution of a set of *means* of samples chosen from our universe of numbers in Article 4. This is a very important experiment, but since it is lengthy, it is suggested that the reader perform it in cooperation with other students, each student taking a separate part of the work.

(a) Choose twenty pairs of numbers from Table 10-3-1 at random, average each pair, then find the mean and standard deviation of the resulting distribution of means. As an illustrative example, the mean of the first number in the first column (66) and the first number in the second column (77) is 71.5; the mean of the two numbers below these (70 and 67) is 68.5, and if we continue, reading down the first two columns in this way, we obtain twenty means of pairs continuing 69.0, 66.0, and so forth. The standard deviation of these twenty means is 3.58. Thus we see that the standard deviation of the mean of two variates is smaller than the standard deviation of a single variate, but not related to it in any simple or obvious way.

(b) Choose twenty sets of five numbers at random; average each set; then find the standard deviation of these twenty means of five. To continue our illustrative example, let us use the left-hand five columns in the table as a sample and obtain our twenty means by averaging the variates in each row. The first result will be the mean of the first five numbers in the top row, (66, 77, 78, 71 and 75), which is 73.4; the mean of the second row is 68.4, and so forth. The standard deviation of this group of twenty means of five is 1.89. We see that the standard deviation of a mean of five is somewhat smaller than that of the mean of two.

(c) Repeat the experiment, choosing now ten numbers in each mean. Continuing our illustrative example, let us now choose the variates in the first ten columns, and average each row of this group. The results are 73.0, 70.6, and so forth, with a standard deviation of 1.56. We see that the standard deviation continues to decrease, but rather slowly.

(d) Repeat the experiment, choosing now fifteen numbers in each mean. For our illustrative example we must use the entire table to get twenty means, and we obtain each mean by averaging an entire row. The means are now 73.4, 69.9, and so forth, and the standard deviation of the group of means is 1.23.

Now let us tabulate our results:

Number of Variates in Each Mean	Standard Deviation of Mean
1	4.87
2	3.58
5	1.89
10	1.56
15	1.23

We see that the standard deviation of a mean depends strongly upon the number of variates included in the mean, but that the exact relationship between the two is not obvious.

To find the theoretical relationship between the standard deviation of a mean and the number of variates included in the mean, let us study first some preliminary principles:

(1) The formula for the standard deviation of a sum of two uncorrelated variables can be extended to include the sum of any number of variables. This can be proved by successive applications of equation 10-6-2:

$$\sigma_{x+y+z} = \sigma_{(x+y)+z} = \sqrt{\sigma_{x+y}^2 + \sigma_z^2} = \sqrt{\sigma_x^2 + \sigma_y^2 + \sigma_z^2}$$

or, in general,

$$\sigma_{x_1+x_2+\cdots+x_N} = \sqrt{\sigma_1^2 + \sigma_2^2 + \cdots + \sigma_N^2} \qquad (10\text{-}7\text{-}1)$$

where we have used x_1, x_2, $\cdots x_N$, to denote N variables, and σ_1, σ_2 $\cdots \sigma_N$, to denote their standard deviations.

(2) If we form the sum of N random variates, all from the same table, then there is no correlation between them, and the above formula is applicable. Furthermore, the standard deviation of each one will be simply the standard deviation of a single variate, and we have

$$\sigma_{\Sigma x} = \sqrt{\sigma_1^2 + \sigma_2^2 + \cdots + \sigma_N^2} = \sqrt{N\sigma_x^2} = \sqrt{N}\,\sigma_x \qquad (10\text{-}7\text{-}2)$$

or, the standard deviation of the sum of N similar variates is equal to the standard deviation of a single variate times the square root of the number of variates.

(3) The standard deviation of any constant, C, times a variate, v, is, by 4-4-1,

$$\sigma_{Cv} = \sqrt{\overline{(Cv)^2} - \overline{Cv}^2}$$

This reduces simply to

$$\sigma_{Cv} = \sqrt{C^2(\overline{v^2} - \bar{v}^2)} = C\sigma_v \qquad (10\text{-}7\text{-}3)$$

or, the standard deviation of any constant times any variate equals the constant times the standard deviation of the variate. We have already used this result in a slightly different form in equation 4-5-7.

(4) We are now ready to assemble these preliminary conclusions to find the formula for the standard deviation of the mean. We can write this standard deviation in the form

$$\sigma_{\bar{x}} = \sigma_{(1/N)\Sigma x}$$

and then, using our third preliminary conclusion (10-7-3) we can place the factor $1/N$, which is a constant multiplier, in front:

$$\sigma_{\bar{x}} = (1/N)\sigma_{\Sigma x}$$

Using the second preliminary conclusion, we can replace $\sigma_{\Sigma x}$ by $\sqrt{N}\,\sigma_x$,

$$\sigma_{\bar{x}} = (1/N)\sqrt{N}\,\sigma_x$$

or, combining the factors containing N,

$$\sigma_{\bar{x}} = \frac{\sigma_x}{\sqrt{N}} \tag{10-7-4}$$

This is an important and far reaching conclusion. In words, it is: *The standard deviation of the arithmetic mean is equal to the standard deviation of a single variate, divided by the square root of the number of variates included in the mean.*

If we apply this formula to our experimental data, we have the following results:

Number of Variates	Experimental Standard Deviation	Theoretical Standard Deviation
1	4.87	4.87
2	3.58	3.44
5	1.89	2.18
10	1.56	1.54
15	1.23	1.26
300	—	0.28

In each case the agreement between the experimental and the theoretical values is fairly good. It should be remembered that the theoretical value is the number which we expect the experimental value to approach as the sample size is increased. If, for example, we had used *fifty* groups of five numbers to find the standard deviation of the mean of five variates, the resulting experimental standard deviation would probably have come closer to the theoretical value than it did with a sample of only *twenty* groups.

The importance of the above formula can be seen if we consider that the statistician generally wishes to find the standard deviation of the mean of *all* of his variates, in order to estimate the uncertainty of the mean, and that the experimental method will not give him this, but will give him only the standard deviation of a subgroup.

The use which is generally made of the standard deviation of the mean is an indirect one. If a scientist measures the percentage of impurity in twenty-five samples of a substance and finds that the average percentage is 3.46 and the standard deviation of his measures is 0.40, he can use equation 10-7-4 to find that the standard deviation of the mean of 25 measures is 0.08. The scientist is seeking the true value of the percentage of impurity, and he assumes that this true value is the mean of the universe of possible measurements of it. Let us call this unknown mean of the universe X. Now let us consider the universe of possible means of twenty-five drawn from this first universe. This universe of means will have a mean of X and a standard deviation of 0.08, and the probability is 0.68 that any mean of twenty-five chosen at random will be within 0.08 of X. Therefore the probability is 0.68 that our sample mean of 3.46 is within 0.08 of X, or, if we invert this, the probability is 0.68 that X is within 0.08 of our sample mean of 3.46. In other words, the probability is 0.68 that X lies between 3.38 and 3.54. While we do not know the value of X, we can compute the likelihood that it is between any given limits. We can assert, for example, that since the area corresponding to $t = 3$ is 0.4987, the probability is 0.9974 that X is between $3.46 - 0.24$ and $3.46 + 0.24$; in other words, we can assert that X is almost certainly between 3.22 and 3.70. We can set wider limits if the practical situation requires a still more stringent level of probability.

In drawing such conclusions, the scientist makes a far reaching and sometimes dangerous assumption. He assumes that the only errors of measurement are random, that is, that they are just as likely to be positive as negative. If a systematic error is present, as it might be for example if his instruments are out of adjustment, then he will draw a totally erroneous conclusion about the *likelihood* that the true value is within any given limits. The random errors can be controlled by statistical analysis, but the systematic errors must be detected by the alertness and ingenuity of the investigator.

PROBLEMS

1. The ratio of the weights of bromine and hydrogen which combine to form hydrobromic acid was determined experimentally. The results of ten independent determinations are as follows: 79.2863, 79.3055, 79.3064, 79.3197, 79.3114, 79.3150, 79.3063, 79.3141, 79.2915, and 79.3108.* (a) What value should the investigators report for the result of their investigations? (b) What is the standard deviation of this value? (c) What is its probable error? (d) Write the value with its probable error as it would be reported in scientific literature. (e) In the light of these

*Weber, *Bulletin of Bureau of Standards*, Volume IX, page 131.

measurements, how likely is it that the true value of this ratio is less than 79.3000?

2. Answer illustrative question B near the end of Article 1.

3. For the data in Table 1-4-3, what is the probability that the mean of a sample of five wires will be below 202 pounds?   That the mean of a sample of twelve wires will be below 202 pounds?

4. Using the normal curve theory, and your answer to Problem 3, Article 10, Chapter 6, answer all problems VI, VII, and VIII of Article 4 in Chapter 1.

5. Using equation 10-7-4, answer Question 12 of Article 4, Chapter 1.   What would prevent him from obtaining unlimited accuracy by increasing the number of observations indefinitely?

8.   SUMMARY

In many statistical problems, the investigator studies a relatively small body of data, and from it he draws conclusions about a much larger body of similar data.   The small body of data under study is called the *sample*, and the larger body from which it was drawn is called the *universe*.   Because of the random variation from one sample to the next, the properties* of any sample can be expected to differ a little from the corresponding properties of the universe.   When we estimate the properties of the universe from the properties of a sample, we therefore usually introduce an error.   The central objective of this chapter is to draw some conclusions about the probable sizes of these errors of estimation, and to show how much reduction in their size is to be expected if a larger sample is used.   A second objective, closely related to the first, is to predict the range of variation from one sample to the next, when the properties of the universe are known.

The theoretical standard deviation of a property of a sample is the standard deviation which we would expect if we could collect a large number of samples, measure the required property for each one, and form a frequency tabulation of the results.   For example, the standard deviation of the arithmetic mean of a sample containing N variates is

$$\sigma_{\bar{x}} = \frac{\sigma_x}{\sqrt{N}}$$

If, for instance, a large number of samples, each containing 100 variates, are taken from a universe which has a standard deviation of 25, and the mean of each sample is computed, these means will form a distribution which will have a standard deviation of approximately 2.5.   It follows from the theory of the normal curve that if any one sample mean is chosen at random, the probability is 0.68 that it will differ from the mean of the universe by less than 2.5.

An inversion of this argument is needed for us to determine the re-

---

*Some "properties" of a sample are its mean, its standard deviation, its skewness, and so forth.

liability with which we can deduce the properties of the universe when we know only the properties of one sample. If the mean of one sample is 34, and the probability is 0.68 that this mean differs from the mean of the universe by less than 2.5, then it is obvious that the probability is 0.68 that the mean of the universe is between 31.5 and 36.5. In this way the probability that the mean of the universe will lie between any other given limits can be calculated from equation 10-7-4 and the normal curve tables. Examples of this computation are shown in Article 7.

The standard deviations of some other quantities are as follows. If x and y are measures of two properties of a single individual (such as height and weight of a man) then the standard deviation of a difference between x and y is given by

$$\sigma_{x-y} = \sqrt{\sigma_x^2 + \sigma_y^2 - 2r_{xy}\sigma_x\sigma_y}$$

where r_{xy} is the correlation coefficient between x and y.

If instead x and y are simply random variates selected from two universes, then there is no correlation between them and the standard deviation of the difference is

$$\sigma_{x-y} = \sqrt{\sigma_x^2 + \sigma_y^2}$$

Similar equations (10-6-1 and 10-6-2) give the standard deviation of the sum of two variates. Examples of the uses of these equations are given in Articles 5 and 6.

CHAPTER
. 11 .
TESTING STATISTICAL HYPOTHESES

1. INTRODUCTION

We have seen that the statistical investigator usually works with a sample, drawn in a random way from a much larger universe which is in general inaccessible to him, and we have seen also that the objective of the investigator frequently is to deduce the properties of the universe. Unfortunately it is impossible, from a sample, to deduce the exact properties of the universe, because of the presence of the element of chance in the selection of the sample. In view of this, any specific statement about a property of the universe has the status of a hypothesis, which may or may not be true. It is the purpose of this chapter to explain methods of testing the truth of such hypotheses.

It is not in general possible to prove beyond any possible doubt that a given hypothesis is true or false; instead we must confine ourselves to a discussion of the likelihood that it is true. Even here we must usually proceed indirectly, since our mathematical formulation is set up to tell us the probability of drawing various sorts of samples from a *specific known universe*, while we wish to know the probability that various sorts of universes could have been the parents of our *specific known sample*. In particular, if we must choose between two hypotheses about the universe from which the given sample was drawn, we must compute the probability, under the first hypothesis, that a sample such as the one under study will occur, and then compute, under the second hypothesis, another probability of the observed sample, and choose between the two hypotheses on the basis of these two probabilities. If the observed sample would have been almost impossible to draw by chance under one hypothesis, it is reasonable to reject that hypothesis. This principle is sometimes called the principle of maximum likelihood. A formal statement of it is as follows: *Between two or more competing hypotheses, we must choose the one in the light of which the observed sample has the greater probability of occurring, if the hypotheses are otherwise equal in merit.* We have already made use of this principle in Article 6 of Chapter 8, in establishing the Principle of Least Squares for the line of best fit.

2. DIFFERENCES BETWEEN MEANS

A specific kind of hypothesis which is of great importance in statistical analysis arises when two sets of data are being compared. The hypothesis is that *the two sets of data constitute two samples drawn from the same universe.* To see why this is important, let us consider an example.

A doctor suspects that the convalescence period for a given illness can be shortened a little if the patients are given a new drug. He tests this hypothesis by giving the drug to 100 patients (the experimental group) and withholding it from 100 others (the control group) who are otherwise comparable to the first group so far as the doctor's selection can make it so. A careful record is kept of the convalescent period of all 200 patients.

The durations for the control group are found to vary from seven days to thirty-three days, with a mean of 19.7 and a standard deviation of 6.1. Those for the experimental group vary from eight days to thirty-one days, with a mean of 17.1 and a standard deviation of 5.7. Thus there appears to be, in the difference between the two means, some evidence for the effectiveness of the drug in shortening the duration of convalescence. However, the difference is so small, and the scatter of each group is so large, that it is perhaps possible to believe that the difference arose solely by chance, and has nothing to do with the drug. Let us state these two competing hypotheses exactly.

A. The observed difference of 2.6 days is due to the drug and we can expect a similar difference to occur between any future treated groups and their control groups. In other words, there is a difference between the universe of treated patients and the universe of untreated patients.

B. The observed difference of 2.6 days is due to chance, and we can expect future differences between such groups to be sometimes positive and sometimes negative, with a most likely value of about zero. In other words, the two sample means came from the same universe, and the observed difference is simply an example of the expected random variation between different samples from a universe.

We can test the significance of the difference either by attempting to prove that A is true, or that B is untrue. Of these two statements, B lends itself much more readily to mathematical analysis, and we accordingly devote our attention to it. Let us call it the "null hypothesis." To test this hypothesis, we must begin by making some preliminary computations.

First we compute the standard deviations of both of the means, from equation 10-7-4:

$$\sigma_{\bar{x}} = 6.1/\sqrt{100} = 0.61 \qquad \sigma_{\bar{y}} = 5.7/\sqrt{100} = 0.57$$

where x is used to indicate the duration for a control patient and y the duration for an experimental patient. Next we compute the standard deviation of the difference between the two means, by applying equation 10-4-2 to the above results:

$$\sigma_{\bar{x}-\bar{y}} = \sqrt{0.61^2 + 0.57^2} = 0.835$$

To take the next step, *we assume as a working hypothesis that the null hypothesis is true*. This does not mean that we believe it to be true, it means only that we wish to investigate the consequences which would result if it were true. According to this hypothesis, the universe consisting of all the possible differences between means of 100 durations has an average value of zero and a standard deviation of 0.835.

If we accept the null hypothesis, we must also accept the conclusion that in performing our experiment we selected at random one of these possible differences and found it to be 2.6. If the probability of having picked so large a difference at random is absurdly low, then doubt is cast upon the validity of the null hypothesis, upon which this probability is based. If, on the other hand, the probability of having obtained so large a difference is high, then the null hypothesis is a reasonable one. Let us therefore, compute exactly the probability that a difference chosen at random from such a universe of differences will be at least as large as 2.6. We convert 2.6 into t units by subtracting the mean value (zero) and dividing by the standard deviation (0.835); we then find the resulting value of t (3.11) in the tables and read the corresponding value of area, which in this case is 0.4991. This tells us that the probability of obtaining by chance a difference between zero and 2.6 is 0.4991. The probability of obtaining a difference between zero and -2.6 is of course also 0.4991. The remaining probability, 0.0018, is the probability that two means of 100 chosen at random will differ by 2.6 or more. In other words, if we accept the null hypothesis, then we must also accept its consequence, namely, that an event occurred even though it had a probability of less than 2 in 1000 of occurring. It would be unreasonable to accept this consequence of the null hypothesis, and we must therefore reject the null hypothesis itself. Having rejected it, we must accept its alternative, and we therefore conclude that *the two samples could not have come from the same universe*, or that *there is a significant difference between the means*, or, in our example, that *the drug does have an effect on duration of convalescence*.

The conclusion which we drew in the above paragraph is not quite an absolute one, since there remains the probability of 0.0018 that the observed difference could have arisen by chance. This probability we may consider to be, for practical purposes, the probability that the null hypothesis is correct, and we can state our conclusions exactly as follows: The available evidence indicates that the probability that the drug does *not* affect the duration of convalescence is only 0.0018, while the probability that it does affect duration is 0.9982. Since the probability in its favor is so overwhelming, we can state flatly that we have proved beyond a reasonable doubt that the drug affected the duration of convalescence.

Let us summarize the operations involved in this analysis:

First step: Compute the mean and standard deviation of both x and y.

Second step: Compute the standard deviations of $\bar{x}$ and $\bar{y}$ from equation 10-7-4.

Third step: Compute the standard deviation of $\bar{x} - \bar{y}$ from equation 10-4-2.

Fourth step: Compute t from

$$t = \frac{\bar{x} - \bar{y}}{\sigma_{\bar{x}-\bar{y}}} = \frac{\text{Diff.}}{\sigma_{\text{Diff.}}} \qquad (11\text{-}2\text{-}1)$$

Fifth step: Look up the area corresponding to this value of t.

Sixth step: Compute P from

$$P \text{ (of null hypothesis)} = 1 - 2A \qquad (11\text{-}2\text{-}2)$$

This value of P is the probability that a difference as large as or larger than the observed difference could have arisen by chance, assuming that the two samples came from the same universe. It is commonly interpreted as the probability that the null hypothesis is correct, and if P is so small as to be negligible, then the difference between the two means is proved to be real.

If the probability is small, but not so small as to be ignored, then we must state our conclusions accordingly. An example of such a less favorable probability is the following: A farmer who has been raising one variety of tomatoes believes that he might be able to obtain an increased yield with a new variety. He plants nine of the new variety (the experimental group) and nine of the old variety (the control group), spacing them alternately in a row to reduce the likelihood of systematic differences in growing conditions of any kind. The yields per plant are as shown in Table 11-2-1.

TABLE 11-2-1.   Yield from Two Varieties

Control Group (x)			Experimental Group (y)		
18	13	12	14	17	13
16	12	13	14	16	16
16	14	12	15	18	12

The details of the computations are:

First step: $\bar{x} = 14$ $\bar{y} = 15$
    $\sigma_x = 2.1$ $\sigma_y = 1.8$
Second step: $\sigma_{\bar{x}} = 2.1/\sqrt{9} = 0.7$ $\sigma_{\bar{y}} = 1.8/\sqrt{9} = 0.6$
Third step: $\sigma_{\bar{x}-\bar{y}} = \sqrt{0.7^2 + 0.6^2} = 0.92$
Fourth step: $t = (15 - 14)/0.92 = 1.09$
Fifth step: $A = 0.362$
Sixth step: $P = 1 - 2(0.362) = 0.276$

Thus we see that there is a probability of 0.28 that a difference this large or larger could have arisen solely by chance upon selecting two samples of nine from the same universe, and, by implication, this tells us that the probability that the null hypothesis is correct is 0.28, which is far too large a probability to permit us to reject the hypothesis. Our conclusion therefore is that no significant difference between the two varieties has been proved to exist.

PROBLEMS

1. Compute the probability that the difference between the mean of Table 1-4-1 and the mean of Table 1-4-2 is due to chance, upon the hypothesis that the two sets of temperatures came from the same universe. What is your conclusion about the effectiveness of the treatment given the experimental patients?

2. This year's freshman class, consisting of 538 men, had an average grade of 76.4, with a standard deviation of 17. Last year's class, with 620 men, had a grade average of 77.4 with a standard deviation of 19. Is the difference between the two classes significant?

3. The mean height of 1428 men in one geographical region is 66.4 inches, with a standard deviation of 2.7 inches, while that of 1193 men in another region is 66.7, with a standard deviation of 2.5. Would you predict that further samples of men from the two regions will show a similar difference?

3.   CONFIDENCE LIMITS

The conclusions in a study of the significance of a difference between means can never be stated in absolute terms, since there always remains a residual probability that the difference arose by chance. Nevertheless, it is frequently convenient to adopt arbitrary limits of significance, and several such arbitrary limits are widely used. One such set of rules is the following:

> If P is greater than 0.20, no significance is indicated.
> If P is between 0.05 and 0.20, the difference is probably significant.
> If P is less than 0.05, the difference is certainly significant.

$$(11\text{-}3\text{-}1)$$

These results are frequently expressed in somewhat different terms, which the student should be prepared to recognize in statistical reports. If P is less than 0.05, the difference is said to be "significant at the 0.05 level," if P is less than 0.01, "at the 0.01 level," and so forth. The limits most frequently used are 0.1, 0.05, 0.02, 0.01, and 0.001, but the terminology can be used to express any "level of significance."

Another way of expressing the conclusions in terms of confidence limits is to compute only t, and not A or P, and to interpret the results according to the following table:

> If t is less than 2.5, no significance is proved.
> If t is between 2.5 and 3.0, the difference is probably significant.
> If t is greater than 3.0, the difference is certainly significant.

$$(11\text{-}3\text{-}2)$$

The fact that 11-3-1 disagrees completely with 11-3-2 emphasizes the fact that all limits are arbitrary. The use of arbitrary limits is an inexact way to express our conclusions, and in general it is better to state the exact probability that the results could have occurred by chance. It is obviously ridiculous, for example, to state that when t is 2.5001 the difference is probably significant, but when t is 2.4999 there is no evidence for significance; yet this is what the use of arbitrary limits compels us to do.

Another reason for stating our conclusions in terms of probability is the fact that different situations require different degrees of certainty. Suppose that a rope manufacturer installs some new machinery and performs a statistical analysis to find whether the strength of the rope produced by the new machinery is significantly different from that produced by the old machinery. He finds a small difference, but reports to his customers that "it is not significant." One of his customers resells the rope in the form of clotheslines and is completely satisfied with the conclusion. After all, if there is one chance in a thousand that a cord will break, the consequences are not very serious, and if a rope should break, the irate housewife could be easily compensated for the resulting damage. Another customer buys the rope for use in the manufacture of parachutes. Here the consequences of a break are much more serious, and the user must know whether the probability of a break under the proposed load is one in a thousand or one in a million. The purchaser in this case would insist rightly upon a far smaller probability that the rope would break under the proposed load than would the first purchaser. The manufacturer should therefore state his conclusions exactly in terms of the probability that the null hypothesis is correct and leave it to the user to decide whether the probability is low enough to meet his needs.

PROBLEMS

1. Restate your answers to problems 1 and 3 in the preceding section in terms of "levels of significance," and then in terms of the criteria 11-3-1, and finally in terms of the criteria 11-3-2.

2. Write a brief statement comparing the value of criteria 11-3-1 and 11-3-2 with each other, and both with the use of levels of significance.

4. DESIGN OF EXPERIMENTS

In Article 2 we considered the question of whether the data in Table 11-2-1 proved that the experimental plants shown at the right of the table differed significantly from those shown at the left. We concluded that the difference between the two means was too small to be statistically significant, and that no difference was proved to exist.

This does not mean that no difference between the two varieties exists. It means only that if a difference does exist, the sample size chosen by the farmer was too small to reveal it. The farmer may perhaps reason as follows: "A difference of yield of one pound per plant is large enough to justify replacing the old variety by the new one, since the two varieties are alike in all other respects. It is therefore worth experimenting further to discover whether this apparent difference is real or is only an accident of sampling. How many experimental plants must I put in next year in order to settle the question decisively?"

To answer this question, we must first decide exactly how "decisively" the question must be answered. Suppose that we decide that it should be answered at the 0.05 level of significance. This means that we wish to design an experiment in such a way that, if such a difference between the means continues to appear, it will be proved to be significant at the 0.05 level. To find the number of experimental plants necessary, we must follow our previous procedure in the reverse order. If $1 - 2A$ is to equal 0.05, then A must equal 0.475. From the normal curve tables we find that t must equal 1.96. Assuming that there is a real difference of 1.00 between the two varieties, equation 11-2-1 becomes

$$1.96 = \frac{1.00}{\sigma_{\bar{x}-\bar{y}}}$$

from which we see that $\sigma_{\bar{x}-\bar{y}}$ must equal 0.51. If we insert this in equation 10-4-2, applying it to the means, we have

$$0.51 = \sqrt{\sigma_{\bar{x}}^2 + \sigma_{\bar{y}}^2}$$

If we replace $\sigma_{\bar{x}}$ by σ_x/N and $\sigma_{\bar{y}}$ by σ_y/N, according to equation 10-7-4, this becomes

$$0.51 = \sqrt{\frac{\sigma_x^2}{N} + \frac{\sigma_y^2}{N}}$$

The standard deviations of the larger samples which the farmer plans for next year will probably not differ much from the standard deviations of this year's small samples, and we can replace σ_x by 2.1 and σ_y by 1.8. The above equation can then be solved for N. The exact result is:

$$N = \frac{2.1^2 + 1.8^2}{0.51^2} = 29$$

Our conclusion is then that if a true difference of about 1 pound per plant does exist, it will require a sample size of at least twenty-nine plants to prove it beyond a reasonable doubt.

PROBLEMS

1. Suppose that the farmer in the above illustration believes that a proved difference of $\frac{1}{2}$ pound per plant would be enough to justify the adoption of the new variety, but that a smaller difference would not justify a change. How large should his experimental group be to insure the proof of significance? (Use $P = 0.05$ as before.)

2. Suppose that the farmer not only wishes to test for differences as small as $\frac{1}{2}$ pound, but is not satisfied with a result which permits one chance in twenty that he is wrong. If he insists that the probability of the null hypothesis must be reduced to 0.01 for any difference greater than $\frac{1}{2}$ pound, how many plants should he include in his next experiment?

3. In Problem 1, Article 7, Chapter 10, how many observations would be necessary to reduce the probable error of the mean below 0.001? Below 0.0005?

4. A preliminary study of ten criminals indicates an average IQ of 89, with a standard deviation of 15. For comparable sociological groups, the mean IQ of a large number of non-criminals is known to be 96, with a standard deviation of 12. If the difference in mean IQ is real, how many criminals should be included in subsequent studies in order to demonstrate the reality of the difference at the 0.005 level of significance? At the 0.001 level?

5. HYPOTHESES CONCERNING VARIABILITY

In Article 2 we discussed the procedure for finding whether the difference between the means of two sets of data is compatible with the hypothesis that the two sets came from the same universe. We will now consider the problem of finding whether the difference between the *standard deviations* of two sets of data is compatible with this hypothesis.

To see why this is useful, let us consider a specific application. In a factory a bolt-cutting machine turns out bolts with a mean diameter of 0.2508 inch, with a standard deviation of 0.0017 inch. In a routine check it was found that a sample of 100 bolts had a mean diameter of 0.2506, which is well within the tolerance limits of size, but that the standard deviation of the sample was 0.0027. The operator accepts this as evidence that the machine has become worn to the point of being erratic in its output. Is it reasonable to believe that the machine will continue to turn out bolts with the higher variability, or is it more reasonable to believe that the apparent high variability was due to chance and to expect future samples to have a standard deviation of around 0.0017? Assuming that an increase of variability of this size cannot be tolerated, should the machine be replaced?

To answer this question, we must know the equation for the standard deviation of a standard deviation, which we introduce here without proof.

$$\sigma_\sigma = \frac{\sigma}{\sqrt{2N}} \tag{11-5-1}$$

To apply this to our problem, we must compute the standard deviation of the standard deviation of 100 variates, if the standard deviation of the universe is 0.0017. From 11-5-1 we have

$$\sigma_\sigma = \frac{0.0017}{\sqrt{2 \times 100}} = 0.00012$$

Thus we see that the observed standard deviation (0.0027) differs from the predicted standard deviation (0.0017) by eight times its own standard deviation, and the hypothesis that the sample of 100 came from the specified universe is totally untenable. It is nearly impossible that the difference could have arisen by chance, and we must conclude that the machine has become defective.

PROBLEMS

1. In Problem 4, Article 4, we discussed the hypothesis that criminals have lower IQ's than non-criminals, in the mean. Do the figures given also indicate that the IQ's of criminals tend to be *more variable* than those of non-criminals? Discuss this hypothesis.

2. Assuming that the difference between the standard deviations of IQ's of criminals and non-criminals is real, how many criminals would have to be studied to demonstrate the reality at the 0.01 level? At the 0.001 level?

3. For Table 11-2-1, discuss the hypothesis that the experimental group is less variable than the control group.

4. For the data in Tables 1-4-1 and 1-4-2, discuss the hypothesis that the experimental treatment reduces the variability of temperatures.

5. In Problem 3, Article 2, Chapter 11, would you regard the difference between the two standard deviations as significant?

6. STANDARD DEVIATION OF A FREQUENCY

In the preceding articles we have studied the methods by which a study of a sample can give us information about the range of reliability of quantities deduced from the sample. The quantities so studied have all been functions of the variates. In this article we shift our attention away from the sizes of the variates and direct it instead to the frequencies of occurrences of variates of various sizes. The purpose of this will be made clear by an illustrative example:

Example 1. In a sample of 500 bolts from a day's production of a bolt-making machine, 15 were found to be defective. In earlier tests, the average number of defective bolts had been about 10 per 500. Would you call in a repair man to check the machine or would you attribute the increase to chance?

To solve this problem, we recall from the chapter on the normal curve, that if p is the probability that a given event will succeed, $1 - p$ is the probability that it will not succeed, n is the number of trials, and s is the number of successes, then the standard deviation of s is equal to $\sqrt{np(1 - p)}$, by equation 6-6-1. In the terminology we have used for frequency tabulations, f is the frequency of occurrence of any given class, in other words, the number of "successes" with respect to that class; N is the total number of variates, and f/N is the best guess we can make about the probability of a success in the universe from which the sample was drawn. In other words, equation 6-6-1 becomes

$$\sigma_f = \sqrt{N \frac{f}{N} \left(1 - \frac{f}{N}\right)}$$

or

$$\sigma_f = \sqrt{f\left(1 - \frac{f}{N}\right)} \tag{11-6-1}$$

In many cases the frequency of the class in which we are interested is very small in comparison with the total number of variates. In this case, f/N is nearly zero and we can use the approximate formula

$$\sigma_f \cong \sqrt{f} \quad \text{(if } f/N \text{ is small)} \tag{11-6-2}$$

where $\cong$ means "is approximately equal to." For our illustrative problem, we make the hypothesis that the day's production is a random sample from a universe in which 10 bolts per 500 are defective. The expected frequency of defective bolts in the day's production is therefore 10, with a standard deviation of $\sqrt{10}$ or 3.16. The observed frequency of 15 is therefore only 1.58 standard deviations away from the expected value. The normal curve tables tell us that a deviation this large or larger can be expected in about 11 per cent of the trials. We conclude that the difference may easily be due to chance and that there is no justification for overhauling the machine.

Example 2. An identical examination was given in two classes. In the first class, 8 students out of 32 made perfect scores, and in the second class, only 5 out of 35 made perfect scores. Should you, on the basis of this evidence, expect consistently better performance from the first class or should you attribute the difference to chance?

Answer. As usual, we begin by adopting the hypothesis that the two samples came from the same universe, and we investigate the consequences of this hypothesis. The best guess about the hypothetical single universe is obtained by combining the two samples, which tells us that 13 out of 67 made perfect scores, or 19.4 per cent. On this basis we would expect 6.2 perfect scores in the first class, and 6.8 in the second class. To obtain the standard deviations of these predictions, we cannot use the approximate equation 11-6-2 because f/N is too large, and we use instead equation 11-6-1. The standard deviation of the first predicted frequency (6.2) is $\sqrt{6.2\left(1 - \frac{6.2}{32}\right)}$ or 2.2, and that of the second is 2.3. The observed frequencies are both less than one standard deviation from their expected values, and we conclude that our hypothesis that the two samples came from the same universe is tenable. In other words, we conclude that there is not sufficient reason to believe that the first class will be consistently better than the second. This problem will be treated more fully in Section 8.

PROBLEMS

1. In a state with a population of six million, there were 984 automobile accident fatalities last year. In an effort to reduce the number of accidents, the traffic authorities increased their severity in dealing with violations. In the following year there were only 951 fatalities, and the authorities claimed to have saved 33 lives by means of their campaign. Comment upon the validity of this claim.

2. A given city usually has about 15 cases of typhoid fever per year, but this

year there have been 28 cases. Should the health authorities investigate the
cause of the increase, or should they simply dismiss it as due to the random variation to be expected from year to year?

3. A patient has a blood count of 13,200. This "count" is based upon the actual
counting of 264 blood cells in a standardized volume. Two days later his count
has risen to 13,800, based upon an actual count of 276 cells. Should this be regarded as evidence of a change in his condition, or should it be attributed merely
to random differences between successive samples?

7. STANDARD DEVIATION OF A PERCENTAGE

If the data are in the form of percentages the procedure in Article 6
can be shortened somewhat by using a modified form of equation 11-6-1.
If we let P stand for the frequency of any group expressed as a percentage
of the total variates that is, if we let $P = 100f/N$, then we can rewrite
equation 11-6-1 as follows: The standard deviation of P is $100/N$ times
the standard deviation of f, since $100/N$ is a constant (see equation
10-7-3), and we have

$$\sigma_P = \frac{100}{N} \sqrt{f\left(1 - \frac{f}{N}\right)}$$

or, if we replace f by $PN/100$ and simplify,

$$\sigma_P = \sqrt{\frac{P(100 - P)}{N}} \tag{11-7-1}$$

As an illustration of this equation, let us consider the following problem.
On a public opinion survey, 37 per cent of the people polled in a given
state expressed a preference for a given tax measure. In one county of
that state, in which 1523 people were interviewed, only 32 per cent expressed a preference for the measure. Can you reasonably predict, on
the basis of this poll, that the actual election will also show a lower percentage of positive votes in the county than in the state, assuming that
there is no shift in public opinion between the time of the opinion poll and
the actual vote?

To answer this question, we must again begin by formulating a specific
hypothesis, and we choose the hypothesis which is most easily tested. In
this case we adopt (for testing) the hypothesis that the opinion in the
county is the same as that in the state; in other words, we assume that the
percentage of favorable votes in the county would have been 37 per cent
if all the voters had been polled. On this hypothesis, the actual percentage
of 32 per cent which we observed in the sample differed from the true
value of 37 per cent solely as a result of chance. To test this hypothesis,
we compute the standard deviation of the percentage from equation 11-7-1;

it is $\sqrt{\dfrac{37(100-37)}{1523}}$, or 1.24 per cent.   The observed value of 32 is therefore 4.0 standard deviations away from the expected value, and the probability that the difference could have arisen by chance under this hypothesis is less than 0.0001.   We conclude that the hypothesis is untenable, and that we can safely predict (ignoring other sources of error) that the actual vote in the county will agree with the opinion poll in showing a lower percentage in the county than in the state.

PROBLEMS

1.   An instructor in Ohio University gave an examination to a class of 74 members, which met at 8 A.M.   He told them that he planned to give the identical examination to a section (containing 82 members) which was to meet later in the day, and he asked them not to reveal the content of the examination.   In the early section 31 men failed, and in the later section only 11 failed.   The sections had been evenly matched in ability on earlier examination.   Is it more reasonable to believe that information was given to the second section by the first, or to believe that the difference is due to chance?

2.   In a sample of 100 students, it was found that 13 per cent smoked cigarette A and only 11 per cent smoked cigarette B.   Would you definitely expect cigarette A to be more popular on the average in the entire student body?

3.   If you believe that the difference in Problem 2 is significant, how many students would you interview in order to be reasonably certain of establishing the difference at the 0.01 level of significance?

4.   In the 1946-47 term, the voting record* of the Supreme Court in cases involving alleged civil rights violations was as follows:

Justice	For Claimed Right	Against Claimed Right
Rutledge	11	1
Murphy	10	1
Douglas	8	4
Black	8	4
Burton	3	9
Jackson	2	9
Frankfurter	2	10
Reed	2	10
Vinson	0	12

Does this indicate a systematic and predictable difference of voting attitude in civil rights cases between Murphy and Douglas?   Between Douglas and Jackson? Between Black and Frankfurter?   Between Murphy and Reed?

---

*Reprinted from *Truman Reshapes the Supreme Court* by Irving Dilliard, December, 1949, by permission of the Atlantic Monthly and Mr. Dilliard.   Copyright by the Atlantic Monthly, 1949.

5. In the 1947-48 term, the voting record was as follows:

Justice	For Claimed Right	Against Claimed Right
Rutledge	26	1
Murphy	25	2
Douglas	23	4
Black	19	7
Frankfurter	12	15
Jackson	7	20
Burton	6	21
Vinson	6	21
Reed	4	23

Is Rutledge's voting record significantly different between the two sessions?

6. Is Frankfurter's record significantly different between the two sessions? Assuming that such a difference exists, is it more reasonable to attribute it to a change in his attitude or to a change in the nature of the cases under consideration? (Hint: The hypothesis that there has been a change in the nature of the cases under consideration can be tested by comparing the total votes of the entire court in the first session with that in the second session.)

8.   CHI-SQUARE TEST

The procedure given in Article 6 is adequate for testing any hypothesis which predicts the frequency of occurrence in any single class. Frequently, however, the hypotheses which we wish to test contain predictions about a set of frequencies. As an example of such a situation, let us consider the problem of a set of dice which are to be tested for balance. One of them is thrown 360 times, with the results shown in Table 11-8-1. Would you conclude that the dice are probably defective, or probably not defective?

In order to proceed, we must make a definite hypothesis which will enable us to predict a set of frequencies. The hypothesis that the die is defective is of course useless, since it does not lead to a definite set of expected frequencies. We therefore adopt the opposite hypothesis, that the die is perfectly balanced. This leads us to a set of predicted frequencies, equal to 60 for each face. Now let us begin by considering the probability that the number of sixes will be exactly 58. By equation 11-6-2, the standard deviation of the expected frequency of 60 is 7.7. The deviation of the observed frequency from the predicted frequency in t units is $\frac{60-58}{7.7}$, or 0.26, and the probability per t unit of such a value of t is, by equation 6-5-1,

$$P(t) = \frac{1}{\sqrt{2\pi}} e^{-\frac{1}{2}[(60-58)/\sqrt{60}]^2}$$

or 0.39. The probability of occurrence of exactly 58 sixes is obtained by multiplying the probability per t unit by the number of t units contained in the interval from 57.5 to 58.5, which is simply 1/7.7 or 0.13. The probability of obtaining exactly 58 sixes is therefore 0.39×0.13 or 0.051. If we

TABLE 11-8-1.   Results of 360 Throws

Face	Frequency
6	58
5	42
4	87
3	61
2	63
1	49

generalize this, we have, for the probability of occurrence of a given frequency f_1, whose predicted value is f_p :

$$P(f_1) = Ce^{-\frac{1}{2}[(f_1-f_p)/\sqrt{f_p}]^2} = Ce^{-\frac{1}{2}[(f_1-f_p)^2/f_p]}$$

where C is used as an abbreviation for the constant multiplier. If f_2 is the observed frequency of the second class, its probability will be given by the same equation with f_2 replacing f_1, and with the meaning of f_p changed to indicate the predicted frequency of the *second* class. The probability that the frequency of the first class will be f_1 *and* that of the second class will be f_2 is the product of the two probabilities. If we continue this throughout all of the classes, the probability that all of the frequencies will be exactly those observed is

$$P(f_1 \text{ and } f_2 \text{ and } \cdots) = Ce^{-\frac{1}{2}[(f_1-f_p)^2/f_p]} \times Ce^{-\frac{1}{2}[(f_2-f_p)^2/f_p]} \times \cdots$$

We can simplify this by adding the exponents of e, according to equation 3-3-1:

$$P(f_1 \text{ and } f_2 \text{ and } \cdots) = C^m e^{-\frac{1}{2}[(f_1-f_p)^2/f_p+(f_2-f_p)^2/f_p+\cdots]} \qquad (11\text{-}8\text{-}1)$$

Let us abbreviate the sum in the exponent by means of a single symbol:

$$\chi^2 = \Sigma(f - f_p)^2/f_p \qquad (11\text{-}8\text{-}2)$$

This symbol is read "Chi-squared." With it, equation 11-8-1 becomes

$$P \text{ (of observed set of frequencies)} = C^m e^{-\frac{1}{2}\chi^2} \qquad (11\text{-}8\text{-}3)$$

This probability, however, is not a satisfactory measure of the degree of success of our hypothesis, for two reasons:

1. Any probability of a set of *specific* frequencies will be low. The probability of a frequency of 58, for example, was found to be only 0.051,

although it is obvious that 58 has a higher probability than any other frequency except 59, 60, 61, and 62. We are not so much interested in the probability of getting *exactly* 58 sixes as we are in knowing how its probability compares with the probability of other possible frequencies, that is, in *whether it is in a region of relatively high probabilities or not*. In the discussion of the reality of a given difference between means, we met this problem by computing the total probability that a difference this large or larger would occur by chance; in other words, we computed the *total probability of occurrence of all differences which were less likely than the observed difference*. If we apply the same principle here, we must sum equation 11-8-3 for all sets of frequencies which are less likely than the observed set. Since equation 11-8-3 itself measures the likelihood of occurrence of a set of frequencies, this means that we must sum it for all values of χ^2 which are larger than the observed value of χ^2.

2. We must make a distinction between a hypothesis which is independent of the observations and one which is shaped in part by the observations. It is always possible to contrive a hypothesis which is adjusted to fit the sample perfectly if we are permitted to make the hypothesis elaborate enough, but the success of the fit should not be accepted as a measure of the probability of the hypothesis. For instance, we could make the following hypothesis: The die is defective in such away that a four comes up 24.2 per cent of the time, while the others are all equally likely. In this way we have taken care of the largest discrepancy and the quality of the fit is greatly improved. The probability of a large deviation is now greatly reduced, and we must modify equation 11-8-3 to express this fact. If we had adjusted two constants, instead of one, to being about an exact agreement with the observations, we would have to reduce the probability of large deviations still farther. To accomplish this modification of equation 11-8-3 we must make use of a concept called the *number of degrees of freedom*, which is the number of classes for which we are comparing the observed to the predicted frequencies, minus the number of constants in the hypothesis which are adjusted to fit the data.

The modifications of equation 11-8-3 to allow for the *number of degrees of freedom*, and the summing of the resulting equation to measure the probability of all equally likely or less likely distributions, are too complex mathematically for us to discuss here. The resulting probability equation is very complex, and the values of the probability are in practice usually obtained from precomputed tables rather than from the equation. Such a table is contained in Appendix VI. To use it, we find the number of degrees of freedom in the left-hand column headed "n," we look across this line until we find the value nearest to the observed value of χ^2, and we then read at the top of the corresponding column the total probability of occurrence of all equally likely or less likely distributions. The use of the tables is straightforward and simple except for the determination of the number of degrees of freedom. This can be made clear most rapidly by means of illustrative examples:

I. Let us first test the hypothesis that the die described in Table 11-8-1 is correctly balanced. The procedure (demonstrated in Table 11-8·2), is as follows:

(1) Tabulate the observed and the predicted frequencies of each class (columns 2 and 3 in Table 11-8-2).

(2) If any class contains fewer than five variates, it is advisable to combine it with an adjacent class. (This rule is not applicable to Table 11-8-2 but is included here for future reference. For its use, see the example in Table 11-8-3.)

(3) List the differences between each observed frequency and the corresponding predicted frequency (column 4 of Table 11-8-2).

(4) List the squares of these differences (column 5).

(5) Divide each of these squares by the corresponding predicted frequency (column 6).

(6) Add this column, obtaining χ^2.

TABLE 11-8-2.   Chi-Square Test

x	f	f_p	$f - f_p$	$(f - f_p)^2$	$(f - f_p)^2/f_p$	
6	58	60	-2	4	0.07	Number of classes: 6
5	42	60	-18	324	5.40	Number of adjusted constants: 1
4	87	60	27	729	12.15	(total throws = 360)
3	61	60	1	1	0.02	Degrees of freedom: 5
2	63	60	3	9	0.15	$\chi^2 = 19.81$
1	49	60	-11	121	2.02	Prob. <0.01
					19.81	

(7) Count the number of constants contained in the hypothesis or the predicting equation which have been adjusted to fit the sample exactly. For the data in Table 11-8-2, the hypothesis is that all faces are equally likely, and in order to predict the frequency it is necessary to use the fact that the total number of throws must be 360. This number is fitted exactly to the data in the sample. The number of adjusted constants is therefore 1.

(8) Subtract this number from the final number of classes used in computing χ^2; obtaining n, the number of degrees of freedom. In the example, there are six classes and one adjusted constant, therefore there are five degrees of freedom.

(9) Find this value of n in the left-hand column of the tables; find the tabulated value on this row which is nearest to the observed value of χ^2; read the probability at the top of this column. In our example we find,

opposite $n = 5$, that the tabulated value of χ^2 which is nearest to our observed value (19.81) is 20.52. From the top of the column we see that the probability is therefore between 0.01 and 0.001, and nearer to the latter. Thus we see that the probability that the observed frequency could have occurred by chance if the die were perfectly balanced, plus all the probabilities than any other equally likely or less likely frequency could have occurred by chance, totals much less than 0.01. Thus if we accept the hypothesis that the die is balanced, we are forced to accept with it the conclusion that in selecting our sample we chanced upon an excessively unlikely distribution, so unlikely in fact that in scarcely more than one trial in a thousand would we expect to obtain this distribution or any other distribution of comparable likelihood. Being unwilling to accept the consequence, we are forced to relinquish the hypothesis, and we conclude that the hypothesis that the die is properly balanced must be rejected.

(10) The probability obtained in step 9 can be regarded as the conclusion of the χ^2 test and can be used as it stands as the basis for a practical decision about the hypothesis. However, some workers prefer to use an arbitrary scale such as the following:

> If P is greater than 0.1, the hypothesis is acceptable.
> If P is between 0.1 and 0.05, the hypothesis is doubtful.
> If P is less than 0.05, the hypothesis is not acceptable.

II. As a second example of the use of the chi-square test, let us consider the data in Table 6-9-1. This frequency tabulation appears to fit the normal curve fairly well, and the question arises as to whether the

TABLE 11-8-3.   Hypothesis of Normal Distribution

f	f_p	$f - f_p$	$(f - f_p)^2$	$(f - f_p)^2/f_p$		
1 ⎫						
2 ⎬	6.8	−1.8	3.2	0.47	Number of classes:	11
2 ⎭						
10	9.2	+0.8	0.6	0.07	Adjusted constants:	3
15	16.4	−1.4	2.0	0.12		
27	25.2	+1.8	3.2	0.13	$(\bar{x}, \sigma, N)$	
37	31.2	+5.8	33.6	1.08		
30	33.4	−3.4	11.6	0.35	Degrees of freedom:	8
34	30.4	+3.6	13.0	0.43		
18	23.3	−5.3	28.1	1.21	Probability of an	
13	13.4	−0.4	0.2	0.01	equally or less	
10	8.2	+1.8	3.2	0.39	likely set of	
4 ⎫					frequencies:	>0.5
2 ⎬	5.9	+1.1	1.2	0.20		
1 ⎭						
			$\chi^2 = 4.46$			

universe from which this sample was drawn is or is not normal, within the limits of observation. We must begin as usual by making a specific hypothesis which will permit the prediction of a set of frequencies; for this reason we adopt the hypothesis that the distribution is normal rather than that it is not. The chi-square test of this hypothesis is shown in Table 11-8-3.

To carry out the test, we begin by computing the predicted frequencies for each class. This step has been carried out in Table 6-9-1 and will not be repeated here. We next combine the small classes as shown in Table 11-8-3, so that there will be no predicted frequencies less than five. Finally, we must count the adjusted constants, in order to obtain the number of degrees of freedom.

To count the adjusted constants, let us review the procedure of fitting a normal curve. To compute the predicted frequencies we first convert the values of x into t units from the equation $t = (x - \bar{x})/\sigma$. In this equation, both $\bar{x}$ and σ have been computed from the observations and are therefore adjusted constants. Later, when the probabilities per class have been obtained, these are multiplied by N, the total number of observations, in order to obtain the predicted frequencies. Since N is determined by the sample size, it is also an adjusted constant. The total number of adjusted constants is therefore three ($\bar{x}$, σ, and N), and the number of degrees of freedom is therefore $11 - 3$, or 8. We see that the final probability is larger than 0.50, from which we conclude that the hypothesis of a normal distribution is acceptable.

PROBLEMS

1. Using the chi-square test, answer question XI, Article 4, Chapter 1.

2. In the data in Problem 4 of the preceding article, test the following hypothesis: The Justices are all alike in their attitudes toward civil rights cases, and the differences in their voting records are due to chance variations rather than to systematic and predictable differences of attitude. (Hint: Assign a half-vote in cases of abstention, and consider only the "for" votes.)

3. Test the hypothesis that the attitudes of all the Justices toward civil rights cases have remained unchanged between the 1946-1947 session and the 1947-48 session. (Hint: Use the percentage of "for" votes in the first session as a basis for predicting votes in the second session.)

4. Test the hypothesis that the attitudes of all the Justices except Frankfurter have remained unchanged between the two sessions.

5. Test the hypothesis that the two sets of temperatures in Tables 1-4-1 and 1-4-2 came from the same universe. (Hint: Compute the *percentages* of temperatures in the various classes in the first set, and use these as a basis for predicting the frequencies in these classes in the second set.)

6. Test the hypothesis that the temperatures in Table 2-3-2 (and Figure 2-4-1) were drawn from a normal universe.

7. Test the hypothesis that the distribution which Table 4-3-2 represents is

normal. (Note that the predicted frequencies are given in the answer to Problem 1, Article 9, Chapter 6.)

9. SUMMARY

When an investigator studies a sample, and deduces from it the properties which he believes the universe to have, he is forming a hypothesis which may or may not be true. The likelihood of such a hypothesis is determined indirectly by computing the likelihood that a sample drawn at random from such a universe will have the properties possessed by the actual sample.

The simplest such hypothesis arises when the investigator measures the properties of two samples, obtained under somewhat different conditions, and raises the question of whether or not there is a significant difference between the two; that is, of whether they could have come from the same universe or whether they probably came from two different universes. To answer this important question we compute the probability that, if two random samples are drawn from such a hypothetical single universe, the difference will be as large as or larger than the observed difference. The procedural details of this computation are summarized near the end of Article 2.

If it is found that the difference is not proved to be significant, but that there is some reason to believe that a significant difference may exist, then it may be desirable to plan a further experiment to answer the question decisively by increasing the size of the samples. The required sample size can be computed by the procedures described in Article 4.

In addition to forming hypotheses about the arithmetic mean of the universe, it is sometimes necessary to make a hypothesis about the dispersion of the universe. Such hypotheses can be tested by using the equation for the standard deviation of a standard deviation:

$$\sigma_\sigma = \frac{\sigma}{\sqrt{2N}}$$

The use of this equation is illustrated in Article 5.

Another kind of hypothesis about a universe is that concerning the size of a given frequency or a set of frequencies. To test such hypotheses we use the equation for the standard deviation of a frequency:

$$\sigma_f = \sqrt{f\left(1 - \frac{f}{N}\right)}$$

If the frequency is expressed as a percentage (P) of the variates, then its standard deviation is

$$\sigma_P = \sqrt{\frac{P(100 - P)}{N}}$$

The use of these equations is discussed in Articles 6 and 7.

If the hypothesis about the universe consists of an assertion about the relative abundance of the variates in several classes, then we must use a somewhat more elaborate test, called the chi-square test. To perform this test, we first compute the frequencies to be expected in the various classes if the hypothesis is correct and then compare these predicted frequencies with the actual observed frequencies. The details of the test are summarized in Article 8.

$\cdot$ 12 $\cdot$

MULTIPLE AND PARTIAL CORRELATION

1. INTRODUCTION

In Chapter 9 we studied the methods by which we can predict the value which any variable will have if we know the corresponding value of any related variable. We showed how the range of uncertainty of such a prediction could be estimated, and, finally, we set up a measure of the degree of relatedness of the two variables. This theory was adequate for any problem involving only two variables, but if we have instead three variables, all related to each other, several important questions arise.

(1). If we wish to predict a variable z and know the values of two related variables x and y, then the methods of Chapter 9 enable us to predict z from either x or y, but not both. In either case we may waste some potentially useful information. How can we make a prediction based upon x and y simultaneously and thus combine the usefulness of the two variables?

(2) How can we measure the total effectiveness of such a joint prediction; that is, how can we measure the degree of relatedness between z on the one hand and x and y *together* on the other?

(3) If x affects y, which in turn affects z, then there will be a statistical relationship between x and z. If, in addition, x affects z directly, this relationship will be still stronger. It would be helpful in untangling the cause-effect relationships involved if we could distinguish between these two situations. Is there any way to separate them mathematically?

The theory of multiple and partial correlation will cast some light upon these and related questions.

2. PREDICTION FROM TWO VARIABLES

The problem of predicting one variable from known values of two related variables can best be discussed by following a specific example. In a study of the factors affecting the grades of 450 students at Syracuse University, the intelligence of each student was measured by standard tests, and the number of hours per week which each student studied was recorded. If we let I stand for intelligence, S for hours of study per week, and G for the cumulative grade of any student, measured in honor points, then the results of the study were as follows:*

$$\bar{I} = 100.6 \qquad \sigma_I = 15.8 \qquad r_{IG} = +0.60$$

$$\bar{S} = 24 \qquad \sigma_S = 6 \qquad r_{SG} = +0.32$$

$$\bar{G} = 18.5 \qquad \sigma_G = 11.2 \qquad r_{IS} = -0.35$$

where the bars above the letters indicate arithmetic means, and where the terms r_{IG}, r_{SG}, and r_{IS} stand for the ordinary correlation coefficients between these variables in pairs.

Now let us set ourselves the problem of making the best possible prediction of the grade which any particular student might be expected to make, in the light of what we know about his intelligence and his study habits. In particular, if a student named John Schreiber has an intelligence measure of 121 and tells us that he usually studies about twenty-nine hours per week, what grade should be expect to make?

Before approaching this problem directly, let us see what can be done with it by the methods of Chapter 9. If we use equation 9-7-1 to predict his grade from his intelligence alone, we have

$$G_p = \bar{G} + \frac{\sigma_G}{\sigma_I} r_{IG}(I - \bar{I})$$

or, for our present problem,

$$G_p = 18.5 + \frac{11.2}{15.8} 0.60(121 - 100.6) = 27.2$$

The standard error of estimate of this prediction is given by 9-9-1:

$$S_G = \sigma_G \sqrt{1 - r_{IG}^2} = 11.2 \sqrt{1 - 0.6^2} = 9.0$$

This tells us that the best predicted value for Mr. Schreiber's grade average is 27.2 or 8.7 points above the average grade. But the standard error of estimate of this prediction is 8.96, and we see that the prediction is not very reliable. The probability, for example, that Mr. Schreiber will have a grade *below* the average, in spite of the prediction that his grade will be far above the average, is 0.166, as we find by the methods of Article 9 of Chapter 9.

If we follow the alternative procedure of predicting his grade average solely from his hours of study, we have the following result:

$$G_p = \bar{G} + \frac{\sigma_G}{\sigma_S} r_{GS}(S - \bar{S}) = 21.5$$

and $$S_G = \sigma_G \sqrt{1 - r_{GS}^2} = 10.6$$

*Based upon data from "Predicting Academic Success" by Mark A. May, *Journal of Educational Psychology*, 1923, Volume 14, pages 7 and 429, by permission of the publishers.

Here we find that the predicted grade is only three units above the average, and the standard error of estimate is even larger than before! Clearly what we need is a method of making a single prediction which utilizes all the available information. This is the first objective of the theory of multiple correlation.

The mathematical treatment of prediction from two variables follows the same principles as the treatment of prediction from a single variable, but the details are much lengthier. In view of this similarity, you should review the corresponding treatment of prediction from a single variable, using the following outline as a guide.

(1) In Chapter 8, Article 6, we showed that an important property which the prediction equation must possess is that it must minimize the sum of the squares of the errors of prediction.

(2) In Chapter 8, Article 8, we showed that for a prediction equation of the form $y_p = mx + b$, the values which m and b must have in order for the least squares criterion to be fulfilled are

$$m = \frac{\overline{xy} - \bar{x}\bar{y}}{\sigma_x^2} \quad \text{and} \quad b = \bar{y} - m\bar{x}$$

(3) In Chapter 9, Article 7, we showed that the resulting prediction equation could be simplified by introducing r, giving us finally the very simple form shown in equation 9-7-1,

$$y_p = \bar{y} + \frac{\sigma_y}{\sigma_x} r(x - \bar{x})$$

or, if we transpose the $\bar{y}$ and divide by σ_y, this takes the symmetrical form

$$\frac{y_p - \bar{y}}{\sigma_y} = r \frac{x - \bar{x}}{\sigma_x} \tag{12-2-1}$$

Now to extend this procedure to the prediction of a third variable, z, from known values of x and y, we begin by writing an equation similar to 12-2-1, but containing one additional variable:

$$\frac{z_p - \bar{z}}{\sigma_z} = A \frac{x - \bar{x}}{\sigma_x} + B \frac{y - \bar{y}}{\sigma_y} \tag{12-2-2}$$

where A and B are as yet unknown multipliers which we must choose in such a way that the criterion of least squares is satisfied. We must, in other words, choose A and B in such a way as to make the sum of the squares of the errors of prediction, that is, $\Sigma(z - z_p)^2$, as small as possible. If we insert the value given by 12-2-2 for z_p, we have

$$\Sigma(z - z_p)^2 = \Sigma\left[z - \bar{z} - \sigma_z\left(A \frac{x - \bar{x}}{\sigma_x} + B \frac{y - \bar{y}}{\sigma_y}\right)\right]^2 \tag{12-2-3}$$

or, if we divide both sides by N in order to secure the advantages of working with arithmetic means, and remove σ_z^2 as a factor,

$$\overline{(z - z_p)^2} = \sigma_z^2\left(\frac{z - \bar{z}}{\sigma_z} - A\frac{x - \bar{x}}{\sigma_x} - B\frac{y - \bar{y}}{\sigma_y}\right)^2$$

The right-hand side consists of three terms. If we square it out, leaving each of these three terms intact, we will obtain three squares and three cross products. The first of the square terms will be $\overline{(z - \bar{z})^2}/\sigma_z^2$, which is equal to σ_z^2/σ_z^2, or one. The first of the cross terms is $-2A\overline{(x - \bar{x})(z - \bar{z})}/\sigma_x\sigma_z$, which is equal to $-2Ar_{xz}$, as we can see from equation 9-6-2. If we simplify all the six terms in this way, we will have

$$\overline{(z - z_p)^2} = \sigma_z^2(1 - 2Ar_{xz} + A^2 - 2Br_{yz} + 2ABr_{xy} + B^2) \qquad (12\text{-}2\text{-}4)$$

Following the principles used in Article 8, Chapter 8, we group these terms as follows:

$$\overline{(z - z_p)^2} = \sigma_z^2[A^2 - 2A(r_{xz} - Br_{xy}) + \text{terms not containing } A]$$
$$= \sigma_z^2[A - (r_{xz} - Br_{xy})]^2 + \text{terms not containing } A$$

The terms $\sigma_z^2[A - (r_{xz} - Br_{xy})]^2$ must always be positive, since it is squared, and the smallest value which it can possibly take on is zero. To give it this smallest value, we must give A the value

$$A = r_{xz} - Br_{xy}$$

In the same way, we find that the value which we must give B to make the mean in 12-2-4 a minimum is

$$B = r_{yz} - Ar_{xy}$$

These two equations are not yet useful for finding A and B because the right-hand sides contain the quantities which we are trying to find. If we combine the two equations and solve for A and B, we obtain

$$\left.\begin{aligned} A &= \frac{r_{xz} - r_{xy}r_{yz}}{1 - r_{xy}^2} \\[2mm] B &= \frac{r_{yz} - r_{yx}r_{xz}}{1 - r_{xy}^2} \end{aligned}\right\} \qquad (12\text{-}2\text{-}5)$$

These two equations, together with 12-2-2, enable us to make a prediction of the most likely value of any variable from two other variables related to it. For the problem of predicting grades, these become

$$A = \frac{r_{IG} - r_{IS}r_{SG}}{1 - r_{IS}^2} = 0.81$$

$$B = \frac{r_{SG} - r_{SI}r_{IG}}{1 - r_{IS}^2} = 0.60$$

and the prediction equation is

$$\frac{G_p - \overline{G}}{\sigma_G} = 0.81 \frac{I - \overline{I}}{\sigma_I} + 0.60 \frac{S - \overline{S}}{\sigma_S} \qquad (12\text{-}2\text{-}6)$$

which gives us, for the case of Mr. Schreiber, a predicted grade as follows.

$$\frac{G_p - 18.5}{11.2} = 0.81 \frac{121 - 100.6}{15.8} + 0.60 \frac{29 - 24}{6}$$

or, upon solving, $G_p = 35.8$

To find the confidence limits of this prediction, we must derive an equation for the *standard error of estimate*. This quantity, it will be recalled, is defined as the square root of the mean of the squares of the errors of prediction:

$$S_z = \sqrt{\overline{(z - z_p)^2}}$$

We will use the same definition here, but will now use the notation $S_{z.xy}$, as a reminder that z is now being predicted from both x and y. We can obtain an equation for $S_{z.xy}$ by taking the square root of both sides of equation 12-2-4, and then substituting for A and B the values given by equations 12-2-5. The result, after simplifying, is

$$S_{z.xy} = \sigma_z \sqrt{1 - \frac{r_{xz}^2 - 2r_{xz}r_{xy}r_{yz} + r_{yz}^2}{1 - r_{xy}^2}} \qquad (12\text{-}2\text{-}7)$$

which is the required equation for the standard error of estimate for prediction from two variables. If we apply this to our illustrative example of the prediction of grades, we have

$$S_{G.IS} = \sigma_G \sqrt{1 - \frac{r_{IG}^2 - 2r_{IG}r_{IS}r_{SG} + r_{SG}^2}{1 - r_{IS}^2}} = 6.3$$

Thus we see that the *standard error of estimate of grades is much lower when we predict it from both intelligence and study than when we predict it from either factor alone.* If we express our results in terms of probable error, we see that Mr. Schreiber's predicted grade is 35.8 ± 4.2, whereas in the prediction from intelligence alone it was 27.2 ± 6.1, and from study alone it was 21.5 ± 7.1. If, instead, we express our results in terms of confidence limits at the 0.10 level, then the result tells us that we can expect Mr. Schreiber's grade to be between 25.8 and 47.0.

PROBLEMS

1. Complete the derivation of equations 12-2-5, supplying and explaining all the missing steps.

2. (More difficult) Complete the derivation of equation 12-2-7.

3. Using the data in Article 2, predict the grade which you would expect from a student with an intelligence measure of 87 who studies 14 hours per week.

4. What is the probability that the student in Problem 3 will actually make a grade of 20 or above?

5. Using the results of Problems 1 and 3, Article 11, Chapter 9, write the equation for predicting mathematics grades from both the old entrance test and the experimental test used together.

6. Compute the standard error of estimate of this prediction, and compare it with the standard error obtained when the old test is used alone. Is the improvement enough to justify the retention of the experimental test along with the old one?

7. Compute the standard error of estimate which you would obtain if you predicted language grades from both the old entrance test and the new experimental test. How does this compare with the standard error obtained by the use of the old test alone? Does the improvement justify the retention of the experimental test along with the old one?

3.   THE MULTIPLE CORRELATION COEFFICIENT

Before studying the definition of the multiple correlation coefficient, you should review briefly the derivation of the simple correlation coefficient described in Chapter 9, Articles 2, 3, and 4. An outline of the essential steps is as follows:

(1) Using y to denote the observed value and y_p to denote the predicted value, $y_p - \bar{y}$ becomes the predicted deviation of any variate from the mean, $y - y_p$ becomes the error of the prediction, and $y - \bar{y}$ becomes the total deviation from the mean. We pointed out that if these three quantities are averaged in any way, the average of $y_p - \bar{y}$ divided by the average of $y - \bar{y}$ is a measure of the degree to which the prediction has succeeded, and the average of $y - y_p$ divided by the average of $y - \bar{y}$ is a measure of the degree to which the prediction has failed.

(2) We then pointed out that these ratios could be interpreted as a "percentage of success" and a "percentage of failure" only if the averages are performed in such a way that the two ratios total 100 per cent.

(3) We showed that this condition is fulfilled if we square each deviation before averaging.

(4) Taking advantage of this fact, we then defined the coefficient of determination (D) as $\overline{(y_p - \bar{y})^2}$ (the explained variance) divided by $\overline{(y - \bar{y})^2}$ (the total variance). We also defined the coefficient of alienation (A) as $\overline{(y - y_p)^2}$ (the unexplained variance) divided by $\overline{(y - \bar{y})^2}$. These can be interpreted loosely as the "percentage of relatedness" and the "percentage of independence."

(5) For convenience in computation, we defined the coefficient of correlation (r) as the square root of D.

If we are to apply this same procedure to the case in which a variable z is predicted from two other variables, x and y, we must show that the sum of these two ratios is again equal to 1, in other words, that $\overline{(z_p - \bar{z})^2}$ plus $\overline{(z - z_p)^2}$ is equal to $\overline{(z - \bar{z})^2}$. We will again call these three quantities the explained variance, the unexplained variance, and the total variance. The first one is

$$\text{Expl. Var.} = \overline{(z_p - \bar{z})^2} = \sigma_z^2\left(A\,\frac{x - \bar{x}}{\sigma_x} + B\,\frac{y - \bar{y}}{\sigma_y}\right)^2$$

where we have substituted for $z_p - \bar{z}$ the value given by 12-2-2. If we now square out the right-hand side and separate the result into three separate means, the first term will be $\dfrac{A^2(x - \bar{x})^2}{\sigma_x^2}$, or $\dfrac{A^2\sigma_x^2}{\sigma_x^2}$, or simply A^2.

The cross product will be $\dfrac{2AB\overline{(x - \bar{x})(y - \bar{y})}}{\sigma_x\sigma_y}$, or $2ABr_{xy}$. The third term, in the same way, will become simply B^2. Inserting these values, we have

$$\text{Expl. Var.} = \sigma_z^2(A^2 + 2ABr_{xy} + B^2)$$

If we now substitute in this expression the values of A and B given by equation 12-2-5, we obtain, after simplifying,

$$\text{Expl. Var.} = \sigma_z^2\left[\frac{r_{yz}^2 - 2r_{yz}r_{xy}r_{xz} + r_{xz}^2}{1 - r_{xy}^2}\right] \tag{12-3-1}$$

The unexplained variance is $\overline{(z - z_p)^2}$, which is simply the square of the standard error of estimate. From 12-2-7 we have

$$\text{Unexpl. Var.} = \overline{(z - z_p)^2} = S_{z.xy}^2$$

$$= \sigma_z^2\left[1 - \frac{r_{yz}^2 - 2r_{yz}r_{xy}r_{xz} + r_{xz}^2}{1 - r_{xy}^2}\right] \tag{12-3-2}$$

By comparing equations 12-3-1 and 12-3-2 we observe that the important additive property of the variances holds also for multiple correlation. *The explained variance plus the unexplained variance equals the total variance.* The reasoning used in defining the simple coefficient of determination therefore applies to the case of multiple correlation as well, and we therefore define the coefficient of multiple determination as the ratio of the explained variance to the total variance;

$$D_{z.xy} = \frac{\overline{(z_p - \bar{z})^2}}{\overline{(z - \bar{z})^2}}$$

and the coefficient of multiple correlation as the square root of $D_{z.xy}$

$$r_{z.xy} = \sqrt{\frac{\overline{(z_p - \bar{z})^2}}{\overline{(z - \bar{z})^2}}}$$

Thus the coefficient of multiple correlation is the square root of the ratio of that part of the variance in z which is predictable by joint use of x and y to the total variance in z. To obtain an efficient equation for computing it we have only to divide the explained variance (as given by 12-3-1) by the total variance $(\sigma_z)^2$ and take the square root. The result is

$$r_{z.xy} = \sqrt{\frac{r_{xz}^2 - 2r_{xz}r_{xy}r_{yz} + r_{yz}^2}{1 - r_{xy}^2}} \qquad (12\text{-}3\text{-}3)$$

For the example of the relationship between grades, intelligence, and hours of study given in the preceding article, this equation gives us

$$r_{G.SI} = 0.82$$

To give this a concrete meaning, we must square it to obtain the coefficient of determination:

$$D_{G.IS} = 0.68.$$

Thus we see that 68 per cent of the variance in grades is related to the students' measurable intelligence and hours of study, leaving 32 per cent which is related to other variables.

PROBLEMS

1. Complete the derivation of equation 12-3-3, supplying and explaining all the missing steps.

2. Compute the coefficient of multiple correlation between mathematics grades and the two test scores, using the results which you obtained in Problems 1, 3, and 4, Article 11, Chapter 9.

3. What fraction of the total variance in math grades is predictable (a) from the old test alone? (b) From the new test alone? (c) From both tests used jointly? (d) What fraction is independent of both tests?

4 and 5. Repeat problems 2 and 3, applied now to the prediction of language grades instead of math grades.

4. PARTIAL CORRELATION

In the introduction to this chapter we raised three questions which were left unanswered or only partly answered by the simple theory of correlation. We have answered the first two of these questions by the theory of multiple correlation, and are now ready to devote our attention to the third. If a correlation exists between two variables, how can we tell whether it is a direct relationship or a relationship operating through a third intermediary variable? The significance of this question will become clear in the light of a specific example.

The United States was divided up into eighteen regions for statistical purposes, and the following three quantities were tabulated for each region for the year 1930: the number of suicides per 100,000 population; the mean age of the inhabitants, and an index measuring the frequency of business failures. The correlation coefficient between suicide rate and business failure was 0.40, that between suicide rate and age was 0.77, and that between age and business failure was 0.46*. The first of these

---

*These data are reprinted by permission of Prentice-Hall from *Applied General Statistics* by Croxton and Cowden, copyright 1939 by Prentice-Hall, Inc.

three figures suggests that failure in business might be an important direct factor in the motivation of suicide. However, an alternative possibility is that suicide is frequently motivated by factors connected with old age (such as ill health) and that business failure is caused by factors connected with old age (such as a decline of ability or of initiative). If this is true, it might be possible that the entire apparent relationship between business failure and suicide rate is due to the connection of both with the third variable and that business failure in itself is not an important motive for suicide. It is to give us some insight into problems like this that the theory of partial correlation has been developed.

Let us first state the problem in general terms. Two variables, x and y, are related to each other, directly or indirectly, with a known simple correlation coefficient r_{xy} . Both x and y are connected, to some extent, with a third variable, z, and we know the coefficients of correlation r_{xz} and r_{yz} . Can we, by means of mathematics, separate the direct causal relationship between x and y from the indirect causal relationship which operates through z?

To attack this problem, let us recall that the theory of simple correlation makes it possible to separate each value of x into a part (x_p) which is completely predictable from z, and a part (x_r) which is completely independent of z, as described in Article 2, Chapter 9. In the same way we can separate y into y_p and y_r , where the latter is completely independent of z. If we should now find the ordinary coefficient of correlation between *the part of x which is independent of z* and *the part of y which is independent of z*, we will have a measure of that part of the relatedness between x and y which does not operate through z or through anything related to z. Such a measure is called the partial correlation coefficient between x and y. It will be denoted by the symbol $r_{xy.z}$, where the z in the subscript is a reminder that the effect of z has been removed from both variables. It is obvious that $r_{xy.z}$ can be interpreted as the ordinary correlation coefficient which we would obtain between x and y in any subsample in which the values of z were all of the same size.

It would be possible, in any given problem, to carry out the operation described in the preceding paragraph and so derive the partial coefficient of correlation, but shorter methods can readily be derived. To avoid cumbersome subscripts, let us use the symbol X for the part of x which is independent of z, and Y for the part of y which is independent of z. In other words, let us let $X = x - x_p$, where x_p is the best value of x which can be predicted from a knowledge of z. This best predicted value can be found (with a suitable change of variables) from equation 9-7-2:

$$x_p = \bar{x} + \frac{\sigma_x}{\sigma_z} r_{xz}(z - \bar{z})$$

so that

$$X = (x - \bar{x}) - \frac{\sigma_x}{\sigma_z} r_{xz}(z - \bar{z}) \qquad (12\text{-}4\text{-}1)$$

Similarly,

$$Y = (y - \bar{y}) - \frac{\sigma_y}{\sigma_z} r_{yz}(z - \bar{z}) \tag{12-4-2}$$

The partial correlation coefficient $(r_{xy.z})$ which we wish to compute is simply the ordinary correlation coefficient between X and Y, which is, from equation 9-6-1,

$$r_{xy.z} = r_{XY} = \frac{\overline{XY} - \overline{X}\,\overline{Y}}{\sigma_X \sigma_Y} \tag{12-4-3}$$

We will evaluate the ingredients in this equation separately.

(1) If we take the arithmetic mean of both sides of equation 12-4-1, we have

$$\overline{X} = (\bar{x} - \bar{x}) - \frac{\sigma_x}{\sigma_z} r_{xz}(\bar{z} - \bar{z}) = 0$$

Similarly, $\overline{Y} = 0$.

(2) The standard deviation of X can be obtained by applying equation 4-4-1. Remembering that $\overline{X} = 0$, this becomes $\sigma_X = \sqrt{\overline{X^2}}$, or, inserting 12-4-1, squaring, and simplifying,

$$\sigma_X = \sqrt{\overline{(x - \bar{x})^2} - 2\overline{(x - \bar{x})(z - \bar{z})}r_{xz}\left(\frac{\sigma_x}{\sigma_z}\right) + r_{xz}^2\left(\frac{\sigma_x}{\sigma_z}\right)^2\overline{(z - \bar{z})^2}}$$

We recognize $\overline{(x - \bar{x})^2}$ and $\overline{(z - \bar{z})^2}$ as σ_x^2 and σ_z^2 respectively, and from 9-6-2 we recognize $\overline{(x - \bar{x})(z - \bar{z})}$ as $r_{xz}\sigma_x\sigma_z$. Making these substitutions and simplifying, we have

$$\sigma_X = \sigma_x \sqrt{1 - r_{xz}^2}$$

Similarly,

$$\sigma_Y = \sigma_y \sqrt{1 - r_{yz}^2}$$

(3) We obtain $\overline{XY}$ by multiplying together the values given by 12-4-1 and 12-4-2, forming the mean, and simplifying as before:

$$\overline{XY} = \sigma_x \sigma_y (r_{xy} - r_{xz} r_{yz})$$

Substituting these results in 12-4-3, we have

$$r_{xy.z} = \frac{r_{xy} - r_{xz} r_{yz}}{\sqrt{(1 - r_{xz}^2)(1 - r_{yz}^2)}} \tag{12-4-4}$$

We thus see that $r_{xy.z}$ can be obtained directly from the separate correlation coefficients, without the labor of computing the portions of each individual x and y which are independent of z. To apply this result to the problem of the relationship between business failure and suicide rate, let us denote the suicide rate by S, the business failure index by F, and the average age by A. Then, applying 12-4-4,

$$r_{SF.A} = \frac{r_{SF} - r_{SA}r_{FA}}{\sqrt{(1 - r_{SA}^2)(1 - r_{FA}^2)}}$$

$$= \frac{0.40 - (0.77)(0.46)}{\sqrt{(1 - 0.77^2)(1 - 0.46^2)}} = 0.081$$

Thus we see that when the effect of age has been removed from both factors, there remains only a negligibly small relationship between business failure and suicide rate. Stated in another way, we see that if it were possible to obtain a sufficiently large subsample of communities all with the same average age, then the ordinary correlation coefficient between business failure and suicide rate within this subsample would be only 0.081. We conclude that business failure is of extremely little importance in the motivation of suicide.

The partial correlation coefficient in the above example turned out to be smaller than the original correlation coefficient between the two variates. To see that this is not always the case, let us consider the data given in the preceding articles for the intelligence (I) of 450 students at Syracuse University, their grade average (G) in terms of honor points, and their hours of study (S) per week:

$$r_{GS} = +0.32$$

$$r_{GI} = +0.60$$

$$r_{IS} = -0.35$$

If a student examines these results with the purpose of estimating the grade improvement which he could expect if he were to study more hours per week, he might reason as follows: "The first coefficient, 0.32, indicates a moderate relationship between study and grades, and one explanation for this relationship is that more study causes higher grades. On the other hand, it is possible that the more intelligent students are motivated to study more, and it is certain that the more intelligent students get higher grades because of their greater intelligence. Thus the apparent relationship between grades and study may reflect merely the degree to which both are controlled by intelligence, in which case, since I cannot alter my intelligence, more study would be useless. For my purposes, it would be better to know the correlation coefficient between study and grades *for the subgroup of students who have nearly the same intelligence that I have.*" This latter quantity can be obtained from 12-4-4:

$$r_{GS.I} = \frac{0.32 - (0.60)(-0.35)}{\sqrt{(1 - 0.60^2)(1 - 0.35^2)}} = 0.71$$

Thus we see that the relationship between grades and study *for students of a given intelligence* is much stronger than it is for the student body as a whole.

To cast further light upon this situation, let us compute the partial correlation coefficient between intelligence and grades, with the effect of study removed,

$$r_{IG.S} = 0.80$$

which is again larger than the simple correlation coefficient (0.60) between these variables. In other words, intelligence has a strong effect upon grades, for students who study a fixed number of hours per week, but in the general student body this effect is partially obscured because we mix together students of various study habits.

The explanation of these interrelationships is obviously that a student with a high intelligence can use it in either of two ways: first, he can study an average amount and make high grades; second, he can content himself with average grades, in which case he needs to study only a very little. If many of the intelligent students make the latter choice and work only a few hours a week to secure mediocre grades, then the intelligent students as a whole will have little higher grades than the others. In this case the causal relationship between intelligence and grades will not appear very strongly in an overall tabulation, but will become apparent when we compare students who study the same number of hours per week. Since this is exactly what we observe, it appears that many of the intelligent students make the second of the two choices.

To verify the sad conclusion that intelligent students frequently become very lazy, let us compute the relationship between intelligence and hours of study for any subgroup of students all receiving the same grades:

$$r_{IS.G} = -0.72$$

Thus we would expect that for all the students who have a "C" average (for example) there is a *very high negative correlation* between intelligence and hours of study. The group therefore includes many gifted students who work very little, and many intrinsically poor students who work very hard to compensate for their shortcomings.

One word of caution may be appropriate before we leave the topic of partial correlation. When we find that $r_{AB.C}$ is very much smaller than r_{AB}, it is customary to accept this as evidence that the causal relationship between A and B operates through C, rather than directly between A and B, since the relationship vanishes upon removing the effect of C upon both A and B. But a review of the method will show that we not only remove the effect of C upon A and B, but also remove the effect of any variable which is strongly related to C, and we must therefore make our conclusion a little weaker: If $r_{AB.C}$ is very much smaller than r_{AB}, then it is likely that the original causal relationship operated not directly between

A and B, but indirectly through C, or through some variable or variables which are related to C.

PROBLEMS

1. In a study of college dating, it was shown that there was a negative correlation between the number of dates per week and the grades obtained in school. This was interpreted to mean that "too much dating is bad for the students' minds" and diminishes their ability to concentrate on their work. An alternative explanation was simply that dating took time which might otherwise be spent on study. The correlation coefficients are:

$$r_{DG} = -0.42$$

$$r_{DS} = -0.55$$

$$r_{SG} = 0.77$$

where D is the number of dates per week, S is the hours of study per week, and G is the student's grade. Compute $r_{DG.S}$ and comment upon the tenability of the second explanation.

2. Given the information that r_{EI} is 0.72, r_{AI} is 0.64, and r_{AE} is 0.51, where I is the income of each individual, E is the number of years of education which he has received, and A is his native ability as measured by intelligence tests. Does this indicate that more education is likely to increase the income of any individual, or does it simply reflect the fact that people with higher ability have more earning power on the one hand and are likely to remain in school longer on the other hand?

3. Using the results of the problems in Article 11, Chapter 9, compute $r_{LE.X}$, and discuss the possible reasons for its difference from r_{LE}.

4. Compute $r_{ME.X}$. How does this differ from the situation in Problem 3?

5. SUMMARY

There are two central topics in this chapter. The first is that of multiple correlation and regression, which is concerned with the prediction of one variable from several other variables used simultaneously. The second, which is related mathematically but is quite different in objective, is that of partial correlation, which is concerned with the analysis of the channels through which various causes may operate on a given variable. The operational procedures and interpretations of these two topics will be summarized separately.

I. Multiple Correlation and Regression

1. PREDICTION EQUATIONS. If a variate z is to be estimated or predicted, and two related variates x and y are known, then a much better prediction can generally be secured by using x and y simultaneously in a single equation than can be secured by using either of them alone. To make such a prediction, the successive steps are as follows:

(a) Compute $\bar{x}$, $\bar{y}$, $\bar{z}$, σ_x, σ_y, and σ_z. This step can conveniently be combined with step b.

(b) Compute the ordinary coefficients of correlation between x, y, and z. Call these r_{xy}, r_{xz}, and r_{yz}.

(c) Compute A and B from equations 12-2-5:

$$A = \frac{r_{xz} - r_{xy}r_{yz}}{1 - r_{xy}^2}$$

$$B = \frac{r_{yz} - r_{xz}r_{xy}}{1 - r_{xy}^2}$$

(d) Insert these in equation 12-2-2:

$$\frac{z_p - \bar{z}}{\sigma_z} = A\,\frac{x - \bar{x}}{\sigma_x} + B\,\frac{y - \bar{y}}{\sigma_y}$$

This is the required regression equation. Its use is illustrated in Article 2.

2. STANDARD ERROR OF ESTIMATE. When a prediction has been made by means of the above equations, its standard error can be computed by equation 12-2-7:

$$S_{z.xy} = \sigma_z\sqrt{1 - \frac{r_{xz}^2 - 2r_{xz}r_{xy}r_{yz} + r_{yz}^2}{1 - r_{xy}^2}}$$

This has the same meaning as the standard error of estimate in simple correlation theory. It is the square root of the mean of the squares of the errors of estimation. It can be used, with the normal curve tables, to compute the probability that the true value will lie between any given limits.

3. COEFFICIENT OF MULTIPLE CORRELATION. This quantity is computed by means of equation 12-3-3:

$$r_{z.xy} = \sqrt{\frac{r_{xz}^2 - 2r_{xz}r_{xy}r_{yz} + r_{yz}^2}{1 - r_{xy}^2}}$$

To interpret a given value of $r_{z.xy}$, it is desirable first to square it to obtain the coefficient of multiple determination, $D_{z.xy}$, which is then the fraction of the total variance which is explained or predicted by the multiple regression equation. It can be thought of as that fraction of the total causation of z which is related to x and y. The computation and interpretation of this quantity is illustrated in Article 3.

II. Partial Correlation

1. COEFFICIENT OF PARTIAL CORRELATION. This is computed from equation 12-4-4:

$$r_{xy.z} = \frac{r_{xy} - r_{xz}r_{yz}}{\sqrt{(1 - r_{xz}^2)(1 - r_{yz}^2)}}$$

This quantity is the ordinary coefficient of correlation between the part of x which remains when the effect of z is removed, and the part of y which remains when the effect of z is removed.

2. INTERPRETATION. If we assume that variations in x are causing variations in y, then $r_{xy \cdot z}$ measures the part of the causation which acts directly rather than through the intermediate quantity z. If the coefficient of partial correlation is very nearly zero, then we know that any causative effect of x on y does not act directly but instead acts entirely through the intermediate variable z or through variables related to z. If, on the other hand, the partial coefficient of correlation is of about the same size as the ordinary coefficient, then we know that the causation does not act through z or through variables related to z, but instead acts directly upon y, or possibly through other variables not under consideration which are independent of z. As in the case of simple and multiple correlation theory, it should be borne in mind that the mathematical analysis contains no information about the *nature* of the causal relationship, but only about the *strength* of the relationship. Some applications of the partial correlation coefficient are discussed in Article 4.

CHAPTER
. 13 .
STATISTICS AND COMMON SENSE

1. INTRODUCTION

It is customary in many circles to be suspicious of conclusions drawn from mathematical analysis of statistical data. This is to some extent attributable to the fact that the methods of statistical analysis have frequently been misused. Some of this misuse has undoubtedly arisen from intentional dishonesty, but by far the larger share has been due to carelessness or ineptness on the part of the investigator. In this chapter we shall point out a few of the pitfalls against which you should guard, both in performing statistical analyses of your own and in interpreting the results of others. These pitfalls have been grouped into somewhat similar classes for convenience, but the classification is based upon differences of emphasis rather than differences of kind, and many of the illustrative cases could have been placed in any of several classifications with equal validity.

2. INADEQUATE INFORMATION ABOUT DATA

This first classification of statistical fallacies covers a variety of errors which arise because the investigator allows himself to lose touch with the exact meaning of the original data upon which he is basing his study. It should always be remembered that the data in statistical tabulations constitutes a much abbreviated description of events which may have been very complex, and if the investigator is to use the data intelligently, he must know exactly how these complex events were reduced to numbers in tables. If, for example, you should find that an annual report of traffic accidents shows a 5 per cent increase in accidents due to intoxication as compared to last year, you might perhaps regard this as evidence of a real increase in drunken driving. But, totally aside from the question of whether the difference is large enough to be statistically significant, there is a strong question of whether the numbers in the table mean exactly what they appear to mean. If Mr. John Oatman, while driving his 1940 Plymouth home after having had two cocktails, speeds up to 35 miles per hour in a 25 mile zone and bumps the rear end of another car, what is the cause of the accident? Poor visibility? It was raining but there was "no actual fog." Physical handicaps of driver? Mr. Oatman was not wearing his glasses and has a driver's license which permits him to drive only with glasses. Defects in vehicle? The brakes were passed at the last inspection; maybe they've gotten a little out of adjustment since then. At some point a complex judgment has to be made to convert Mr. Oatman into a statistic. Perhaps the increase in the percentage of accidents due to drunkenness (as tabulated) represents a true increase in drunken driving. Perhaps it merely represents the fact that as a result of a few serious accidents involving drunkenness the enforcement officers have become more severe with drivers who have been drinking, so that more borderline cases get into this classification. The only persons who are qualified to interpret the results are those who are thoroughly familiar with the details of the machinery for collecting the original data.

The same problem of subjective effects on the part of the original collector of data is sometimes conspicuous in tabulations of vital statistics. Doctors have frequently commented upon the fact that in tabulations of causes of death there is a tendency for people to die of "fashionable" diseases. To see why this is so, we have only to picture a typical case of an elderly patient who is clearly approaching the end of his life span, and who is suffering from heart disease, high blood pressure, and kidney disease, any of which might result in death. The patient's condition deteriorates steadily and terminates in death, and the attending physician must then assign the cause of death. If we suppose that the doctor has recently read some important new articles about treatment of kidney disease, then he is likely to be particularly aware of this illness in the patient and perhaps is likely to emphasize it in choosing the cause of death. It would obviously be very unwise to accept at face value a small apparent increase in deaths due to such an illness.

The above examples are both concerned with a failure on the part of the investigator to be aware of possible *subjective effects* on the part of the man who first makes an entry in a table to describe an event. Another danger is that the investigator might be insufficiently informed about the exact *criteria of classification* of the original data. Given the figures on the number of farms in a given state, the number of hired men on these farms, and the total volume of farm products, all for two successive years, can you find whether the productivity per farm is increasing or decreasing, and whether the farmers are hiring more or fewer men than they did formerly? Before you could safely draw these conclusions, you would have to know exactly what the investigators in each of the two years meant by "farm," and "farmer," and "farm employee," and "farm product." If a retired policeman raises an acre of vegetables primarily for his own use, you would probably agree that he should not be counted as a farmer in a statistical tabulation; if he raises twenty acres of crops and sells 90 per cent of them, you would perhaps include him. If his brother helps him on the farm during a two-week vacation, he would hardly be described as a farm employee, but what if he works two months, or five months? Somewhere in this range an arbitrary line must be drawn. If the data have been properly collected, this line has been drawn exactly by means of a carefully worded quantitative definition, which admits of no uncertainty when it is applied to a specific case, and it is the duty of anyone who subsequently uses the data to know exactly what this definition is. In 1905, for instance, the United States Census of Agriculture defined a "farm" in such a way as to exclude any tract of land of less than 3 acres, unless agricultural products to the value of $250 or more were produced on it in the previous year. In 1910 the definition was changed somewhat. Clearly a direct comparison between these two years would be misleading unless the investigator was aware of the change of classification.

3. NON-REPRESENTATIVE SAMPLE

This is a statistical pitfall which probably outweighs in frequency of occurrence all the others combined; it is easily the most important pitfall of statistical analysis. We have seen that a statistician must frequently limit his study to a sample chosen at random, either for reasons of economy or because the sample is all that is available for study, and that he must draw his conclusions about the universe from his study of the sample. In any such study, a basic assumption is that the sample is random, that is, that it has been drawn in such a way that no particular kind of variate has any higher likelihood of being included in the sample than any other. At first glance, the selection of a random sample appears to be a simple matter, but in practice it is filled with unexpected difficulties. A few examples will indicate the nature of some of the difficulties to be encountered.

Public opinion polls in which the information is collected by phone or by mail are frequently unreliable. Even if the pollees are chosen at random from a telephone directory, they still represent only a random sample of *that part of the population which has telephone service*, which is quite different in economic level and in other ways from the part of the population which does not have telephone service. Mailing lists are sometimes chosen at random from the files of public utilities, and here the same kind of selection arises. The people who do not have electricity in their homes, for example, might be excluded from such a poll, and these people are likely to be from a lower than average economic level and therefore are likely to have a somewhat different political orientation from that of other groups. One of the classic examples of a non-representative sample of this sort was the 1936 public opinion poll carried out by the Literary Digest. More than ten million questionnaires were mailed out, and almost two and a half million were returned. On the basis of the opinions expressed, it was predicted that Landon would win 370 electoral votes to 161 for Roosevelt, while in the actual election Landon won 3 and Roosevelt 523! Here there was a second kind of selection operating as well, inasmuch as only about one-fourth of the questionnaires were returned.   The one-fourth who were sufficiently motivated to return the questionnaires were presumably the ones who felt most strongly about political matters, and it is possible that the ones who felt most strongly about political matters were primarily those who proposed to upset the status quo, that is, the Landon supporters! The case is particularly interesting because a careful study of the results of the poll itself would have revealed evidence of non-random selection.   Some of the pollees were asked "How did you vote in 1932?" and the results of this question indicated that about 50 per cent of the people answering the questionnaire voted for the Republican candidate in 1932.   But the overall vote in 1932 was almost 60 per cent Democratic!   The sample was therefore obviously drawn somewhat more heavily from the Republican voters than from the Democratic.   A similar situation occurred in the opinion polls preceding the Truman-Dewey election.

Examples of this kind of non-random sampling or bias can be enumerated indefinitely.   In one local tabulation the average size of the families in the region turned out to be surprisingly high.   Upon investigation it was found that: (1) the data was collected by door-to-door interviewers; (2) if no one was at home, an attempt was made to revisit the home later, but this had not been completely carried out and some of the homes were missed and not revisited.   Now it is obvious that in general the larger the family the greater is the probability that someone will be home when the interviewer calls, and that the omission of families where no one was at home represents a non-random omission with regard to family size.

A somewhat different kind of non-random sampling arose in the following case.   An article appeared recently by a physician who specialized in women's illnesses.   He participated in a semi-charity clinic and also carried on a private practice, and he wrote that he had become increasingly aware of the fact that the incidence of a certain illness among his private patients was much higher than it was among the "lower classes" whom he attended in the clinic.   Since the illness often resulted in sterility, he concluded that the "better classes" were being menaced by this extra margin of fertility in the "lower classes." His results were strongly criticized on the grounds that the clinic patients represented a more or less random sampling of various illnesses, while his private patients were strongly selected by the fact that he was a well-known specialist in this particular illness and would naturally tend to be chosen by people suffering from it who could afford to pay for their medical care!

Another sort of non-random sampling in medical statistics has been commented upon by Professor Wiener in his delightful book *The Human Use of Human Beings*: "In connection with mental cases, but also with many others, I wish to deplore the fast-and-loose way with which most doctors play with statistics. A disease is first recognized in those cases in which it assumes an acute or even fulminating form. Accordingly, the early statistics give a disease, whatever it may be, a high mortality rate, and a large list of complications. Later on, similar physiological or mental changes are recognized in patients who are less ill and who would probably have recovered anyhow. At least, many of them might have led a useful life for several years even without treatment. When treated, these less serious cases respond far better than the cases already doomed. 'Ah-ha,' says the doctor. 'Look at my statistics. My esteemed predecessors saved only half their patients, and I saved nine-tenths.' What a triumph for medicine.''*

Another particularly troublesome kind of non-random sampling arises in cases where the original selection of individuals is random, but in which the process of carrying out the investigation alters those individuals so that they are no longer representative. This problem appears in many guises. It is an easily demonstrated fact, for example, that interviewees sometimes tend to modify their answers in such a direction as to win the approval of the questioner.** A specific instance of a sample which is altered by the investigation is the following: There is currently being conducted in one of our large cities an experiment to determine all the long-range effects of good or ill health in children, and a set of representative families have been asked to cooperate by permitting the investigators to make periodic detailed physical examinations of their children and to study a number of possibly health-related factors such as, for example, grades in school and social adjustment. It is inevitable that the act of participation in the study, and the frequent health checkups, will increase the awareness of health problems in these families, so that their behavior in matters of health will no longer be representative of the population at large, no matter how successful the original random selection may have been.

The Fish and Game authorities in Ohio have been accustomed to estimate the fish population of the various lakes by netting large numbers of fish, marking them by clipping the end of one fin, returning them to the lake, and finally, after the marked fish have had time to mix thoroughly with the general population of the lake, netting samples of this mixed population. From the records of the number of marked fish known to be in the lake, and the observed percentage of fish which are found to be

---

*Reprinted from *The Human Use of Human Beings* by Prof. Norbert Wiener, by permission of the Riverside Press. Copyright by the Riverside Press.

**It is said that in rural areas investigators who ask "How many times a week on the average do you take a bath?" will receive answers centering around two or three, but if they ask "Which night of the week do you generally take your bath?" the answer is usually "Saturday"!

marked in the later samples, the total population of the lake can be found in an obvious way. The method yields results of high accuracy for small lakes, but for larger lakes the results are more and more obviously in error, and the authorities are now searching for a better method. Here the trouble is that the fish do not mix thoroughly, but tend to swim in schools, so that no sample can be trusted to be random with respect to the percentage of marked fish. Also there is a possibility that the process of netting and marking the fish alters their future behavior (for example, they may learn to avoid the net), and so alters their probability of being netted again in future. Here again we see that the investigator is unable to prevent his experiment from altering the properties of his sample.

4. CORRELATION AND CAUSATION

In the chapters on correlation we emphasized the fact that a correlation coefficient measures the degree to which two variables are related, but that it does not provide any direct information about the nature of the causal relationship. Failure to remember this leads to many a statistical absurdity. A popular joke among statisticians concerns the high coefficient of correlation which can be found between the average pay for school teachers and the total number of dollars per year spent for whiskey over the last century! This, it is pointed out, clearly indicates that it is folly to increase the pay of teachers, since it is obvious that any increase which they obtain will only be spent on whiskey! In this case the true explanation of the correlation is not difficult to find. During the interval covered, there was a steady decline in the purchasing power of money. Two dollars once represented a day's work, while ultimately it came to represent little more than an hour's work. This change produced a great increase in the monetary valuation of all commodities, including whiskey, teachers' labor, and many other things.

More serious examples are not difficult to find. For example, a typical misleading correlation is that between the suicide rate in various communities and the church attendance in these communities. Instead of indicating that religious people are more likely to commit suicide than non-religious people, this is again a case in which the two variables are not directly related causally, but are instead both related to a third variable, which in this case is the size of the community.

Another such example is the high correlation between the number of Jewish bakeries in various communities and the average wage of bakery employees in these communities. An inexperienced statistician might easily conclude that this indicated that wages in Jewish bakeries were higher than in comparable non-Jewish bakeries. Upon investigation, however, this turns out to be not the case. Instead, it can be shown that all bakeries in large cities have higher wage scales than those in small cities or rural communities, and it can also be shown that the percentage of Jewish population in large cities is generally higher than in rural areas. The Jewish bakeries and the non-Jewish bakeries *in any given community* are likely to have about the same wage scale. These are obviously problems in which partial correlation theory would clarify the causal relations.

5. INAPPROPRIATENESS OF DATA

Many statistical discussions are sound in logic but faulty because the data chosen to support the argument are not appropriate for the purpose. A simple example of inappropriate data is the following. Suppose that you are planning to travel from New York City to San Francisco by train or by air, and are curious about the relative safety of the two modes of travel. If you found that in 1950 there were 111 commercial aviation fatalities, in a total of 48,000,000 man hours of flying, or an average of 2.3 fatalities per million man hours of flying, while in railroad travel there were 3627 fatalities in 630,000,000 man hours of travel, or an average of 5.8 per million man hours of travel, would this justify you in choosing the plane on the grounds of its greater safety? Certainly not, for several obvious reasons and several not so obvious. In the first place, a given trip will require far more rail hours than air hours, and a better basis for comparison would be that of fatalities *per passenger mile*. In the second place, since accidents in flying frequently occur at takeoff or landing, a long trip has a lower fatality rate per passenger mile than a short trip, and we should investigate the fatalities per passenger mile for trips as long as the one you contemplate.

But these are secondary considerations; the important consideration is: Were the original data collected in such a way as to be applicable to the question under consideration? In this case a closer investigation will show that of the 3627 rail fatalities, 399 victims were railway employees, and these should obviously be excluded if we wish to evaluate the hazard to a passenger. Furthermore, 1218 were what the railway tabulators describe as "trespassers," and these should be excluded for the same reason, unless you are contemplating a trip to San Francisco on the rods underneath a freight car! But this is not the end; 1698 of the fatalities involved people killed at grade crossings, and in short, only 184 of the 3627 were ordinary paying passengers! When we have made a similar scrutiny of the data for air travel to be certain that the data are applicable to our problem, then we can draw a conclusion about relative safety.*

A special kind of inappropriateness of data arises when we choose an

---

*These figures are reprinted, with permission, from the 1950 report of the National Safety Council. For 1950, domestic scheduled air lines had 96 passenger deaths in 8,363,000,000 passenger miles, or 1.1 fatalities per 100,000,000 passenger miles, while the railroads had 184 passenger deaths in 31,800,000,000 passenger miles, or 0.58 per 100,000,000 passenger miles.

inappropriate average to sum up a complex situation. Suppose that you were working with a list of all the factories in a given community and that the data included the mean weekly wage in each factory. If you wished to know the mean weekly wage paid in factories in the community, would it be permissible to take a straight mean of these mean salaries? To do so would give equal weight to a large factory employing several thousand workers and a small factory employing half a dozen, and the result would be very misleading if, for example, the small factories paid lower wages. A more representative average would be obtained by weighting the individual means in proportion to the number of men employed at each factory.

6. FALLACY OF LARGE NUMBERS

This article will discuss a kind of statistical fallacy which is somewhat different from the preceding ones. The fallacies which we have already discussed are logical fallacies, while this one is psychological and overlaps several of the others.

Let us first comment upon the opposite fallacy, that of *small* numbers. When John Doe reads an advertisement which asserts that in a poll of ten famous film stars, five were found to smoke Brand A cigarettes, while only two smoked Brand B and only one Brand C, he will presumably be influenced to smoke Brand A in future. As a student of statistics, you might not agree with Mr. Doe's decision. Aside from the perplexing question of why you should be motivated to smoke Brand A simply because they are preferred by film stars, you might reasonably raise the question of whether the figures prove beyond a reasonable doubt that Brand A is in fact preferred by movie stars in general. With the methods of Chapter 11, you can readily prove that this is not a conclusion which you are justified in accepting as proved by the given facts.

The fallacy of large numbers, on the other hand, is one to which trained statisticians are unfortunately more susceptible. Let us describe it by means of an example. In a recent master's thesis, an education student attempted to show that a new experimental course which he conducted resulted in a demonstrable gain in understanding of motivations of people in problem situations. He distributed a mimeographed account of a problem situation at the beginning of the course and asked the students to write an analysis of it. At the end of the course he asked them to analyze the same case again, and he then distributed the pairs of analyses (without identification) to cooperating members of the faculty and asked them to decide which of the two showed more understanding of the problems involved. Each pair of papers was read by several judges, so that the scatter of the answers was available as a measure of the uncertainty of the measurement. The number of experimental students in the class was sufficiently large so that the probable error of the class mean was small, and the difference between the class ability at the beginning of the term and the end of the term turned out to be many times its probable error. The difference was thus overwhelmingly proved to be significant, and the investigator concluded that the value of the experimental course was established.

The fallacy of his conclusion lies in the fact that the argument is not merely a two-sided one but a three-sided one. The observed improvement may have been due to chance, or it may have been due to the effect of the experimental course, *or it may have been due to some totally different cause.* The investigator secured so overwhelming a defeat over the hypothesis of chance that he assumed that the job was finished, and overlooked the third antagonist altogether! During the time in which the experiment was in progress, the students of course were subjected to many influences besides the experimental class; they were attending other classes, meeting new people, and indulging in new activities, and any of these might have produced the observed improvement in understanding. The investigator's results proved that a significant improvement had occurred in the students, but he did not prove that his experimental course produced the change.

An excellent example of the "fallacy of large numbers" can be found in some of the analyses of the results of the intelligence tests given to United States soldiers in World War I. The tests were given to hundreds of thousands of men, so that the standard deviation of the mean of any subgroup is very small. Even a rather small difference between two subgroups will therefore be very large in comparison with its standard deviation, and the argument for its being statistically significant is therefore extremely strong. The difference between the intelligence scores of white and Negro soldiers, for example, is more than thirty times its probable error, and this constitutes a demonstration of statistical significance which is usually beyond the ordinary statistician's most ambitious hopes. This has sometimes led to the uncritical conclusion that Negro intelligence is inferior to that of whites. Subsequent investigations, however, have indicated that alternative explanations should be investigated. In particular, many of the questions used in the intelligence tests were based upon the assumption that the examinee is familiar with the household objects of everyday life in an average American home, and it is likely that this assumption is not fulfilled for people of very low economic status.

For an even more striking example, let us look again at the Literary Digest presidential poll. Both because of the dangers of faulty sampling, and the possibility of a systematic change of opinion between the poll and the actual election, it would be unrealistic to expect to be able to predict the actual outcome much more closely than 3 or 4 per cent, and this precision could be reached with a well-selected sample of about 500 in each state, according to equation 11-7-1. Since the investigators actually used a sample of more than two million (for all states combined) we must conclude that their procedure was very wasteful, and that furthermore the apparently high precision attainable by so large a sample led them to overvalue their results—a typical example of the "fallacy of large numbers!"

It should not be supposed from these remarks that the theoretical precision has no meaning. With a sample of two million, divided into two approximately equal groups, the standard deviation of the percentage in each group is 0.035 per cent, by 11-7-1. This represents *the precision with which the investigators can expect to duplicate their original results if they repeat their experiment under the same conditions.* In this case, however, the faulty sampling methods necessarily lead to a wrong result, and by using a large sample the investigators are merely measuring the wrong quantity with a higher and higher precision.

A special case of this fallacy occurs in the interpretation of the results of scientific measurements. When a scientist measures a single quantity by finding the mean of a number of repeated measurements, he usually computes the standard deviation of the mean, and, from it, the probable error. It is customary to accept such a result as indicating that the probability is one-half that the true value will lie within this distance of the scientist's value. This is, however, a stronger statement than is justified by the data; instead we can only say that the probability is one-half that the mean of the universe of measurements made *in the same way* will lie within this distance from the scientist's value. To equate the two statements we must assume that *the mean of the universe of similar measurements is the same as the true value of the quantity which he is attempting to measure,* and this is true only if the errors of measurement are random. If there is a systematic error, that is, an error which is always of the same size and in the same direction for all measurements, then the assumption is not valid, and the mean of the universe of measurements will differ from the true value of the quantity being measured. In such cases a small probable error obtained by combining a large number of observations is very misleading. It is paradoxical that a scientist can control the effects of a random—or unpredictable—error by statistical analysis, but has no defense against a systematic—or potentially predictable—error except through common sense study of his equipment and methods.

7. EXCESSIVE REFINEMENT OF WEAK DATA

This paragraph again concerns a topic which overlaps several of the preceding ones, namely, the tactical error of applying high-precision methods to basically poor data. In itself this is not a fallacy, since it does not necessarily lead to erroneous conclusions, but leads only to wasted time and effort. In its simplest and most harmless form, it is exemplified by the scientist who publishes a probable error to three decimals in a field where there is a strong likelihood that a systematic error will negate even the first decimal. In the problems of fish populations described in Article 3, the method now in use (1951) involves an application of the principle of maximum likelihood to each day's catch, so that the computation of the population for an entire season's catch requires many hours for each lake studied. Since the failure of the fish to mix thoroughly renders the entire computation highly uncertain, it would be better to average the results for the season and apply a single computation.

This fallacy has been commented upon very pungently by Sir Josiah Stamp, as follows: "Harold Cox, when a young man in India, quoted some Indian statistics to a judge. The judge replied, 'Cox, when you are a bit older, you will not quote Indian statistics with that assurance. The government are very keen on amassing statistics—they collect them, add them, raise them to the nth power, take the cube root and prepare wonderful diagrams. But what you must never forget is that every one of those figures comes in the first instance from the chowty dar (village watchman), who just puts down what he damn pleases.' "*

8. SOME USEFUL PRECAUTIONS

Some of the errors described in the preceding articles can be avoided by specialized techniques which will be described here, while others require no more than common sense and an alertness to the dangers of carelessness. The following suggestions will include both of these:

A. Keep in touch with the source of your data. If you are using data gathered by others investigators, make certain that you understand exactly what each number means and learn as much as you can about the exact process by which it was gathered. If you plan to collect your own data, then make certain that the principle of classification is specific and see that it includes exactly stated criteria for borderline cases. If your investigation requires the questioning of people, make the questions unambiguous and objective, and plan to ask them always in the same way. It may be desirable to test the questions on a small experimental group before deciding on their final form.

B. Plan your sampling technique so that every factor which might possibly contribute a bias is eliminated. If, for example, you wish to draw a sample of fifty names from an alphabetical list of 500, do not take the first fifty on the list. The first fifty might possibly contain, for instance, a large number of people named "Anderson," and the people with this name might consist of a large fraction of people of Scandinavian descent, who in turn might differ significantly from the population as a whole. Rather than investigate each of these rather remote possibilities, it is easier to

---

*Reprinted from *Some Economic Factors in Modern Life* by Sir Josiah Stamp, by permission of Staples Press, Ltd.

avoid any possibility of bias by choosing names distributed uniformly throughout the alphabet.

This problem is so important that statisticians have devised a special technique for combatting it, consisting of choosing a separate sample from each subgroup which might be suspected of differing from the entire population. If, for example, a public opinion poll is to be taken in a community in which 30 per cent of the population is Catholic, and if the investigator believes that there is any possibility that Catholic opinion might differ from the non-Catholic opinion on the point under investigation, then he should take care to select 30 per cent of his sample from the Catholic population and 70 per cent from the non-Catholic population. This is called *stratified sampling*.

An interesting contribution to the problem of avoiding bias has been offered by Professor Kinsey in *The Sexual Behavior of the Human Male*.* Professor Kinsey and his associates interviewed a large number of students in American colleges concerning their sexual behavior, the students being selected on the basis of their having volunteered for the interviews. It has been suggested that the results of the study are not representative of college students in general, since the sample consisted only of those students who were willing to discuss their sexual behavior, and the behavior of the more reticent students might be expected to be somewhat different. To meet this criticism, Professor Kinsey selected a few small colleges for saturation questioning and by appealing for cooperation he was able to interview the entire male student body. The results for this "One hundred per cent sample" did not differ appreciably from the preceding results from a volunteer sample, and the validity of his original sampling technique was thus established.

C. Analyze causes. If you are planning an experiment of your own, in which you wish to measure the effect of one variable upon another, then plan the experiment in such a way that any other possible causes of the variation are excluded. A widely used and well-known method for accomplishing this is the use of a "control group," a simple example of which is the following. A large university recently undertook to test the effectiveness of a proposed immunization against common colds. Half of the students who volunteered for the experiment were given an inoculation of the vaccine, and the other half, without knowing it, were given an inoculation of water instead. Any difference in the number of colds subsequently reported by the two groups must then have been due to the inoculation. If the control group had not been used, any apparent decrease in the number of colds might have been attributed to the milder weather, or to subjective effects in the reports made by the students, or to any of several possible causes other than the treatment. The graduate student

---

*W. B. Saunders Co., 1948.

mentioned in Article 6 could have validated his experiment by using a control group.

If you are using statistical data which was not obtained under control group conditions and if the cause of the observed effect is in doubt, then the use of partial correlation will often aid in eliminating or substantiating groups of possible causes. And finally, if you have not sufficient data for this and can obtain only a simple correlation coefficient, you should remember in reporting your results that the correlation coefficient measures only the *strength* of the relationship and that any statement you make about the *cause* of the relationship is an opinion, which must be based upon your knowledge of the situation and not upon your statistical analysis.

APPENDIX CONTENTS

• • •

LOGARITHMS   PROPORTIONAL PARTS

N	0	1	2	3	4	5	6	7	8	9	1 2 3	4 5 6	7 8 9
10	0000	0043	0086	0128	0170	0212	0253	0294	0334	0374	4 8 12	17 21 25	29 33 37
11	0414	0453	0492	0531	0569	0607	0645	0682	0719	0755	4 8 11	15 19 23	26 30 34
12	0792	0828	0864	0899	0934	0969	1004	1038	1072	1106	3 7 10	14 17 21	24 28 31
13	1139	1173	1206	1239	1271	1303	1335	1367	1399	1430	3 6 10	13 16 19	23 26 29
14	1461	1492	1523	1553	1584	1614	1644	1673	1703	1732	3 6 9	12 15 18	21 24 27
15	1761	1790	1818	1847	1875	1903	1931	1959	1987	2014	3 6 8	11 14 17	20 22 25
16	2041	2068	2095	2122	2148	2175	2201	2227	2253	2279	3 5 8	11 13 16	18 21 24
17	2304	2330	2355	2380	2405	2430	2455	2480	2504	2529	2 5 7	10 12 15	17 20 22
18	2553	2577	2601	2625	2648	2672	2695	2718	2742	2765	2 5 7	9 12 14	16 19 21
19	2788	2810	2833	2856	2878	2900	2923	2945	2967	2989	2 4 7	9 11 13	16 18 20
20	3010	3032	3054	3075	3096	3118	3139	3160	3181	3201	2 4 6	8 11 13	15 17 19
21	3222	3243	3263	3284	3304	3324	3345	3365	3385	3404	2 4 6	8 10 12	14 16 18
22	3424	3444	3464	3483	3502	3522	3541	3560	3579	3598	2 4 6	8 10 12	14 16 17
23	3617	3636	3655	3674	3692	3711	3729	3747	3766	3784	2 4 6	7 9 11	13 15 17
24	3802	3820	3838	3856	3874	3892	3909	3927	3945	3962	2 4 5	7 9 11	12 14 16
25	3979	3997	4014	4031	4048	4065	4082	4099	4116	4133	2 4 5	7 9 10	12 14 16
26	4150	4166	4183	4200	4216	4232	4249	4265	4281	4298	2 3 5	7 8 10	11 13 15
27	4314	4330	4346	4362	4378	4393	4409	4425	4440	4456	2 3 5	6 8 9	11 12 14
28	4472	4487	4502	4518	4533	4548	4564	4579	4594	4609	2 3 5	6 8 9	11 12 14
29	4624	4639	4654	4669	4683	4698	4713	4728	4742	4757	1 3 4	6 7 9	10 12 13
30	4771	4786	4800	4814	4829	4843	4857	4871	4886	4900	1 3 4	6 7 9	10 11 13
31	4914	4928	4942	4955	4969	4983	4997	5011	5024	5038	1 3 4	5 7 8	10 11 12
32	5051	5065	5079	5092	5105	5119	5132	5145	5159	5172	1 3 4	5 7 8	9 11 12
33	5185	5198	5211	5224	5237	5250	5263	5276	5289	5302	1 3 4	5 7 8	9 11 12
34	5315	5328	5340	5353	5366	5378	5391	5403	5416	5428	1 2 4	5 6 8	9 10 11
35	5441	5453	5465	5478	5490	5502	5514	5527	5539	5551	1 2 4	5 6 7	9 10 11
36	5563	5575	5587	5599	5611	5623	5635	5647	5658	5670	1 2 4	5 6 7	8 10 11
37	5682	5694	5705	5717	5729	5740	5752	5763	5775	5786	1 2 4	5 6 7	8 9 11
38	5798	5809	5821	5832	5843	5855	5866	5877	5888	5899	1 2 3	5 6 7	8 9 10
39	5911	5922	5933	5944	5955	5966	5977	5988	5999	6010	1 2 3	4 5 7	8 9 10
40	6021	6031	6042	6053	6064	6075	6085	6096	6107	6117	1 2 3	4 5 6	8 9 10
41	6128	6138	6149	6160	6170	6180	6191	6201	6212	6222	1 2 3	4 5 6	7 8 9
42	6232	6243	6253	6263	6274	6284	6294	6304	6314	6325	1 2 3	4 5 6	7 8 9
43	6335	6345	6355	6365	6375	6385	6395	6405	6415	6425	1 2 3	4 5 6	7 8 9
44	6435	6444	6454	6464	6474	6484	6493	6503	6513	6522	1 2 3	4 5 6	7 8 9
45	6532	6542	6551	6561	6571	6580	6590	6599	6609	6618	1 2 3	4 5 6	7 8 9
46	6628	6637	6646	6656	6665	6675	6684	6693	6702	6712	1 2 3	4 5 6	7 7 8
47	6721	6730	6739	6749	6758	6767	6776	6785	6794	6803	1 2 3	4 5 6	7 7 8
48	6812	6821	6830	6839	6848	6857	6866	6875	6884	6893	1 2 3	4 5 6	7 7 8
49	6902	6911	6920	6928	6937	6946	6955	6964	6972	6981	1 2 3	4 4 5	6 7 8
50	6990	6998	7007	7016	7024	7033	7042	7050	7059	7067	1 2 3	3 4 5	6 7 8
51	7076	7084	7093	7101	7110	7118	7126	7135	7143	7152	1 2 3	3 4 5	6 7 8
52	7160	7168	7177	7185	7193	7202	7210	7218	7226	7235	1 2 3	3 4 5	6 7 7
53	7243	7251	7259	7267	7275	7284	7292	7300	7308	7316	1 2 2	3 4 5	6 6 7
54	7324	7332	7340	7348	7356	7364	7372	7380	7388	7396	1 2 2	3 4 5	6 6 7
N	0	1	2	3	4	5	6	7	8	9	1 2 3	4 5 6	7 8 9

LOGARITHMS   PROPORTIONAL PARTS

N	0	1	2	3	4	5	6	7	8	9	1 2 3	4 5 6	7 8 9
55	7404	7412	7419	7427	7435	7443	7451	7459	7466	7474	1 2 2	3 4 5	5 6 7
56	7482	7490	7497	7505	7513	7520	7528	7536	7543	7551	1 2 2	3 4 5	5 6 7
57	7559	7566	7574	7582	7589	7597	7604	7612	7619	7627	1 1 2	3 4 5	5 6 7
58	7634	7642	7649	7657	7664	7672	7679	7686	7694	7701	1 1 2	3 4 4	5 6 7
59	7709	7716	7723	7731	7738	7745	7752	7760	7767	7774	1 1 2	3 4 4	5 6 7
60	7782	7789	7796	7803	7810	7818	7825	7832	7839	7846	1 1 2	3 4 4	5 6 6
61	7853	7860	7868	7875	7882	7889	7896	7903	7910	7917	1 1 2	3 3 4	5 6 6
62	7924	7931	7938	7945	7952	7959	7966	7973	7980	7987	1 1 2	3 3 4	5 5 6
63	7993	8000	8007	8014	8021	8028	8035	8041	8048	8055	1 1 2	3 3 4	5 5 6
64	8062	8069	8075	8082	8089	8096	8102	8109	8116	8122	1 1 2	3 3 4	5 5 6
65	8129	8136	8142	8149	8156	8162	8169	8176	8182	8189	1 1 2	3 3 4	5 5 6
66	8195	8202	8209	8215	8222	8228	8235	8241	8248	8254	1 1 2	3 3 4	5 5 6
67	8261	8267	8274	8280	8287	8293	8299	8306	8312	8319	1 1 2	3 3 4	5 5 6
68	8325	8331	8338	8344	8351	8357	8363	8370	8376	8382	1 1 2	3 3 4	4 5 6
69	8388	8395	8401	8407	8414	8420	8426	8432	8439	8445	1 1 2	3 3 4	4 5 6
70	8451	8457	8463	8470	8476	8482	8488	8494	8500	8506	1 1 2	3 3 4	4 5 6
71	8513	8519	8525	8531	8537	8543	8549	8555	8561	8567	1 1 2	3 3 4	4 5 6
72	8573	8579	8585	8591	8597	8603	8609	8615	8621	8627	1 1 2	3 3 4	4 5 6
73	8633	8639	8645	8651	8657	8663	8669	8675	8681	8686	1 1 2	2 3 4	4 5 5
74	8692	8698	8704	8710	8716	8722	8727	8733	8739	8745	1 1 2	2 3 4	4 5 5
75	8751	8756	8762	8768	8774	8779	8785	8791	8797	8802	1 1 2	2 3 3	4 5 5
76	8808	8814	8820	8825	8831	8837	8842	8848	8854	8859	1 1 2	2 3 3	4 4 5
77	8865	8871	8876	8882	8887	8893	8899	8904	8910	8915	1 1 2	2 3 3	4 4 5
78	8921	8927	8932	8938	8943	8949	8954	8960	8965	8971	1 1 2	2 3 3	4 4 5
79	8976	8982	8987	8993	8998	9004	9009	9015	9020	9025	1 1 2	2 3 3	4 4 5
80	9031	9036	9042	9047	9053	9058	9063	9069	9074	9079	1 1 2	2 3 3	4 4 5
81	9085	9090	9096	9101	9106	9112	9117	9122	9128	9133	1 1 2	2 3 3	4 4 5
82	9138	9143	9149	9154	9159	9165	9170	9175	9180	9186	1 1 2	2 3 3	4 4 5
83	9191	9196	9201	9206	9212	9217	9222	9227	9232	9238	1 1 2	2 3 3	4 4 5
84	9243	9248	9253	9258	9263	9269	9274	9279	9284	9289	1 1 2	2 3 3	4 4 5
85	9294	9299	9304	9309	9315	9320	9325	9330	9335	9340	1 1 2	2 3 3	4 4 5
86	9345	9350	9355	9360	9365	9370	9375	9380	9385	9390	1 1 2	2 3 3	4 4 5
87	9395	9400	9405	9410	9415	9420	9425	9430	9435	9440	1 1 2	2 3 3	4 4 5
88	9445	9450	9455	9460	9465	9469	9474	9479	9484	9489	0 1 1	2 2 3	3 4 4
89	9494	9499	9504	9509	9513	9518	9523	9528	9533	9538	0 1 1	2 2 3	3 4 4
90	9542	9547	9552	9557	9562	9566	9571	9576	9581	9586	0 1 1	2 2 3	3 4 4
91	9590	9595	9600	9605	9609	9614	9619	9624	9628	9633	0 1 1	2 2 3	3 4 4
92	9638	9643	9647	9652	9657	9661	9666	9671	9675	9680	0 1 1	2 2 3	3 4 4
93	9685	9689	9694	9699	9703	9708	9713	9717	9722	9727	0 1 1	2 2 3	3 4 4
94	9731	9736	9741	9745	9750	9754	9759	9763	9768	9773	0 1 1	2 2 3	3 4 4
95	9777	9782	9786	9791	9795	9800	9805	9809	9814	9818	0 1 1	2 2 3	3 4 4
96	9823	9827	9832	9836	9841	9845	9850	9854	9859	9863	0 1 1	2 2 3	3 4 4
97	9868	9872	9877	9881	9886	9890	9894	9899	9903	9908	0 1 1	2 2 3	3 4 4
98	9912	9917	9921	9926	9930	9934	9939	9943	9948	9952	0 1 1	2 2 3	3 3 4
99	9956	9961	9965	9969	9974	9978	9983	9987	9991	9996	0 1 1	2 2 3	3 3 4
N	0	1	2	3	4	5	6	7	8	9	1 2 3	4 5 6	7 8 9

N	$\log N$
1.005	.002166
1.010	.004321
1.015	.006466
1.020	.008600
1.025	.010724
1.030	.012837
1.035	.014940
1.040	.017033
1.045	.019116
1.050	.021189
1.055	.023252
1.060	.025306

(Based on 100,000 living at age 10)

Age	Surviving	Age	Surviving	Age	Surviving
10	100,000	40	78,106	70	38,569
11	99,251	41	77,341	71	36,178
12	98,505	42	76,567	72	33,730
13	97,762	43	75,782	73	31,243
14	97,022	44	74,985	74	28,738
15	96,285	45	74,173	75	26,237
16	95,550	46	73,345	76	23,761
17	94,818	47	72,497	77	21,330
18	94,089	48	71,627	78	18,961
19	93,362	49	70,731	79	16,670
20	92,637	50	69,804	80	14,474
21	91,914	51	68,842	81	12,383
22	91,192	52	67,841	82	10,419
23	90,471	53	66,797	83	8,603
24	89,751	54	65,706	84	6,955
25	89,032	55	64,563	85	5,485
26	88,314	56	63,364	86	4,193
27	87,596	57	62,104	87	3,079
28	86,878	58	60,779	88	2,146
29	86,160	59	59,385	89	1,402
30	85,441	60	57,917	90	847
31	84,721	61	56,371	91	462
32	84,000	62	54,743	92	216
33	83,277	63	53,030	93	79
34	82,551	64	51,230	94	21
35	81,822	65	49,341	95	3
36	81,090	66	47,361		
37	80,353	67	45,291		
38	79,611	68	43,133		
39	78,862	69	40,890		

t	.00	.01	.02	.03	.04	.05	.06	.07	.08	.09
0.0	.39894	.39892	.39886	.39876	.39862	.39844	.39822	.39797	.39767	.39733
0.1	.39695	.39654	.39608	.39559	.39505	.39448	.39387	.39322	.39253	.39181
0.2	.39104	.39024	.38940	.38853	.38762	.38667	.38568	.38466	.38361	.38251
0.3	.38139	.38023	.37903	.37780	.37654	.37524	.37391	.37255	.37115	.36973
0.4	.36827	.36678	.36526	.36371	.36213	.36053	.35889	.35723	.35553	.35381
0.5	.35207	.35029	.34849	.34667	.34482	.34294	.34105	.33912	.33718	.33521
0.6	.33322	.33121	.32918	.32713	.32506	.32297	.32086	.31874	.31659	.31443
0.7	.31225	.31006	.30785	.30563	.30339	.30114	.29887	.29659	.29431	.29200
0.8	.28969	.28737	.28504	.28269	.28034	.27798	.27562	.27324	.27086	.26848
0.9	.26609	.26369	.26129	.25888	.25647	.25406	.25164	.24923	.24681	.24439
1.0	.24197	.23955	.23713	.23471	.23230	.22988	.22747	.22506	.22265	.22025
1.1	.21785	.21546	.21307	.21069	.20831	.20594	.20357	.20121	.19886	.19652
1.2	.19419	.19186	.18954	.18724	.18494	.18265	.18037	.17810	.17585	.17360
1.3	.17137	.16915	.16694	.16474	.16256	.16038	.15822	.15608	.15395	.15183
1.4	.14973	.14764	.14556	.14350	.14146	.13943	.13742	.13542	.13344	.13147
1.5	.12952	.12758	.12566	.12376	.12188	.12001	.11816	.11632	.11450	.11270
1.6	.11092	.10915	.10741	.10567	.10396	.10226	.10059	.09893	.09728	.09566
1.7	.09405	.09246	.09089	.08933	.08780	.08628	.08478	.08329	.08183	.08038
1.8	.07895	.07754	.07614	.07477	.07341	.07206	.07074	.06943	.06814	.06687
1.9	.06562	.06439	.06316	.06195	.06077	.05959	.05844	.05730	.05618	.05508
2.0	.05399	.05292	.05186	.05082	.04980	.04879	.04780	.04682	.04586	.04491
2.1	.04398	.04307	.04217	.04128	.04041	.03955	.03871	.03788	.03706	.03626
2.2	.03547	.03470	.03394	.03319	.03246	.03174	.03103	.03034	.02965	.02898
2.3	.02833	.02768	.02705	.02643	.02582	.02522	.02463	.02406	.02349	.02294
2.4	.02239	.02186	.02134	.02083	.02033	.01984	.01936	.01889	.01842	.01797
2.5	.01753	.01709	.01667	.01625	.01585	.01545	.01506	.01468	.01431	.01394
2.6	.01358	.01323	.01289	.01256	.01223	.01191	.01160	.01130	.01100	.01071
2.7	.01042	.01014	.00987	.00961	.00935	.00909	.00885	.00861	.00837	.00814
2.8	.00792	.00770	.00748	.00727	.00707	.00687	.00668	.00649	.00631	.00613
2.9	.00595	.00578	.00562	.00545	.00530	.00514	.00499	.00485	.00471	.00457
3.0	.00443	.00430	.00417	.00405	.00393	.00381	.00370	.00358	.00348	.00337
3.1	.00327	.00317	.00307	.00298	.00288	.00279	.00271	.00262	.00254	.00246
3.2	.00238	.00231	.00224	.00216	.00210	.00203	.00196	.00190	.00184	.00178
3.3	.00172	.00167	.00161	.00156	.00151	.00146	.00141	.00136	.00132	.00127
3.4	.00123	.00119	.00115	.00111	.00107	.00104	.00100	.00097	.00094	.00090
3.5	.00087	.00084	.00081	.00079	.00076	.00073	.00071	.00068	.00066	.00063
3.6	.00061	.00059	.00057	.00055	.00053	.00051	.00049	.00047	.00046	.00044
3.7	.00042	.00041	.00039	.00038	.00037	.00035	.00034	.00033	.00031	.00030
3.8	.00029	.00028	.00027	.00026	.00025	.00024	.00023	.00022	.00021	.00021
3.9	.00020	.00019	.00018	.00018	.00017	.00016	.00016	.00015	.00014	.00014

t	0.0	0.2	0.4	0.6	0.8
4.	1.3×10^{-4}	5.9×10^{-5}	2.5×10^{-5}	1.0×10^{-5}	4.0×10^{-6}
5.	1.5×10^{-6}	5.4×10^{-7}	1.9×10^{-7}	6.2×10^{-8}	2.0×10^{-8}
6.	6.1×10^{-9}	1.8×10^{-9}	5.1×10^{-10}	1.4×10^{-10}	3.6×10^{-11}

t	.00	.01	.02	.03	.04	.05	.06	.07	.08	.09
0.0	.00000	.00399	.00798	.01197	.01595	.01994	.02392	.02790	.03188	.03586
0.1	.03983	.04380	.04776	.05172	.05567	.05962	.06356	.06749	.07142	.07535
0.2	.07926	.08317	.08706	.09095	.09483	.09871	.10257	.10642	.11026	.11409
0.3	.11791	.12172	.12552	.12930	.13307	.13683	.14058	.14431	.14803	.15173
0.4	.15542	.15910	.16276	.16640	.17003	.17364	.17724	.18082	.18439	.18793
0.5	.19146	.19497	.19847	.20194	.20540	.20884	.21226	.21566	.21904	.22240
0.6	.22575	.22907	.23237	.23565	.23891	.24215	.24537	.24857	.25175	.25490
0.7	.25804	.26115	.26424	.26730	.27035	.27337	.27637	.27935	.28230	.28524
0.8	.28814	.29103	.29389	.29673	.29955	.30234	.30511	.30785	.31057	.31327
0.9	.31594	.31859	.32121	.32381	.32639	.32894	.33147	.33398	.33646	.33891
1.0	.34134	.34375	.34614	.34850	.35083	.35314	.35543	.35769	.35993	.36214
1.1	.36433	.36650	.36864	.37076	.37286	.37493	.37698	.37900	.38100	.38298
1.2	.38493	.38686	.38877	.39065	.39251	.39435	.39617	.39796	.39973	.40147
1.3	.40320	.40490	.40658	.40824	.40988	.41149	.41309	.41466	.41621	.41774
1.4	.41924	.42073	.42220	.42364	.42507	.42647	.42786	.42922	.43056	.43189
1.5	.43319	.43448	.43574	.43699	.43822	.43943	.44062	.44179	.44295	.44408
1.6	.44520	.44630	.44738	.44845	.44950	.45053	.45154	.45254	.45352	.45449
1.7	.45543	.45637	.45728	.45818	.45907	.45994	.46080	.46164	.46246	.46327
1.8	.46407	.46485	.46562	.46638	.46712	.46784	.46856	.46926	.46995	.47062
1.9	.47128	.47193	.47257	.47320	.47381	.47441	.47500	.47558	.47615	.47670
2.0	.47725	.47778	.47831	.47882	.47932	.47982	.48030	.48077	.48124	.48169
2.1	.48214	.48257	.48300	.48341	.48382	.48422	.48461	.48500	.48537	.48574
2.2	.48610	.48645	.48679	.48713	.48745	.48778	.48809	.48840	.48870	.48899
2.3	.48928	.48956	.48983	.49010	.49036	.49061	.49086	.49111	.49134	.49158
2.4	.49180	.49202	.49224	.49245	.49266	.49286	.49305	.49324	.49343	.49361
2.5	.49379	.49396	.49413	.49430	.49446	.49461	.49477	.49492	.49506	.49520
2.6	.49534	.49547	.49560	.49573	.49585	.49598	.49609	.49621	.49632	.49643
2.7	.49653	.49664	.49683	.49683	.49693	.49702	.49711	.49720	.49728	.49736
2.8	.49744	.49752	.49760	.49767	.49774	.49781	.49788	.49795	.49801	.49807
2.9	.49813	.49819	.49825	.49831	.49836	.49841	.49846	.49851	.49856	.49861
3.0	.49865	.49869	.49874	.49878	.49882	.49886	.49889	.49893	.49897	.49900
3.1	.49903	.49906	.49910	.49913	.49916	.49918	.49921	.49924	.49926	.49929
3.2	.49931	.49934	.49936	.49938	.49940	.49942	.49944	.49946	.49948	.49050
3.3	.49952	.49953	.49055	.49957	.49958	.49960	.49951	.49962	.49964	.49965
3.4	.49966	.49968	.49969	.49970	.49971	.49972	.49973	.49974	.49975	.49976
3.5	.49977	.49978	.49978	.49979	.49980	.49981	.49981	.49982	.49983	.49983
3.6	.49984	.49985	.49985	.49986	.49986	.49987	.49987	.49988	.49988	.49989
3.7	.49989	.49990	.49990	.49990	.49991	.49991	.49992	.49992	.49992	.49992
3.8	.49993	.49993	.49993	.49994	.49994	.49994	.49994	.49995	.49995	.49995
3.9	.49995	.49995	.49996	.49996	.49996	.49996	.49996	.49996	.49997	.49997

t	0.0	0.2	0.4	0.6	0.8
4.	.499 968	.499 987	.499 994 6	.499 997 9	.499 999 21
5.	.499 999 71	.499 999 90	.499 999 967	.499 999 989	.499 999 996 7
6.	.499 999 999 01	.499 999 999 72	.499 999 999 922	.499 999 999 979	.499 999 999 995

P \ n	0.50	0.30	0.20	0.10	0.05	0.02	0.01	0.001
1	0.45	1.07	1.64	2.71	3.84	5.41	6.63	10.83
2	1.39	2.41	3.22	4.60	5.99	7.82	9.21	13.81
3	2.37	3.66	4.64	6.25	7.81	9.84	11.34	16.27
4	3.36	4.88	5.99	7.78	9.49	11.67	13.28	18.46
5	4.35	6.06	7.29	9.24	11.07	13.39	15.09	20.52
6	5.35	7.23	8.56	10.64	12.59	15.03	16.81	22.46
7	6.35	8.38	9.80	12.02	14.07	16.62	18.47	24.32
8	7.34	9.52	11.03	13.36	15.51	18.17	20.09	26.12
9	8.34	10.66	12.24	14.68	16.92	19.68	21.67	27.88
10	9.34	11.78	13.44	15.99	18.31	21.16	23.21	29.59
11	10.34	12.90	14.63	17.27	19.67	22.62	24.72	31.26
12	11.34	14.01	15.81	18.55	21.03	24.05	26.22	32.91
13	12.34	15.12	16.98	19.81	22.36	25.47	27.69	34.53
14	13.34	16.22	18.15	21.06	23.68	26.87	29.14	36.12
15	14.34	17.32	19.31	22.31	25.00	28.26	30.58	37.70
16	15.34	18.42	20.46	23.54	26.30	29.63	32.00	39.25
17	16.34	19.51	21.61	24.77	27.59	30.99	33.41	40.79
18	17.34	20.60	22.76	25.99	28.87	32.35	34.80	42.31
19	18.34	21.69	23.90	27.20	30.14	33.69	36.19	43.82
20	19.34	22.77	25.04	28.41	31.41	35.02	37.57	45.31
21	20.34	23.86	26.17	29.61	32.67	36.34	38.93	46.80
22	21.34	24.94	27.30	30.81	33.92	37.66	40.29	48.27
23	22.34	26.02	28.43	32.01	35.17	38.97	41.64	49.73
24	23.34	27.10	29.55	33.20	36.41	40.27	42.98	51.18
25	24.34	28.17	30.67	34.38	37.65	41.57	44.31	52.62
26	25.34	29.25	31.79	35.56	38.88	42.86	45.64	54.05
27	26.34	30.32	32.91	36.74	40.11	44.14	46.96	55.48
28	27.34	31.39	34.03	37.92	41.34	45.42	48.28	56.89
29	28.34	32.46	35.14	39.09	42.56	46.69	49.59	58.30
30	29.34	33.53	36.25	40.26	43.77	47.96	50.89	59.70

EXPONENTS

3-3-1 $A^x A^y = A^{x+y}$

3-3-5 $A^0 = 1 \quad (A \neq 0)$

3-3-2 $\dfrac{A^x}{A^y} = A^{x-y}$

3-3-6 $A^{-n} = \dfrac{1}{A^n} \quad (A \neq 0)$

3-3-3 $(A^x)^y = A^{xy}$

3-3-7 $A^{1/n} = \sqrt[n]{A}$

3-3-4 $A^1 = A$

ARITHMETIC MEAN

3-10-1 $\bar{x} = \dfrac{\Sigma x}{N}$

4-2-1 $\bar{x} = \dfrac{\Sigma fx}{N}$ (for frequency tabulations)

3-10-2 $\overline{x + y} = \bar{x} + \bar{y}$

3-10-5 $\bar{C} = C$

3-10-3 $\overline{x - y} = \bar{x} - \bar{y}$

4-4-2 $\bar{x} = x_0 + \overline{x - x_0}$

3-10-4 $\overline{Cx} = C\bar{x}$

4-5-4 $\bar{x} = x_0 + C\bar{u}$

STANDARD DEVIATION

4-3-2 $\sigma = \sqrt{\overline{(x - \bar{x})^2}}$

4-4-3 $\sigma = \sqrt{\overline{(x - x_0)^2} - \overline{(x - x_0)}^2}$

4-4-1 $\sigma = \sqrt{\overline{x^2} - \bar{x}^2}$

4-5-5 $\sigma = C\sqrt{\overline{u^2} - \bar{u}^2}$

PROBABILITY

5-2-1 $P(A) = \dfrac{s}{s + f}$

5-2-3 $P(\text{not } A) = 1 - P(A)$

5-7-1 $P(A \text{ and } B) = P(A) \times P(B \text{ if } A \text{ has occurred})$

5-8-1 $P(A \text{ or } B) = P(A) + P(B)$

5-10-2 $P(s) = \dfrac{n!p^s q^{n-s}}{s!(n - s)!}$

NORMAL CURVE

6-3-1 $t = \dfrac{x - \bar{x}}{\sigma}$

6-3-2 $P(t) = \dfrac{f\sigma}{NC}$

6-4-11 $\quad P(t) = \dfrac{n!\sqrt{n}}{\left(\dfrac{n - \sqrt{nt}}{2}\right)!\left(\dfrac{n + \sqrt{nt}}{2}\right)!2^{n+1}}$

6-5-1 $\quad P(t) = \dfrac{1}{\sqrt{2\pi}}\, e^{-t^2/2}$

CORRELATION

9-2-9 $\quad D = \dfrac{\text{Expl. var.}}{\text{Tot. var.}}$

9-3-1 $\quad r = \pm\sqrt{D}$

9-6-1 $\quad r = \dfrac{\overline{xy} - \bar{x}\bar{y}}{\sigma_x \sigma_y}$

9-6-2 $\quad r = \dfrac{\overline{(x - \bar{x})(y - \bar{y})}}{\sigma_x \sigma_y}$

9-10-1 $\quad r = \dfrac{\overline{(x - x_0)(y - y_0)} - \overline{(x - x_0)}\ \overline{(y - y_0)}}{\sigma_x \sigma_y}$

9-11-1 $\quad r = \dfrac{\overline{uv} - \bar{u}\bar{v}}{\sigma_u \sigma_v}$

9-14-5 $\quad r = 1 - \dfrac{6\Sigma(m - n)^2}{N(N^2 - 1)}$

9-15-1 $\quad r_u = \sqrt{r^2 - \dfrac{1 - r^2}{N - 2}}$

12-3-3 $\quad r_{z.xy} = \sqrt{\dfrac{r_{xz}^2 - 2r_{xz}r_{xy}r_{yz} + r_{yz}^2}{1 - r_{xy}^2}}$

12-4-4 $\quad r_{xy.z} = \dfrac{r_{xy} - r_{xz}r_{yz}}{\sqrt{(1 - r_{xz}^2)(1 - r_{yz}^2)}}$

REGRESSION

9-7-1 $\quad y_p = \bar{y} + \dfrac{\sigma_y}{\sigma_x} r(x - \bar{x})$

9-7-2 $\quad x_p = \bar{x} + \dfrac{\sigma_x}{\sigma_y} r(y - \bar{y})$

12-2-2 $\quad \dfrac{z_p - \bar{z}}{\sigma_z} = A\dfrac{x - \bar{x}}{\sigma_x} + B\dfrac{y - \bar{y}}{\sigma_y}$

12-2-5 $\quad \begin{cases} A = \dfrac{r_{xz} - r_{xy}r_{yz}}{1 - r_{xy}^2} \\[2ex] B = \dfrac{r_{yz} - r_{yx}r_{xz}}{1 - r_{xy}^2} \end{cases}$

RELIABILITY

10-4-1 $\sigma_{x-y} = \sqrt{\sigma_x^2 - 2\sigma_x r_{xy}\sigma_y + \sigma_y^2}$

10-6-1 $\sigma_{x+y} = \sqrt{\sigma_x^2 + 2\sigma_x r_{xy}\sigma_y + \sigma_y^2}$

10-7-4 $\sigma_{\bar{x}} = \dfrac{\sigma_x}{\sqrt{N}}$

10-5-1 $\sigma_\sigma = \dfrac{\sigma}{\sqrt{2N}}$

11-6-1 $\sigma_f = \sqrt{f\left(1 - \dfrac{f}{N}\right)}$

11-6-3 $\sigma_P = \sqrt{P\dfrac{100 - P}{N}}$

9-15-2 $\sigma_r = \dfrac{1 - r^2}{\sqrt{N - 1}}$

9-9-1 $S_y = \sigma_y\sqrt{1 - r^2}$

12-2-7 $S_{z.xy} = \sigma_z\sqrt{1 - \dfrac{r_{xz}^2 - 2r_{xz}r_{xy}r_{yz} + r_{yz}^2}{1 - r_{xy}^2}}$

SKEWNESS AND KURTOSIS

7-4-1 $\alpha_3 = \dfrac{\overline{(x - \bar{x})^3}}{\sigma_x^3} = \dfrac{\overline{u^3} - 3\overline{u^2}\bar{u} + 2\bar{u}^2}{\sigma_u^3}$

7-4-2 $\alpha_4 = \dfrac{\overline{(x - \bar{x})^4}}{\sigma_x^4} = \dfrac{\overline{u^4} - 4\overline{u^3}\bar{u} + 6\overline{u^2}\bar{u}^2 - 3\bar{u}^4}{\sigma_u^4}$

Blair, Morris Myers, *Elementary Statistics*, Henry Holt, 1944.

Brunt, David, *The Combination of Observations*, Cambridge University Press, 1931.

Camp, B. H., *Mathematical Part of Elementary Statistics*, D. C. Heath, 1931.

Croxton, F. E., and Cowden, D. J., *Applied General Statistics*, Prentice-Hall, 1939.

Davenport, C. B., and Ekas, M. P., *Statistical Methods in Biology, Medicine, and Psychology*, Wiley, 1936.

Davies, G. R., and Crowder, W. F., *Methods of Statistical Analysis in the Social Sciences*, Wiley, 1933.

Dixon, Wilfrid J., and Massey, Frank J., *An Introduction to Statistical Analysis*, McGraw-Hill, 1951.

Ezekiel, Mordecai, *Methods of Correlation Analysis*, Wiley, 1941.

Fisher, R. A., *Statistical Methods for Research Workers*, Oliver and Boyd, 1944.

Fry, T. C., *Probability and Its Engineering Uses*. Van Nostrand, 1928.

Garett, Henry E., *Statistics in Psychology and Education*, Longmans, Green, 1947.

Gavett, G. I., *A First Course in Statistical Method*, McGraw-Hill, 1937.

Hoel, Paul G., *Introduction to Mathematical Statistics*, Wiley, 1947.

Johnson, Palmer, O., *Statistical Methods in Research*, Prentice-Hall, 1949.

Kenney, J. F., *Mathematics of Statistics, Part One*, Van Nostrand, 1939.

Kramer, Edna E., *A First Course in Educational Statistics*, Wiley, 1935.

Lindquist, E. F., *Statistical Analysis in Educational Research*, Houghton Mifflin Co., 1940.

Mode, Elmer B., *The Elements of Statistics*, Prentice-Hall, 1945.

Mood, Alexander M., *Introduction to the Theory of Statistics*, McGraw-Hill, 1950.

Neyman, J., *First Course in Probability and Statistics*, Henry Holt, 1950.

Pearl, Raymond, *Introduction to Medical Biometry and Statistics*, W. B. Saunders Co , 1930.

Peters, C. C. and Van Voorhis, W. R., *Statistical Procedures and Their Mathematical Bases*, McGraw-Hill, 1940.

Richardson, C. H., *Introduction to Statistical Analysis*, Harcourt Brace, 1935.

Rietz, H. L., *et al.*, *Mathematical Statistics*, Open Court, 1927.

Snedecor, G. W., *Statistical Methods*, Collegiate Press, 1937.

Sorenson, Herbert, *Statistics for Students of Psychology and Education*, McGraw-Hill, 1936.

Walker, Helen M., *Elementary Statistical Methods*, Henry Holt, 1943.

Waugh, Albert E., *Elements of Statistical Method*, McGraw-Hill, 1943.

Yule, G. U., and Kendall, M. G., *An Introduction to the Theory of Statistics*, Charles Griffin, 1937.

Yule, G. U., *Introduction to the Theory of Statistics*, Lippincott, 1940.

ANSWERS TO PROBLEMS

• • ○

Chapter 2

ARTICLE 2

1. 201, 2; 202, 5; 203, 11; 204, 16; 205, 10; 206, 4; 207, 2.
2. (a) The third entry in Table 1-4-3, or 206. (b) The total number of variates, or 50.

ARTICLE 3

1.

Class	Table 1-4-1	Table 1-4-2
103.0–103.4	2	0
103.5–103.9	6	4
104.0–104.4	13	5
104.5–104.9	9	10
105.0–105.4	7	1
105.5–105.9	3	0

2. (a) 99.4; (b) 99.45; (c) 99.3; (d) 99.45; (e) 99.5.
3. (a) 201.5; (b) 201.

ARTICLE 5

1. The class interval should be about 4 or 5.

ARTICLE 6

1. (a) $M = 69$; (b) $Q_1 = 61$; (c) $D_9 = 92$; (d) $P_{73} = 81$. Your answers should not differ from these by more than one if your ogive is properly smoothed.
2. His percentile rating in language is 14; in mathematics, 32.

3.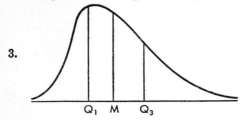

ARTICLE 7

2. (a) 46%; (b) 2%; (c) 4%; (d) 12%.

Chapter 3

ARTICLE 2

1. (a) 7; (b) 3; (c) 32.
2. (a) 2; (b) 3; (c) 9; (d) 125.
3. (a) 64; (b) 64; (c) 8; (d) 64; (e) 128; (f) 4.

ARTICLE 3

1. (a) 1/9; (b) 32; (c) 1; (d) 9; (e) 1/27.
2. (a) -3; (b) 0.5; (c) -2.5.

ARTICLE 4

1. (a) 3.5437; (b) 5.4719; (c) $6.4533 - 10$; (d) $4.9900 - 10$; (e) 0.5844; (f) 8.1653; (g) 0.4732; (h) $9.9117 - 10$.
2. (a) 3865; (b) 0.000,015,04; (c) 2.563; (d) 0.09416; (e) 1,944,000; (f) 9.602; (g) 0.2937; (h) 0.003215.

ARTICLE 5

1. 7,525,000	2. 0.1727.	3. 13.72.	4. 18.65.
5. 0.07158.	6. 15.10.	7. 6.396.	8. 31.80.
9. 0.08084.	10. 45.82.		

ARTICLE 6

1. $5538.   2. $8626.   3. $16,800,000,000,000,000,000,000,000,000.

ARTICLE 7

Your answers should agree with the following with an error not much larger than one part in a thousand:

1. 7.32.   2. 8.46.   3. 9.34.   4. 9.16.   5. 1.456.   6. 3.74.

ARTICLE 8

Your answers should agree with the following with an error not much larger than one part in a thousand.

1. 1635.   2. 16.53.   3. 55.4.   4. 3.58×10^{-8}.   5. 6.58×10^{6}.

6. 63.5.   7. 3.46×10^{-7}.   8. 13.6.   9. 42.9.   10. 527.

11. 0.0527.   12. 605.   13. 3.96.

ARTICLE 9

4. 400.   5. 15,243.   6. 75,625.   7. 2752.

ARTICLE 10

4. $\bar{z} = 97$; $\overline{x + z} = 152$; $\overline{yz} = 956$; $\bar{y}\bar{z} = 970$.

ARTICLE 11

1. 6 and 2650.   2. $31\frac{2}{3}$ and $697\frac{2}{3}$.

Chapter 4

ARTICLE 2

1. 98.93; 98.920. The small difference is due to the rounding off effect of forming a frequency tabulation.
2. 205.3. Yes, because each number in Table 2-2-1 agrees exactly with the corresponding class mark in Table 2-2-2.

ARTICLE 3

1. 3.27.   2. 3.19.

ARTICLE 4

1. 2.89.   2. $\bar{x} = 49639.1$; $\sigma = 4.57$. Equations 4-4-2 and 4-4-3 should be used.

ARTICLE 5

1. $\bar{x} = 104.48$ and $\sigma = 0.64$ for the data in 1-4-1; $\bar{x} = 104.40$ and $\sigma = 0.43$ for the data in 1-4-2. The distributions are nearly alike in arithmetic mean but differ greatly in dispersion.
2. $\bar{x} = 13$; $\sigma = 3.57$.
3. $\bar{x} = 80.93$; $\sigma = 5.11$.

Chapter 5

ARTICLE 2

1. (a) 0.250; (b) 0.500; (c) 0.308.
2. (a) 0.33; (b) 0.67.
3. (a) 0.0278; (b) 0.111; (c) 7.

ARTICLE 3

1. It is extremely unlikely that the kinds of fish are equally numerous in the lake, and the statement is therefore extremely weak.
2. (a) 12/45, or 0.267; (b) 9/45, or 0.200; (c) 8/38, or 0.211. The third of these is the most reliable, since it is based upon the most information.
3. (a) 2/7; (b) 1/6; (c) 1/6.

ARTICLE 4

1. (a) 0.84; (b) 0.63; (c) 0.16; (d) 0.00003.
2. (a) 0.27; (b) 0.038.
3. Between 66 and 67.
4. (a) 9/40; (b) 28/40.

ARTICLE 5

1. (a) $42. (b) $2273.
2. About a quarter of a cent. No; the tickets are worth only about 26¢.
3. $133.

ARTICLE 6

1. 0.24.   **2.** 1/36.   **3.** $(1 - 0.3)$ times $(1 - 0.4)$, or 0.42.
4. $\frac{2}{3} \times \frac{2}{3} \times \frac{2}{3}$, or 0.296.

ARTICLE 7

1. (a) 3/51 or 0.059; (b) 13/204 or 0.064; (c) 19/34 or 0.559.
2. 0.12.
3. $0.72 \times 0.87 \times 0.91$ or 0.570.
4. 0.252.

ARTICLE 8

1. 1/3.   **2.** 1/2.   **3.** $1 - 1/9$, or 8/9.

ARTICLE 9

2. (a) 8! or 40,320; (b) 7! or 5,040; (c) $8 \times 5 \times 4 \times 5!$ or 19,200; (d) $8 \times 3! \times 4!$ or 1152.
3. $P(15,6) = 3,603,600$.

ARTICLE 10

1. (a) 45/512 or 0.088; (b) 405/1024 or 0.396; (c) 1/1024 or 0.00098.
2. 5/3888 or 0.00129.   **3.** $6!/(3!2!)$, or 60.
4. (a) 15/64; (b) 3/32; (c) 1/64.

ARTICLE 11

1. $(150 + 20 + 1)/1296$, or 0.132.
2. $(0.8 \times 0.6) \times (1 - 0.1 \times 0.25 \times 0.7)$, or 0.472.
3. 0.995.
4. The probability that the father will survive is 0.74744; the son, 0.92608. The son's expectation is 0.92608 times 0.74744 times \$20,000, plus 0.92608 times 0.25256 times \$40,000, or, in all, \$23,199. The father's total expectation is \$16,054, and the college's is \$747.
5. 0.403; 0.150; 0.326; 0.121.
6. $1 - (0.748)^{10}$, or 0.925.
7. 0.20.
8. 42/165; 84/165 + 35/165 or 119/165.
9. 50/99; 49/99.

Chapter 6

ARTICLE 2

1. (a) 0.17; (b) 0.44.
2. (a) 0.033; (b) 0.019; (c) 0.21; (d) 22.
3. About \$5000.

ARTICLE 3

1. $P(-1)$ is 0.250, which is about the same as the corresponding value in Figure 6-3-1.

ARTICLE 4

1. $P(0) = 0.375; P(1) = 0.250; P(2) = 0.0625.$

ARTICLE 5

1. $P(0) = 0.399; P(1) = 0.242; P(2) = 0.054; P(2.5) = 0.018.$

ARTICLE 6

1. Yes.
2. (a) No; (b) yes; (c) no. Sex and race differences in (a) and (c) violate the first condition.
3. No. The elements are not independent and the second condition is violated.

ARTICLE 7

1. $P = 0.0104 \times 0.6$, or 0.0062.
2. $P = 0.4986 - 0.4918$ or 0.0068. Yes. The method of Problem 2 is exact.
3. 0.0214.

ARTICLE 9

1. The predicted frequencies for the six classes are 1.4, 5.7, 12.6, 14.1, 8.1, and 2.4. The disagreement is largest for the second class.
2. The predicted frequencies for the six classes are 2.6, 10.7, 23.0, 25.0, 14.3, and 4.3.

ARTICLE 10

1. (a) More than 1100. (b) About 615.
2. The old contract is better. The old contract gives him $920 per hundred turkeys, while the new one would give him only $872.
3. (a) About 6. (b) None. The first contract would be very unstrategic. The second would be very safe, since the probability of a failure in any sample of a thousand wires would be only about 0.000,003.

Chapter 7

ARTICLE 3

1. 1.09 and 3.16.
2. Figure 7-2-1 is strongly leptokurtic, with an α_4 of 4.2, and Figure 7-2-2 is platykurtic with an α_4 of 2.7.

ARTICLE 4

1. For Table 1-4-1, $\alpha_3 = +0.10$ and $\alpha_4 = 2.4$. For Table 1-4-2, $\alpha_3 = -0.39$ and $\alpha_4 = 2.1$.
2. 0.04; 2.4.
3. 0.48; 2.6.

ARTICLE 5

1. (a) 5.25; (b) 3.5; (c) 4.12; (d) 3.43.
2. (a) 98.70; (b) 98.74.

ARTICLE 6

1. 2.3. 2. 2.98. 3. (a) 8.33; (b) 12.8; (c) 576.
4. (a) 3.4; (b) PE from equation 6-8-1 is 3.45.

ARTICLE 7

The following results have been read from a *smoothed* ogive. Your results may differ slightly from them:

1. 0.13. 2. 0.18. 3. (a) 0.42; (b) 0.62.

ARTICLE 8

1. 0.25.

Chapter 8

ARTICLE 4

1. 4. 2. −2. 3. −1. 4. 0.

ARTICLE 5

1. $y = -4x + 4$. 2. $y = x + 2$. 3. $y = \frac{1}{2}x - 1$.

ARTICLE 7

1. A graphical answer: $y = 3.3x - 5.0$, where x is the entrance examination score and y is the subsequent mathematics grade. Your answer may differ somewhat from this.
2. The best possible line is $y = 1.5x + 9.2$. Your result should differ from this only slightly if your curve is well drawn.
3. Line (a) is better. For it, $\Sigma(y - y_p)^2$ is 3.00, while that for line (b) is 3.64.

ARTICLE 8

1. The least squares line is $y = 1.5x + 9.2$. For it, $\Sigma(y - y_p)^2$ is 2.80.
2. $y = 2.8x + 27$.

ARTICLE 9

1. See text.

2. $y_p = \dfrac{926}{x} + 2$.

Chapter 9

ARTICLE 2

1. 50; 0.44; 0.56.   **2.** 80; 0.11; 0.89.   **3.** 45; 50; 0.10.
4. 15; 5; 0.25.   **5.** 30; 50; 0.60.   **6.** 6; 20; 0.70.

ARTICLE 3

1. 0.66.   **2.** 0.33.   **3.** 0.95.   **4.** 0.87.   **5.** 0.77.   **6.** 0.84.

ARTICLE 4

1. 64%.   **2.** 0.60.   **3.** Yes. If temperature is related to rainfall, equation 9-4-1 will not be applicable.

ARTICLE 6

2. $r = 0.97$; $D = 0.94$; $A = 0.06$.
3. $r = 0.82$; $D = 0.67$; $A = 0.33$.

ARTICLE 7

1. $H_p = 2.8A + 27$, where H is height and A is age.
2. 63 inches.   **3.** $A_p = 0.24H - 3$.   **4.** 8 years.   **5.** $P_p = 1.5A + 9.2$.

ARTICLE 8

1. 26.   **2.** 2.68.   **3.** (a) 0.24; (b) 0.26; (c) 0.07; (d) less than 0.00003.

ARTICLE 9

1. $S_H = 2.8$.   **2.** 0.85.   **3.** $S_A = 0.8$.   **4.** 0.006.

ARTICLE 10

2. -0.75.   **3.** 0.56; 0.44.   **4.** $R_p = 0.31 - 0.26(B - 29.1)$, where R is rainfall and B is barometric pressure. The parenthesis on the right has been retained to avoid the use of large numbers in applying the equation.
5. 0.60 inch.   **6.** $S_R = 0.19$ inch; $P = 0.02$.   **7.** 0.99.

ARTICLE 11

1. $r_{EM} = 0.78$.   **2.** $r_{EL} = 0.57$.   **3.** $r_{XM} = -0.41$.   **4.** $r_{XL} = 0.52$.
5. (a) Jackson's mathematics grade, as predicted from his entrance exam score, is 57.2. (b) The standard error of estimate is 8.4, and the probability that Jackson will earn 60 or above, in spite of the prediction, is 0.37. (c) r_{EM} is 0.78, while r_{EL} is only 0.57. The entrance test therefore predicts 61% of the variance in mathematics grades and only 32% of the variance in language grades. (d) The new test is nearly as good as the old one for predicting language grades but much poorer for predicting mathematics grades.
6. $r_{EX} = -0.23$.

ARTICLE 12

1. 0.83. **2.** $W_p = 0.78H + 6.5$, where W and H are the ages of husband and wife.

3. $S_W = 8.5$. **4.** $H_p = 0.88W + 10.6$. **5.** $W_p = 48$. **6.** $P = 0.017$.

ARTICLE 14

1. 0.55. **2.** -0.70.

ARTICLE 15

1. (a) 0.65, 0.13; (b) 0.69, 0.05; (c) 0.699, 0.016; (d) 0.00, 0.14; (e) 0.198, 0.020; (f) 0.86, 0.08.

2. 0.75. **3.** 0.15. **4.** 0.77; 0.06. **5.** 0.829; 0.011.

Chapter 10

ARTICLE 4

1. $\sigma_{M-L} = 16.5$; $P(M - L > 10) = 0.29$.

2. $\overline{H - W} = 0.5$; $\sigma_D = 9.3$; $PE_D = 6.3$; $P(H - W > 10) = 0.15$.

ARTICLE 5

1. $\overline{x - y} = \overline{D} = 6.8$. **2.** $\sigma_D = 6.0$. **3.** $PE_D = 4.0$.

ARTICLE 6

1. $\sigma = \sqrt{0.02^2 + 0.02^2} = 0.028$.

2. $\sigma = \sqrt{0.02^2 - 2 \times 0.4 \times 0.2 \times 0.2 + 0.02^2} = 0.022$.

3. $\sigma_\Sigma = 26.8$; $PE_\Sigma = 18.1$.

ARTICLE 7

1. (a) 79.3067; (b) 0.0031; (c) 0.0021; (d) 79.3067 $\pm$ 0.0021; (e) 0.015.

2. The probability that the true value will lie between 24.50 and 25.00 is 0.997; between 24.70 and 24.80 it is only 0.44.

3. (a) $P = 0.0007$; (b) $P < 0.000,000,8$.

4. (VI and VIII). The risk to the manufacturer can be made negligible by specifying a sample size of ten or more. (VII). We have seen from Problem 6-10-3 that about 0.6% will break at 200 pounds. The contract would clearly be a risky one for the manufacturer.

5. (a) From equation 10-7-4 we see that he can reduce his error to half of its former value by taking the mean of *four times* as many measurements. He must therefore take the mean of twenty measurements of each angle. (b) He can reduce the effect of only the random errors in this way. The limit of accuracy will probably be set by the presence of systematic errors.

Chapter 11

ARTICLE 2

1. The probability that so large a difference would occur by chance is less than 0.00006. We must conclude that the treatment has reduced temperatures.
2. The probability that so large a difference will occur by chance is 0.35, and we conclude that the data fail to prove that a significant difference exists.
3. The probability of so large a difference, under the null hypothesis, is only 0.003. Further samples should be expected to show a similar difference.

ARTICLE 3

1. In Problem 1 the difference is proved to be significant at the 0.0001 level (or at the 0.00006 level). In Problem 3, it is proved to be significant at the 0.01 level (or at the 0.003 level). Using criteria 11-3-1, both are "certainly significant." Using criteria 11-3-2, the difference in temperature is "certainly significant" and the difference in heights is "probably significant."

ARTICLE 4

1. 117.   2. 203.   3. 44; 177.   4. 36; 50.

ARTICLE 5

1. Since σ_σ is 2.7, the observed σ differs from its expected value by only about 1.1 in t units. These data do not therefore prove that there is a difference in variability.
2. If this difference should be real, it would require approximately 53 cases to prove it at the 0.01 level, or 87 to prove it at the 0.001 level.
3. The difference of the standard deviations is 0.3, and the standard deviation of this difference is 0.65. There is no significant difference in variability.
4. σ_σ for the untreated patients is 0.072, and for the treated patients, 0.068. Assuming that the variability is the same for the two groups, the standard deviation of the difference between the standard deviations of two such groups is 0.099. The actual difference between the two standard deviations is 0.21. The actual difference is therefore 2.1 t units away from the expected value, and the probability that this will occur by chance is only 0.034. We conclude that the difference in variability is significant.
5. The difference between the two standard deviations is 0.2, and the standard deviation of this difference is 0.071. The difference is therefore 2.8 t units away from its expected value. The probability that so large a difference will occur by chance is 0.004, and we conclude that the difference in the standard deviations is significant.

ARTICLE 6

1. The standard deviation of these frequencies is about 30, while the difference in frequencies is only 33. Such a difference could easily have occurred by chance.
2. The standard deviation of the usual frequency is 3.9, and the difference is 13. This is a difference of 3.3 in t units, and the probability that such a difference

would occur by chance is only 0.001. We must conclude that a new cause of typhoid, not previously present, is operating.

3. The standard deviations of the *actually counted* frequencies are 16.3 and 16.6, while the difference between these frequencies is 12. The difference is not significant.

ARTICLE 7

1. In the first class, the percentage of failures was 42%, with a standard deviation of 5.7%. In the second class it is 13%, with a standard deviation of 3.7%. The standard deviation of the difference between the two percentages is 6.8%. The actual difference is 29%, or 4.3 t units. This difference is almost impossible on the hypothesis of chance ($P < 0.00002$), and the difference is certainly significant.

2. The standard deviations of the two percentages are 3.4% and 3.1%. Since the difference between the two percentages is only 2%, it is not significant.

3. About 3500.   4. (a) No; (b) yes; (c) yes; (d) yes.   5. No.

6. (a) Yes; (b) The court voted "for" in 43% of the cases in the first session and 53% in the second. Frankfurter voted "for" in 17% of the cases in the first session. Allowing for changes in the nature of the cases (as evidenced by the change in overall vote) he would be expected to vote "for" in 21% of the cases in the second session. His actual vote in the second session is 45% "for", which exceeds the expected vote by six times its standard deviation. We conclude that Frankfurter's change of attitude is real and is independent of any changes in the nature of the cases.

ARTICLE 8

1. $P<0.2$; the die is probably defective.

2. If we assign a half-vote for cases in which a Justice abstained from voting, we find a total of 47 "for" votes. On the hypothesis that the attitudes of the Justices are alike, their predicted number of "for" votes is 47/9, or 5.22, for each Justice. Comparing this with the actual number of their "for" votes, we find that $P<0.001$, and the hypothesis is totally untenable.

3. We find that $P<0.01$, and the hypothesis is untenable.

4. Here we find that $P = 0.2$, and the hypothesis is acceptable.

5. $P<0.02$. The temperatures almost certainly could not have come from the same universe.

6. $P>0.50$; distribution is normal within expected limits of sampling error.

7. $P>0.50$; distribution is normal.

Chapter 12

ARTICLE 2

3. -0.5.   4. 0.0005.   5. $M_p = 0.137X + 2.088E + 47.1$.

6. 7.8. If old test is used alone, S is 8.4, so that the improvement is small and the use of the new test is probably not justified for this purpose.

7. 7.0 If the old test is used alone, S is 12.1. This large improvement in S indicates that it would be desirable to retain both tests and use them jointly for predicting language grades.

ARTICLE 3

2. 0.82.   **3.** 61%; 17%; 67%; 33%.   **4.** 0.88.   **5.** 32%; 27%; 77%; 23%.

ARTICLE 4

1. Less than 0.01. It appears highly likely that dating affects grades only through loss of study time.

2. $r_{EI.A} = 0.60$. This is the coefficient of correlation between education and income which we would expect to find within any subgroup of people with the same ability as each other. Since this is nearly as high as the simple coefficient of correlation, it appears likely that the primary relationship is directly between education and income.

3. 0.83.   **4.** 0.77.

INDEX

•